GW00361465

© 2017 Viacom International Inc. All Rights Reserved. NICKELODEON, SHIMMER & SHINE
and all related titles, logos and characters are trademarks of Viacom International Inc.

SHIMMER & SHINE: 2018 A CENTUM BOOK 978-1-911460-86-2
Published in Great Britain by Centum Books Ltd, 20 Devon Square, Newton Abbot, Devon, TQ12 2HR, UK.
books@centumbooksltd.co.uk CENTUM BOOKS Limited Reg. No. 07641486. This edition published 2017.
A CIP catalogue record for this book is available from the British Library. Printed in China. 1 3 5 7 9 10 8 6 4 2

nickelodeon™

SHIMMER & SHINE™

2018

This book belongs to

....

centum

Better together

Pick your best and boldest colours to make the genie sisters sparkle.

Things can only get better when you try, try and try again!

Flying high

The magical friends love to play hide and seek.
Tick them off when you spot them amongst the clouds.

Find the answers on page 60

Shimmer

Shimmer is full of fun and bursting with lots of energy!

Shimmer and Shine work together to make things right and never give up!

10

Give Shimmer
bright pink hair and
a sparkly outfit.

*Shimmer always
has the time
of her life!*

HAIR COLOUR: pink
EYE COLOUR: blue
JEWEL COLOUR: green
ALWAYS: sweet and kind
LOVES: her sister
Shine's ideas
PET: Tala
MOST LIKELY TO SAY:
Oopsie!

Genie double

Can you spot 2 differences between these pictures of Shimmer practising her dance steps?

How about 4 differences between these pictures of Shine?

Too easy? How about 7 differences between these pictures of the sisters practising their potion making?

Find the answers on page 60

Shine

Courageous and bold, Shine is always ready for a magical adventure.

Shine is the elder genie twin by just one minute.

Shine has lots of words of wisdom!

Add some genie-tastic colours to magical Shine.

HAIR COLOUR: blue
EYE COLOUR: purple
JEWEL COLOUR: pink
ALWAYS: sassy and brave
LOVES: animals
PET: Nahal
MOST LIKELY TO SAY:
Always better together!

15

Dazzling pairs

Can you match these sparkling gems and jewels into matching pairs?

Magic mix up

Oopsie! A magical genie gem has duplicated Zeta! Can you spot the odd one out to reveal the real Zeta?

Find the answers on page 60

Boom Zahramay!

Help Leah make her first wish of the day and finish off these pictures of her genie friends.

Leah

Leah is warm and friendly and thrilled to have magical genies as her best friends!

Kind Leah always thinks of others.

Copy the colours opposite to complete this picture of Leah.

HAIR COLOUR: blonde

EYE COLOUR: green

ALWAYS: kind and caring

LOVES: her genie friends

PET: Parisa

MOST LIKELY TO SAY: That's not exactly what I wished for!

Leah always tries to make her friends happy.

21

Starry sleepover

The genie sisters love a sleepover. Read on to discover how to create your own sleepover fun.

Invite your brothers, sisters, cousins or your best friends.

Play fun games like hide and seek and I spy, or sing and dance along to your favourite songs.

What you'll need:

snacks (for a midnight feast) ⭐

pyjamas ⭐

a cosy onesie ⭐

slippers ⭐

torch ⭐

sleeping bag ⭐

a comfy pillow ⭐

Popcorn, chocolate, fruit, carrot sticks and crisps all make great sleepover snacks.

Make sure you get some sleep as otherwise you'll be very grumpy in the morning!

23

Oopsie!

Shimmer and Shine's spell has gone wrong and made their lovely long locks disappear. Doodle some fun hairstyles for them.

Zac

Bright and goofy, Leah's best friend Zac is always up for lots of fun.

Finish off this picture of Zac with some bright and bold colours.

Zac is so excited when Leah tells him about her secret genies and gets his very own genie called Kaz!

HAIR COLOUR: brown
EYE COLOUR: blue
SOMETIMES: gets a bit mixed up
LOVES: his best friend Leah
GENIE: Kaz
MOST LIKELY TO SAY: No need to explain!

Zac loves exploring Zahramay Falls with his new genie friends.

Lost and found

Can you find all the words below in the grid opposite? When you spot them, tick them off.

 BOOM

 DIVINE

 FRIENDS

 GENIES

 MAGIC

 NAHAL

 LEAH

 SHIMMER

 SHINE

 SPARKLE

 TALA

 WISH

ZAC

ZAHRAMAY

Don't forget to look forwards, backwards, vertically, horizontally and diagonally, too.

28

F	N	X	E	H	J	S	A	C	Z	E	O	S	C	N
N	R	A	Q	L	E	A	K	K	U	N	B	A	D	K
R	D	Q	H	I	K	T	L	F	E	I	Z	C	Q	J
P	P	K	N	A	P	R	R	A	K	V	N	M	W	N
A	Z	E	X	B	L	I	A	M	T	I	V	W	B	F
O	G	H	O	E	E	Y	D	P	J	D	T	Z	R	Y
Z	H	O	T	N	H	W	O	Y	S	M	A	G	I	C
A	M	I	D	V	S	X	V	J	X	M	S	Z	Q	R
H	G	S	L	M	I	X	O	O	W	P	A	U	Q	E
R	A	F	N	E	W	F	B	Z	B	B	G	I	Q	O
A	G	B	J	A	K	J	K	S	J	D	Z	H	R	R
M	J	P	S	W	W	Z	B	H	M	K	N	E	K	I
A	B	W	K	I	F	C	Z	I	A	D	V	O	F	Y
Y	R	E	M	M	I	H	S	N	H	A	E	L	H	T
C	F	J	E	X	Q	L	E	E	S	F	C	B	O	K

Find the answers on page 60

29

Nahal

Fluff up Nahal's fur with your pens and read on to discover lots of fun facts about Shine's pet cub.

Nahal can be a bit of a scaredy cat but is feisty and brave too!

Nahal loves cuddles with Shine and getting up to all kinds of mischief with Tala.

FUR COLOUR: purple and white
EYE COLOUR: blue
ANIMAL: pet cub tiger
ALWAYS: cuddly
LOVES: adventures with Shine
MOST LIKELY TO: leap and pounce

Memory muddle

Take a good look at the picture below, then cover it up and answer the questions opposite.

Shimmer and Shine love zooming around on their flying carpet. Nahal and Tala do too!

Put a tick next to the right answers.

1 What are Shimmer and Shine standing on?

a treasure chest

a skateboard

a magic carpet

2 What are they flying through?

a wave

a cloud

a rainbow

3 Which pets are with them?

Tala and Nahal

Parisa and Nazboo

Roya

4 Which of these characters is not in the picture?

Shimmer

Shine

Leah

5 What colour are Shimmer's clothes?

pink

purple

green

Find the answers on page 60

Friends forever

Leah loves her genie friends. Who are your friends and what fun do you have together?

My best friend is called: ....

My other friends are called: ....

....

Draw a picture of you and your friends here.

**Add some colour to this picture of Leah
with her genie BFF!**

Me and my friends love to:

giggle   play games

tell jokes have fun

share secrets   help each other

*With
genie friends,
every day
is magical!*

Tala

Add some colour to Shimmer's sweet pet Tala, then read on to discover lots of fun facts about her.

FUR COLOUR: yellow

EYE COLOUR: green

ANIMAL: monkey

ALWAYS: up to mischief

LOVES: Shimmer

MOST LIKELY TO: dress up

Tala loves sparkly jewels and gems and will climb anything to get her paws on them.

Perfect pets

Join the dots to finish off the genie sisters playing with their cute pets.

Tala and Nahal love going on magical adventures.

If you could have a pet, what would it be?

Genie adventures

Look at the pictures then use the word bank below to write a few words next to each one, to describe what you can see.

_____

_____

_____

_____

_____

_____

_____

_____

magic carpet	Leah	Princess	Zac
Shimmer	Nahal	Samira	Nazboo
Shine	Tala	Zeta	Parisa

sky   cloud   flowers   bucket

wish   bike   friends   sparkle

genie   bottle   beach   jewels

Dazzling doodles

Fill this page with lots of magical doodles of all the things Shimmer and Shine love!

Shimmer and Shine love dancing, flowers, jewels, playing, flying and having lots of fun!

Doodle Shimmer and Shine on their flying carpet.

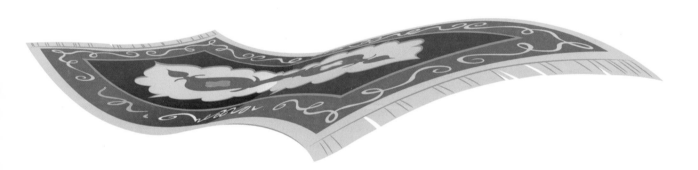

Squiggle some flowers in the space below.

Magical ball

Can you help Shimmer, Shine and Leah
find their way through the maze
to reach the masked ball?

Start

End

Find the answers on page 60

Princess Samira

Kind and generous, this dazzling princess is the most powerful genie in Zahramay falls.

Princess Samira is in charge of all magic and all wishes!

FUR COLOUR: aqua

EYE COLOUR: purple

PET: Roya

ALWAYS: granting wishes

LOVES: magic

MOST LIKELY TO SAY:
Good job genies!

Add some sparkly colours to this magical princess.

Princess Samira is mentor to all genies in training and awards Genie Gems to those who earn them.

Wishful thinking

Use the code cracker below to work out Leah's three wishes, then doodle them in the wish bubble opposite.

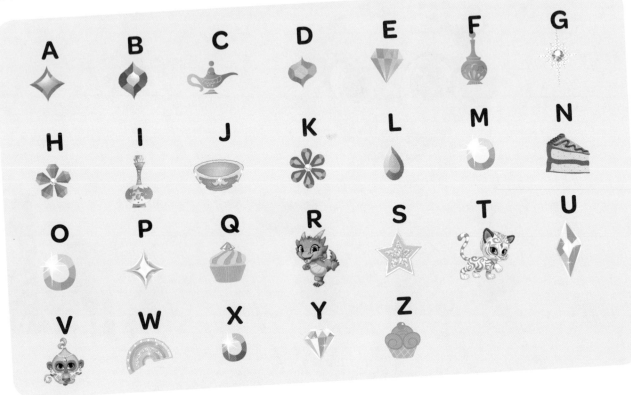

Leah gets
to make three
magical wishes
a day.

Find the answers on page 60

49

Dazzling dress up!

Shimmer and Shine love to dress up. Add some bright colours and sparkly patterns to all the clothes below.

What outfits do you like to dress up in?

shine like a star

Add some sparkly colours and patterns to these stars.

Zeta

The scheming Zeta is determined to be more powerful and magical than anyone else in Zahramay Falls.

Make this sorceress sparkle with your best pens.

Zeta failed her genie training and had to settle for sorceress status instead.

FUR COLOUR: purple

EYE COLOUR: green

PET: Nazboo

ALWAYS: up to no good

LOVES: power

MOST LIKELY TO SAY:
Zip, zow, open now!

Zeta cheats and steals to get her hands on as many Genie Gems as she can.

Picture perfect

Can you work out which jigsaw pieces go where to finish off these pictures?

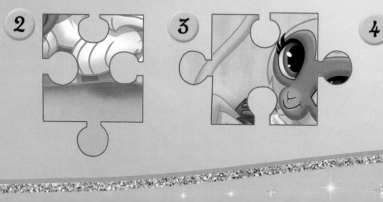

Zac often makes mistakes, it happens a lot!

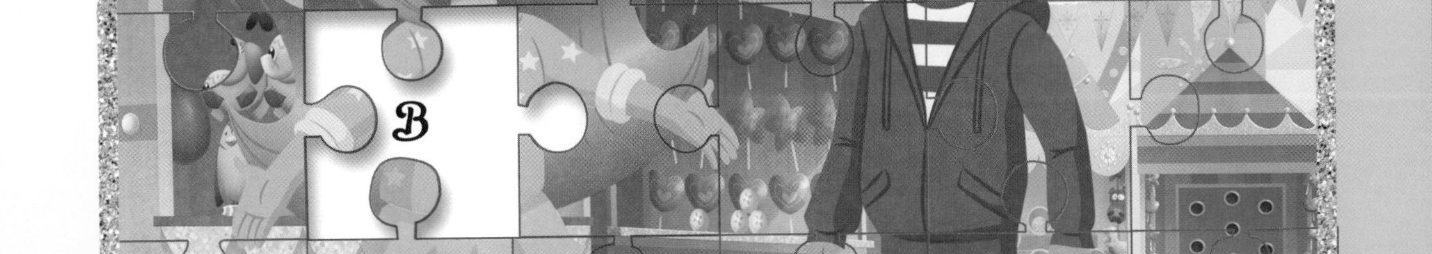

1

2

3

4

Find the answers on page 60

55

Kaz

Kaz makes the perfect genie pal for Zac when he visits Zahramay Falls.

Magic up some fun colours for this picture of Kaz.

Imagine having your very own genie. What would you wish for?

HAIR COLOUR: purple

EYE COLOUR: blue

GENIE TO: Zac

ALWAYS: ready for action

LOVES: magic

MOST LIKELY TO: help his friends

Kaz had never met a non-magical person before he met Leah and Zac.

Genie friends

Can you spot the odd one out in each row of Shimmer and Shine's friends?

Each of Shimmer and Shine's friends is special in their own way!

A   B   C   D

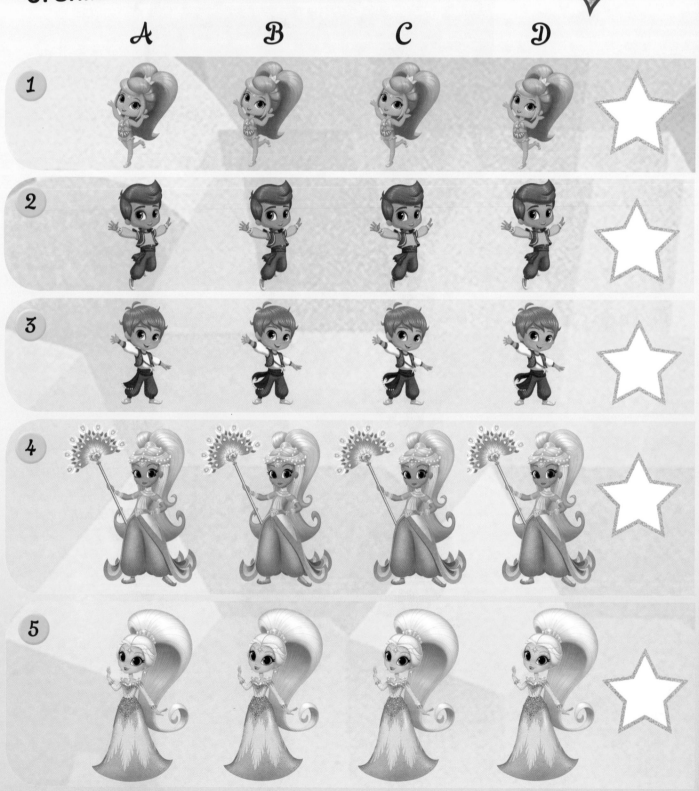

1

2

3

4

5

Find the answers on page 60

Jewel jumble

Oopsie! Leah and Parisa have lost all of the other magical pets in a gem-tastic pile of jewels. Tick them off when you spot them.

Find the answers on page 60

Answers

Pages 8-9

Pages 12

Pages 13

Page 16
A 9, B 2, C 1, D 6, E 7, F 5, G 3, H 4, I 8

Page 17
5

Page 29

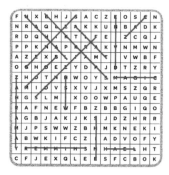

Page 33
1 a magic carpet
2 a wave
3 Tala and Nahal
4 Leah
5 purple

Pages 44-45

Page 48
1 sleepover
2 balloon ride
3 tree house

Page 54

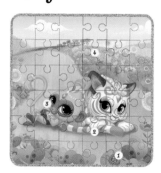

Page 55

Page 58
1 D, 2 B, 3 A, 4 C, 5 D

Page 59

Make a wish

Imagine you had your very own genie. What would it look like?

Draw it here.

Shimmer and Shine's bracelets glow when Leah calls for them.

Think up a fun name for your genie and write it here:

....

GW00362608

DISCOVER
France

DISCOVER
France

AA

Produced by the Publications
Division of the Automobile Association
Fanum House, Basingstoke, Hampshire RG21 2EA

Produced by the Publications Division of The
Automobile Association

Editor Joan Fensome
Art Editor Dave Austin
Editorial Consultant A.N. Brangham
Text Julia Brittain (*Normandy* and
contributors *Brittany*), Sally Howard (*The South of
France*), Barbara Littlewood (*Burgundy and
Champagne*), Jeffrey Robinson (*Paris and the North*),
David Rowlands (*From the Alps to Alsace*), Roger
Thomas (*The Dordogne and South-West France*),
Roland Weisz (*The Loire and Central France*)

Research by the Publications Research Unit of The
Automobile Association

Maps produced by the Cartographic Department of
The Automobile Association

The contents of this book are believed correct at the
time of printing. Nevertheless, the publisher cannot
accept any responsibility for errors or omissions, or
for changes in details given.

ISBN 0 86145 786 2
AA Reference: 10197

© The Automobile Association 1988

Reprinted with amendments 1988
First edition 1983

The Automobile Association retains copyright in the
original edition © 1983 and in all subsequent
editions, reprints and amendments to editions, the
date of copyright in each corresponds to the above
reprint dates.

All rights reserved. No part of this publication may be
reproduced, stored in a retrieval system, or
transmitted in any form or by any means – electronic,
mechanical, photocopying, recording, or otherwise –
unless the written permission of the publisher has
been given beforehand.

Filmset by Tradespools Ltd, Frome, Somerset
Printed and bound in Spain by Artes Graficas.
Toledo SA. D.L. TO 2260–1988

Published by The Automobile Association, Fanum
House, Basingstoke, Hampshire RG21 2EA

Photographs on opening pages
Half-title page: A game of boules in Arles
Title page: The Champs-Élysées, Paris
This page: the vineyards of Monbazillac

Contents

Introduction

France, Western Europe's largest country, is also one of its most enduring delights. *Discover France* portrays many of the numerous and often surprising attractions of this fascinating land. The book features the whole of France in seven regional sections, each of which highlights the special character and appeal of the provinces it covers. Every section is introduced by a general descriptive feature of the area, and this is followed by a comprehensive gazetteer of the most interesting and important places to visit. Illustrated boxes of additional information include France's famous foods and wines, its history, traditions, specialities and local features.

To help the visitor get the most out of a trip to France, eight pages at the beginning of the book contain practical information concerning travel, accommodation, food, shopping and various legal requirements. A four-page atlas and a detailed street plan of Paris will help you to find your way about. For reasons of scale, some of the smaller places mentioned in the gazetteer are not named on the road atlas. In these cases, location details are given in the gazetteer text.

Discover France is an ideal passport to an exciting adventure across the Channel.

A shady walk in the Tuileries Gardens, Paris

Key to Regions

The 95 Departments of France are listed here alphabetically under the regional headings which appear in the book. Each Department has a number, as shown on the map and in brackets, which for postal purposes replaces its name. These numbers also form part of the registration number of French cars, thus indicating the department in which the vehicle was registered.

NORMANDY AND BRITTANY

Calvados	(14)
Côtes-du-Nord	(22)
Eure	(27)
Finistère	(29)
Ille-et-Vilaine	(35)
Manche	(50)
Morbihan	(56)
Orne	(61)
Seine-Maritime	(76)

THE LOIRE AND CENTRAL FRANCE

Allier	(03)
Cantal	(15)
Charente	(16)
Charente-Maritime	(17)
Cher	(18)
Corrèze	(19)
Creuse	(23)
Eure-et-Loir	(28)
Indre	(36)
Indre-et-Loire	(37)
Loir-et-Cher	(41)
Loire (Haute-)	(43)
Loire-Atlantique (44)	Loiret (45)
Maine-et-Loire (49)	Mayenne (53)
Puy-de-Dôme (63)	Sarthe (72)
Sèvres (Deux-) (79)	Vendée (85)
Vienne (86)	Vienne (Haute-) (87)

THE DORDOGNE AND SOUTH-WEST FRANCE

Ariège	(09)
Aveyron	(12)
Dordogne	(24)
Garonne (Haute-)	(31)
Gers	(32)
Gironde	(33)
Landes	(40)
Lot	(46)
Lot-et-Garonne	(47)
Pyrénées-Atlantiques	(64)
Pyrénées (Hautes-)	(65)
Tarn	(81)
Tarn-et-Garonne	(82)

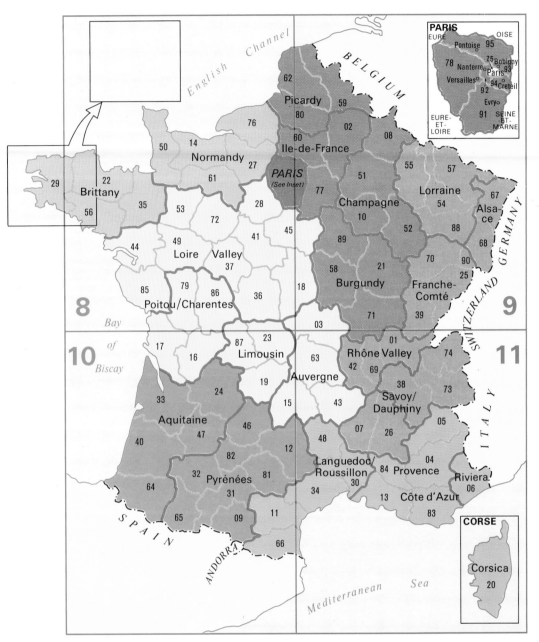

ATLAS LEGEND

	Motorway and Junction
	Toll motorway
	Motorway under construction
	Single carriageway motorway
	Primary route
	Main road
	Secondary road
	Other road
	Mountain road tunnel
	Mountain pass
	Railway
	Road snowbound during winter
N634	Road number
52	Distance in kms
○	Town
Yasso	River and Lake
DOVER-BOULOGNE	Vehicle Ferry
DOVER-CALAIS	Hovercraft Ferry
	International boundary

PARIS (See Inset)
EURE — OISE
Pontoise — 95
78 — Nanterre — 75 Bobigny — 93
Versailles — Paris — 94 Creteil
92
Evry — SEINE-ET-MARNE
EURE-ET-LOIRE — 91

CORSE
Corsica — 20

THE SOUTH OF FRANCE	
Alpes (Basses-)	(04)
Alpes (Hautes-)	(05)
Alpes-Maritimes	(06)
Aude	(11)
Bouches-du-Rhône	(13)
Corse	(20)
Gard	(30)
Hérault	(34)
Lozère	(48)
Pyrénées Orientales	(66)
Var	(83)
Vaucluse	(84)

FROM THE ALPS TO ALSACE	
Ain	(01)
Ardèche	(07)
Belfort (Terrain de)	(90)
Doubs	(25)
Drôme	(26)
Isère	(38)
Jura	(39)
Loire	(42)
Meurthe-et-Moselle	(54)
Meuse	(55)
Moselle	(57)
Rhin (Bas-)	(67)
Rhin (Haut-)	(68)
Rhône	(69)
Saône (Haute-)	(70)
Savoie	(73)
Savoie (Haute-)	(74)
Vosges	(88)

BURGUNDY AND CHAMPAGNE	
Ardennes	(08)
Aube	(10)
Côte-d'Or	(21)
Marne	(51)
Marne (Haute-)	(52)
Nièvre	(58)
Saône-et-Loire	(71)
Yonne	(89)

PARIS AND THE NORTH	
Aisne	(02)
Nord	(59)
Oise	(60)
Pas-de-Calais	(62)
Seine	(75)
Seine-et-Marne	(77)
Seine-et-Oise and Yvelines	(78)
Somme	(80)
Essonne	(91)
Hauts-de-Seine	(92)
Seine-St-Denis	(93)
Val-de-Marne	(94)
Val-d'Oise	(95)

8

ENGLISH CHANNEL

DOVER-CALAIS · FOLKESTONE-CALAIS · DOVER-BOULOGNE · FOLKESTONE-BOULOGNE · NEWHAVEN-DIEPPE · PORTSMOUTH-LE HAVRE · SOUTHAMPTON-LE HAVRE · WEYMOUTH-CHERBOURG · PORTSMOUTH-CHERBOURG · PLYMOUTH-ROSCOFF · PORTSMOUTH-ST MALO

Blériot-P · Wissant · Wimereux · Boulogne · Le Portel · Hardelot-Plage · Le Touquet · Berck-Plage · Le Crotoy · St-Valéry-s-Somme · Abbeville · Le Tréport · Mesnil-Va · Dieppe · Blangy

Alderney · Guernsey · St Peter Port · L'Erée · Sark · CHANNEL ISLANDS · L'Etacq · Trinity · St-Helier · Jersey

Auderville · Cherbourg · Barfleur · Maupertus · St-Vaast-la-Hougue · Les Pieux · Valognes · Utah Beach · Gold Beach · Omaha Beach · Juno Beach · Sword Beach · Bricquebec · Barneville-Carteret · Ste-Mère-Eglise · St-Laurent-sur-Mer · Arromanches · Bayeux · St Aubin-sur-Mer · Bénouville · LE HAVRE · Honfleur · Deauville · Trouville · Houlgate · Caen

Golfe de St Malo · Coutainville · St-Lô · Villers-Bocage · Aunay-sur-Odon · Thury-Harcourt · St Pierre-s-Dives · Lisieux · Bernay · Conches-en-Ouche · Evreux

NORMANDIE

Trégastel · Perros-Guirec · Tréguier · Paimpol · Pontrieux · Lannion · St Michel-en-Grève · Bégard · Morlaix · Guingamp · Callac · Carhaix · Huelgoat · Gourin · Scaër · Rosporden · Quimperlé · Le Pouldu · Pont Aven · Lorient · Port-Louis · Hennebont · Auray · La Trinité-s-M · Carnac · Vannes · Quiberon · Sauzon · Bangor · Le Palais · Locmaria · Belle Île en Mer · St-Nazaire · La Baule · Le Croisic · Pornichet · Paimboeuf · NANTES

St-Brieuc · Lamballe · Moncontour-de-Bretagne · Loudéac · Pontivy · Josselin · Ploërmel · Locminé · Baud · Plouay · Quimperlé · Rennes · Vitré · Laval · Fougères · Mayenne · Ernée · Alençon · Sées · Argentan · Falaise

BRETAGNE

RENNES · Redon · Châteaubriant · Segré · Châteaubriant · Ancenis · Angers · Saumur · Tours · Amboise · Montrichard · Blois · Chambord · Chaumont-sur-L · Contres

Le Mans · Connerré · La Ferté-Bernard · Chartres · Châteaudun · Vendôme · Orléans · Beaugency

La Roche-sur-Yon · Challans · St-Jean de Monts · St Gilles-Croix de Vie · Ile de Noirmoutier · Ile d'Yeu · Les Sables d'Olonne · Luçon · La Tranche-s-Mer · Ars-en-Ré · St-Martin-de-Ré · Ile de Ré · La Rochelle · Ile d'Oléron

Montaigu · Cholet · Bressuire · Thouars · Loudun · Châtellerault · Poitiers · Chauvigny · Niort · Melle · Lusignan · Montmorillon · Châteauroux

BREST inset map: Brignogan · Roscoff · St-Pol-de-Léon · Lesneven · Wrac'h · Landerneau · Daoulas · Camaret · Crozon · Morgat · Pentrez Plage · Ste-Anne-la-Palud · Tréboul · Douarnenez · Audierne · Plozévet · Quimper · Bénodet · Fouesnant · Pont l'Abbé · Beg-Meil · St-Guénolé · Concarneau · Primel-Trégastel · Carantec · St Michel-en-Grève · Morlaix · Guingamp · Callac · Corlay · Rostrenen · Huelgoat · Pleyben · Carhaix · Châteaulin · Châteauneuf-du-Faou · Gourin · Le Faouët · Plouay · Scaër · Rosporden · Quimperlé · Baud · Le Pouldu · Hennebont · Lorient

Scale: 0 — 20 — 40 — 60 mls · 0 — 20 — 40 — 60 — 80 — 100 Kms · 33 miles to one inch (approx)

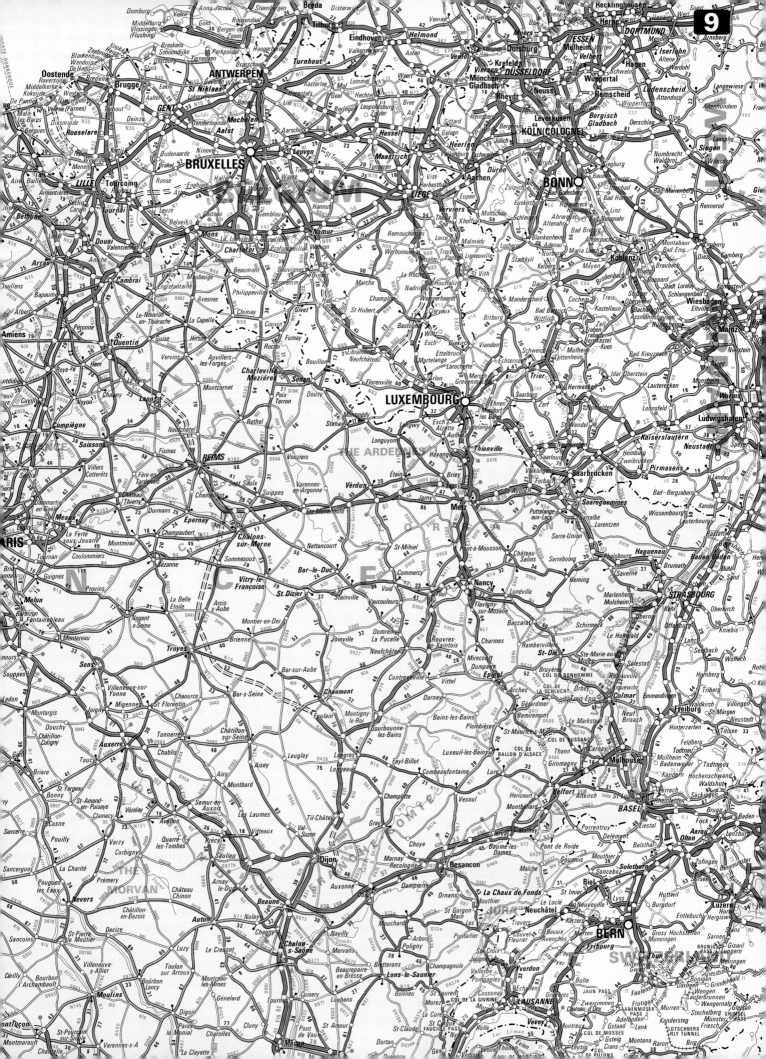

General Information

The following pages attempt to provide basic information of value to the holidaymaker in France. More detailed advice can be obtained for every aspect of your holiday from the sources listed.

Documents

Visitors to France must hold a valid passport (families can obtain a joint passport). A British Visitor's Passport, which lasts for one year, can be obtained over the counter from a main post office (in Northern Ireland only from the Passport Office, Belfast). For a standard British Passport, an application form can be obtained from a main post office and sent to the appropriate Passport Office. Allow at least four weeks for the document to arrive.

A visa is not normally required by British passport holders when visiting for periods of three months or less. However, if you hold a passport of any other nationality, a British passport not issued in this country, or are in any doubt about your position, check with the French Consulate.

Health

There are no obligatory inoculations. Britain has a reciprocal agreement with France for health care. Details are given in leaflet SA30, obtainable from local social security offices of the Department of Health and Social Security. It contains an application for Form E111, which is a certificate of entitlement to treatment within European Community countries. This must be produced when obtaining treatment in France. However, don't rely exclusively on this arrangement as the cover provided is not comprehensive – see *Insurance* below.

Insurance

Comprehensive insurance schemes are widely available to cover vehicles, travel and health, and these are worth investigating. See also page 17 for details of compulsory motor insurance.

Money

There is no limit to the amount of sterling notes you may take abroad. The unit of currency in France is the *Franc* (Fr), which is divided into 100 *Centimes*. There are no restrictions on the import of French or foreign currency, but visitors are advised to complete a currency declaration on arrival if they intend to export bank notes exceeding the equivalent of 5,000Fr. However, it is safer to carry travellers' cheques together with a small amount of French currency to meet immediate expenses. Alternatively if your bankers are part of the Uniform Eurocheque scheme you will be able to obtain a Uniform Eurocheque Card and multi-currency chequebook enabling you to write cheques in French Francs. Approach your bankers well in advance of your departure for further information.

Credit/charge cards

American Express, Carte Bleue (Visa), Eurocard/Mastercard (Access) and Diners Club are accepted at most good hotels and restaurants. Petrol stations and motorway restaurants also accept some credit cards as indicated by symbols displayed outside.

Travel

Air Several airlines operate regularly to France. Air Inter, the national domestic airline, flies between Paris and 30 cities and major towns, and there are several independent companies in operation.

Rail Information and booking facilities concerning rail travel to and in France can be obtained from main British Rail Travel Centres, stations and some travel agents, or from French Railways (SNCF), 179 Picadilly, London W1V 0BA.

Any rail ticket bought in France must be validated (*composté*) by using the automatic date stamping machine at the platform entrance. Inspectors on the trains can impose on-the-spot fines on anyone travelling with an unstamped ticket. *France Vacances* is a rail rover ticket giving unlimited travel on any 9 or 16 days over a period of one month. There are many free bonuses that come with the card which is available in 1st and 2nd Class and attracts reduced fares for children. French Motorail combines car and rail travel to all main holiday areas from Dover and Folkestone.

France boasts the fastest train in the world, TGV (*Train à Grande Vitesse*). This runs from Paris to Lyons, Dijon, Besançon and St-Etienne at 280kph (168mph).

Coach and bus Coach companies operate inclusive services from London to destinations including Paris, Biarritz, Bordeaux, Lyons, Montpellier, Tours and Perpignan; within France there are good local services.

Sea crossings Numerous regular ferry crossings, and some hovercraft crossings, operate across the Channel and your departure and arrival ports obviously depend on where you live and where you are going. For the motorist, the cost varies considerably depending on the length of cross-

	BOULOGNE	CALAIS	CHERBOURG	DIEPPE	DUNKERQUE	LE HAVRE	ROSCOFF	ST MALO	CAEN
DOVER	1¾	1¼-1¾							
FOLKESTONE	1¾								
NEWHAVEN				4					
POOLE			4½						
PORTSMOUTH			4¾ 6½				5¾-8	9	5½-6½
PLYMOUTH							6		
RAMSGATE					2½				
WEYMOUTH			4-6						

The Breton resort of St-Servan-sur-Mer, adjacent to the Channel port of St-Malo. The Port Solidor, a former naval base, is one of three harbours here

ing, but it is worth making a detailed comparison of the various crossings, bearing in mind the distances entailed on the road. This table gives the crossings and the length of each journey.

Car hire You may prefer to hire a car in France, rather than to take your own; this can be arranged in advance through one of the international hire firms. There are also many car-hire agencies in France, a list of which can be obtained from local tourist offices in France. The major airlines have fly-drive facilities and French Railways a train and car-hire service. *France Vacance* card holders enjoy favourable terms for car hire. Note: The minimum age limit for hiring a car varies from firm to firm.

Disabled Travellers If you are disabled tell your travel agent what your special requirements are. Airlines, shipping companies and most hoteliers make provision for those who cannot walk.

Obtaining information

General information about France can be obtained before you leave from the French Government Tourist Office, 178 Piccadilly, London W1V 0AL. The telephone number for general enquiries is 01-491 7622 and for the 24-hr recorded information service 01-449 6911. Once in France you will find *Accueil de France* helpful for booking accommodation within their area for the same night, or up to seven days in advance for **personal callers only**. These 'welcome' offices are situated at main stations and airports. For information about tourist attractions, local events, excursions, religious services, and for specific information about activities such as skiing or horse-riding, contact the *Syndicat d'Initiative* (local tourist office) which is to be found in all larger towns and resorts. If you lose any property you should report the facts to the local police, not the British Consul, and obtain a statement about the loss. If you still need help, such as the issue of an emergency passport or guidance on how to transfer funds, contact the Consulate. The Consular Section of the British Embassy in France is at 75008 Paris, 16 rue d'Anjou, telephone 42669142. There are also Consulates in Bordeaux, Lille, Lyons and Marseilles and Honorary Consuls in Boulogne-sur-Mer, Calais, Cherbourg, Dunkerque, Le Havre, Nantes, Nice, Perpignan, St Malo-Dinard and Toulouse.

Banking and shopping hours

The opening hours of banks in most large towns are 09.00–12.00hrs and 14.00–16.00hrs Monday to Friday and closed on Saturday and Sunday. In the provinces the same hours apply, but they are open Tuesday to Saturday and closed on Sunday and Monday. Generally banks close at midday

on the day prior to a national holiday and all day on Monday if the holiday falls on a Tuesday. The dates of public holidays, some of which vary from year to year, can be obtained from the French Government Tourist office in London.

Shopping hours vary considerably but department stores are usually open Monday to Saturday, 09.00–13.00hrs and 15.00–18.30 or 19.00 hrs. Food shops often open at 07.00hrs and may also open on Sunday mornings.

Post Offices are usually open 09.00hrs–12.00hrs and 14.00–17.00hrs Monday to Friday and 09.00–12.00hrs on Saturday.

Telephones

It is no more difficult to use the telephone in France than it is at home and by using a public callbox you avoid the addition of surcharges imposed by most hotels.

To make a local call from a callbox use a 1Fr coin (2 × 50 *Centimes* in some callboxes), inserting money after lifting receiver. To call one provincial number from another or one Paris area number (Paris, Seine St Dennis, Hauts de Seine and Val de Marne) from another simply dial the 8-digit number. To call a Paris area number from the provinces precede the 8-digit number with 161 and to call a provincial number from the Paris area precede the 8-digit number with 16. To make an international call use a metallic grey callbox and 5Fr coins; to call Britain dial 19, wait for second dialling tone, then dial 44 and your STD code minus the first 0 followed by the number.

Customs

There are very few formalities when taking a car into France for periods of up to three

months, but the vehicle must be taken out of the country when you leave.

As for all EC countries, concessions allow bona-fide holidaymakers to take limited amounts of certain commodities through Customs without paying duty as detailed below. Passengers under 17 are not, however, entitled to tobacco and drinks allowances.

Electricity

The public electricity supply is 220V AC (50 cycles). Screw-in bulbs and plugs with two round pins are usual. Two-pin adaptors which can be used in French lightbulb sockets and shaver points are generally available in the United Kingdom.

Photography

There are no restrictions on photography, except near some military or government establishments, where a clear pictorial sign is displayed.

Sea bathing

Parts of some beaches in southern France are reserved for hotel guests or customers hiring beach facilities. There may be local health hazard signs, and on some beaches a flag system indicates when bathing is safe.

Time

Local time in France is one hour ahead of GMT in winter (GMT + 1) and two hours ahead in summer (GMT + 2).

Metrication

1 kilo = 2.2 lbs
1 litre = 1¾ pints
l gallon = 4.55 litres
1 mile = 1.6 km (5 m = 8 km)

Goods obtained duty and tax free in the EEC or duty and tax free on a ship or aircraft, or goods obtained outside the EEC	Duty and tax free allowances	Goods obtained duty and tax paid in the EEC
	Tobacco products	
200	Cigarettes	300
	or	
100	Cigarillos	150
	or	
50	Cigars	75
	or	
250g	Tobacco	400g
	Alcoholic drinks	
2 litres	Still table wine	5 litres
1 litre	Over 22% vol. (eg spirits and strong liqueurs)	1½ litres
	or	
2 litres	Not over 22% vol. (eg low strength liqueurs or fortified wines or sparkling wines)	3 litres
	or	
2 litres	Still table wine	3 litres
	Perfume	
50g		75g
	Toilet Water	
250cc		375cc
	Other goods but no more than:	
£32	50 litres of beer	£250
	25 mechanical lighters	

Note

Visitors to France entering from an EEC country may also import duty-free 1000g of coffee or 450g of coffee extract and 250g of tea or 80g of tea extract bought duty and tax paid, a reduced allowance applies if bought duty-free.

Where to Stay

Whatever part of France you are visiting there is plenty of accommodation to suit all tastes and pockets. Camp sites, at one end of the scale, are excellent on the whole and greatly favoured by French holidaymakers, while at the other end the luxury hotels of France are among the best in the world. In between the two is a comprehensive range of small hotels and *pensions* at very reasonable prices.

Hotels

The Ministry of Tourism classifies hotels in 5 categories, from 1-star to 4-star and 4-star *de luxe*. The room rate, which is officially controlled, should be displayed in each individual room. It does not include the price of meals.

Some of the world's best hotel accommodation is to be found in the Right Bank/ Champs-Elysées area of Paris and in the fashionable Mediterranean Coast resorts. Here one can expect top-class rooms and service, comfort and every amenity, with prices to match.

For those with their own transport, restaurants listed in the *Relais Routiers* guide offer simple food and sometimes basic accommodation; these are situated on main roads. For rural accommodation it is difficult to beat *Logis de France*: privately owned, usually family-run tourist inns which have high standards and offer good value for money, a friendly welcome and regional cooking. A list of *Logis*, of which there are about 4,000, and *Auberges*, which offer simpler accommodation, can be obtained from the French Tourist Office for a small fee.

When touring during the peak season it is a good idea to telephone ahead to book accommodation. This does not, however, constitute a legal contract (as it does in Britain) and when you arrive you will be expected to examine your rooms and make sure they are satisfactory before registering. *Logis*, and many other good hotel associations such as *France Accueil*, *Petits Nids* and Inter Hotels, will ring ahead and help you book your next stop. It is advisable to arrive at your hotel by 6 pm.

Do check how much you will be charged and ascertain just what is covered by the tariff. Usually the quotation is for bed only, based on two sharing a room, and breakfast is an additional set price per person.

Many hoteliers speak English but when writing to book accommodation – especially at a *pension* or farmhouse – it is better to write in French. When writing enclose an International Reply Coupon, obtainable from post offices. The hotelier's letter of confirmation may include a request for a deposit – *verser des arrhes*.

Self-catering

Nowadays many people prefer to cater for themselves and France offers plenty of choice, ranging from tents already erected and equipped to purpose-built chalet complexes, and from luxurious villas on the Mediterranean to simple farm cottages in the heart of the countryside.

Holiday homes in the country at reasonable prices are what *Gîtes de France* are all about. There are some 23,000 *gîtes* in 4,000 rural locations, including some on farms, governed by the charter of the *Fédération Nationale des Gîtes ruraux de France*, which is Government sponsored. Details of these can be obtained from *Gîtes de France*, 178 Piccadilly, London W1V 0AL (enclose s.a.e.), and travel agents. It is advisable to book early as they are very popular.

Camping and caravanning

France has a large number of campsites, over 7,000 of them officially graded. There are over 100 'Tourist Camps', most of them in pleasant settings, registered with the Ministry of Tourism, and more than 40 *Castels et Camping-caravanning* which are all within the grounds of châteaux. Some state forests (*forêts domaniales*) allow camping on application to the *garde forestier*, who will indicate the site where you may erect your tents.

At most campsites you must produce evidence of insurance cover, including third-party cover while you and your vehicles are on the site. The best way is by showing an International Camping *carnet*, obtainable from motoring organisations; this is obligatory at some sites including *Castels et Camping-caravanning*.

Camping Gaz International and Butagaz are the only types of gas easily obtainable in France. Shell Butane is on sale but is supplied in cylinders which do not fit British butane regulators. A suitable regulator may be obtained on loan from a Shell agent. If your stove uses paraffin buy your supplies at a large town as it may be difficult to find in many country districts.

Tents and camping equipment for holidays in Europe can be hired in Britain. This includes camping packs, a tent, beds, tables, chairs and roofrack, as well as such items as wheel chains, warning triangles and emergency windscreens.

It is as well to book your site or sites in advance, though local *Syndicats d'Initiative* will help you to find a site.

Opulent hotels, two casinos and several yacht harbours are all part of the appeal of Cannes, which has attracted the world's wealthy for over a hundred years

France for the Motorist

Driving in France should be a relaxed and rewarding method of transport. The choice for the tourist is either to take his own car or to hire one, and the advantages of each are worth comparing. Hiring has the advantage of saving wear and tear on one's own car and the left-hand drive offers a better view of the road. Against this is the inconvenience involved in getting to the ferry port, which may involve train fares, transferring luggage from your own car and car parking charges if you leave your own car at the port.

Motoring regulations are as wide and complicated as in the UK but need not worry the driver who is careful and courteous. The main change for British drivers entering France is that cars keep to the right.

Accidents

Fire tel. 18, Police tel. 17. For *Ambulance* use the number given in telephone boxes or call the police. If you have an accident you *must* stop and use hazard warning lights, or a warning triangle.

Breakdown

If your vehicle breaks down do your best to move it to a position where it will not cause obstruction. Use hazard warning lights and/or a warning triangle (see above).

There is no nationwide road assistance service in France. If you break down on a motorway telephone the police (*brigade de gendarmerie*) from an emergency telephone. On other roads seek local help. All garages should display a list of their charges and any invoice should detail separately costs of labour, parts etc. You should recover any parts which have been replaced.

Lights

Headlights should be adjusted for driving on the right. The adjustment can be made by using headlamp converters or beam deflectors which may be purchased from AA Centres. However, beam deflectors must not be used with halogen lamps. In France all locally registered vehicles are equipped with headlights which emit a yellow beam and visitors are advised to comply. Beam deflectors emit a yellow beam, but with beam converters it is necessary to coat the outer surface of the headlamp glass with yellow plastic paint. It is important to remember to remove the deflectors or converters as soon as you return to the UK.

The use of dipped headlights during the day is compulsory for motorcycles exceeding 125cc and generally they must be used by all vehicles in poor daytime visibility. It is recommended that visiting motorists have a set of replacement bulbs, as drivers unable to replace a faulty bulb when stopped by the police may be fined.

Mirrors

It is essential to have clear all-round vision. Ideally external rear-view mirrors should be fitted to both sides of your vehicle, but certainly on the left to allow for driving on the right.

Nationality plate

It is compulsory to display a nationality plate of the approved design (oval with black letters on a white background) and size (GB at least 6.9in by 4.5in) at the rear of your vehicle.

Straight, well-surfaced country roads – often attractively tree-lined – make motoring in rural France a real pleasure

Parking

Regulations are similar to those in Britain and kerb markings are yellow. In most principal towns there are short-term parking areas (blue zones) where you may park for up to one hour if you display a special disc which you can buy at the police station or obtain free from tourist offices and other organisations. In grey zones parking meters are installed and must be used between 09.00hrs and 19.00hrs. If a ticket is issued this must be displayed on the windscreen or near-side front window. Vehicles parked illegally may be towed away and recovery is expensive. There are reserved parking places for the disabled, indicated by the international symbol, but no formal system of concession operates in France.

Crash helmets

It is compulsory for motorcyclists and their passengers to wear crash helmets.

Documents

Driving licence A valid full licence (not provisional) issued in the UK is acceptable for driving in France. The minimum age at which a UK licence holder may drive a temporarily imported car is 18, motorcycle (not exceeding 80cc) 16, motorcycle (exceeding 80cc) 18. See also *Car hire* page 13 and *Speed limits* below.

Registration document You must carry the original vehicle registration document with you. If the vehicle is not registered in your name you should have a letter from the owner authorising you to use it. If you are using a UK registered hired or leased vehicle the registration document will not be available and you should obtain a Hired/Leased Vehicle Certificate from the AA.

Drinking and driving

The only safe rule is – if you are driving don't drink. The laws are strict and penalties severe in France.

Insurance

Third-party motor insurance is compulsory in France and an International Green Card of Insurance is strongly recommended. Therefore, before taking your car to France contact your insurer for advice and to ensure that you are adequately covered.

Passengers

Children under 10 are not permitted to travel in a vehicle as front-seat passengers when rear seating is available.

Petrol

Most petrol stations sell two grades of leaded petrol *Essence Normale* (90 octane) and *Essence Super* (98 octane). Unleaded petrol is sold as *Essence Super* (95 octane),

Two well-known Paris sights – the Arc de Triomphe, overlooking the city's busiest junction, and the familiar gendarme directing the traffic

but pumps are marked *Super sans plomb* (Super grade unleaded). If a car designed to run on leaded petrol is filled with unleaded petrol it will do no immediate harm, provided it is the correct octane rating and the next fill is of leaded petrol.

Police deposits ('fines')

The French police have the power to impose and collect on-the-spot deposits, often mistakenly called fines, for traffic offences. The deposit must be paid in local currency and can be very high even for minor infringements. Court proceedings are always taken on a subsequent date and you can appear in court if you wish. If there is an acquittal the deposit is returned; if there is a conviction the fine is normally the amount of the deposit. It is usually easier to pay the deposit (making sure that you get a receipt), as the authorities can impound the vehicle and sell it if the deposit is not paid.

Priority including roundabouts

In built-up areas slow down and be prepared to stop at all road junctions. You have priority on roads bearing the sign *Passage protége*, but where there are no priority signs give way to traffic from the right. At roundabouts with signs bearing the words *Vous n'avez pas la priorité* or *Cédez le passage* traffic on the roundabout has priority; where no such sign exists traffic entering the roundabout has priority.

Roads

France has a comprehensive system of roads, most of which are kept in good condition. Tolls are charged on most motorways (*autoroutes*) and you may feel they are expensive (for instance Calais to Nice will cost the equivalent of around £33 for a single journey). On most toll motor-

ways a travel ticket is issued on entry and the toll is paid on leaving. The travel ticket gives all relevant information about the toll charges including the toll category of your vehicle. At the exit point the ticket is handed in and the amount due shows up on an illuminated sign at the toll booth. On some motorways the toll collection is automatic; have the correct amount ready to throw into the collecting basket. If change is required use the marked separate lane. The main roads are divided into 'N' (National) and 'D' (Departmental) categories. Some 'N' roads have recently been renumbered as 'D' roads, so an up-to-date road map is useful.

When approaching a small town, if your destination is not signposted follow the *toutes directions* or *autres directions* signs.

In towns there are sometimes special lanes for buses and taxis, marked by a continuous yellow line parallel with the kerb. These are usually in one-way streets and the vehicles in the special lanes may travel in the opposite direction.

During July and August and especially at weekends traffic on main roads is likely to be very heavy. Special signs are erected to indicate alternative routes with the least traffic congestion. Wherever they appear it is usually advantageous to follow them although you cannot be absolutely sure of gaining time. The alternative routes are quiet but they are not as wide as the main roads. They are **not** suitable for caravans. Maps showing alternative routes can be obtained from tourist information offices (*Syndicats d'Initiative*).

Speed limits

The beginning of a built-up area is indicated by a sign bearing the placename in blue letters on a light background; the end by the placename sign with a thin red line diagonally across it. Unless otherwise signposted speed limits are:

Built-up areas 60 kph (37 mph). Outside built-up areas on normal roads 90 kph (56 mph) On dual carriageways separated by a central reservation 110 kph (68 mph) On motorways 130 kph (80 mph) (Note: A driver travelling in the fast lane of a motorway at less than 80 kph (49 mph) on a level stretch of road during good daytime visibility is liable to be fined. The maximum speed on urban stretches of motorway is 110 kph (68 mph).

In wet weather speed limits outside built-up areas are 80 kph (49 mph). 100 kph (62 mph) and 110 kph (68 mph) on motorways. Both French residents and visitors to France, who have held a driving licence for less than one year, must not exceed 90 kph (56 mph) or any lower signposted limit when driving in France. Motorcycles up to 80cc are subject to a special maximum speed limit of 75 kph (45 mph).

Food in France

One of the delights of a holiday in France is – or should be – food, and you do not need to be a *gourmet* to enjoy it, or to appreciate the wines which accompany it. Being adventurous about food may introduce you to pleasures of the table which you did not know existed; and if you are conservative in your tastes you will still be impressed by the French flair for cooking.

Meal times

Traditionally the French start the day with a light 'Continental' breakfast – either coffee, tea or chocolate with rolls, toast or rusks, and jam (butter is not always provided automatically).

The main meal is customarily taken in the middle of the day and a lighter dinner is usual at night although restaurants tend to serve more evenly balanced menus these days. Morning coffee and afternoon tea are rarely taken although a growing number of establishments serve snacks.

Guests are usually expected to eat their evening meal at the hotel, even if they have only booked in for the night.

Where to eat

As in Britain, eating establishments are by no means all of a type. For the wealthy there are *haute cuisine* restaurants where cooking is an art taken seriously by connoisseurs. Any place which calls itself a restaurant will serve drinks only with meals, though in hotels there is usually a separate bar. *Bistros* are small restaurants which may be smart and expensive, especially in Paris, but more usually offer good food at moderate prices. The word *brasserie* originally meant 'brewery' and these places sell beer – including draught beer; they often serve inexpensive light meals and snacks throughout the day as well. Cafés are social eating and drinking places and range from the small and simple to the large and elaborate. They all serve a range of drinks, sandwiches and other snacks, ice-creams etc, but do not usually serve full meals unless they are 'café restaurants'. Many have tables and chairs outside and this area is known as *la terrasse*. The café is the nearest equivalent to a British pub; *cabaret* also denotes a public

house, though these establishments are usually fashionable and expensive. *Un salon de thé* serves tea, coffee and cakes, although these tend to be more expensive than cafés. On the road you may come across *une restauroute*, which serves quick meals, or a kiosk known as *une buvette* where you can buy drinks and snacks. You will also find *crêperies*, which serve a variety of both savoury and sweet pancakes.

Menus

Outside every French restaurant and café a menu with prices should be displayed. As well as the *à la carte* menu there is almost always at least one fixed price (*prix fixe*) set meal, usually with a choice of two or three main dishes. There may be a *menu touristique*, also a set meal but at a rather higher price. The *menu gastronomique* is a more elaborate meal which may be more expensive. A set meal is likely to consist of soup or *hors d'oeuvres*, fish, meat with a vegetable (often just potato), possibly salad, cheese or dessert.

If you order *à la carte* remember that main dishes *garni* include some vegetables so you may not need to order additional portions. Butter is not usually put on the

table and if asked for may cost extra. Salads are usually dressed with oil and vinegar.

Look out for the *plat du jour* (dish of the day) on the menu; this will usually incorporate something in season and therefore be at its best. House or regional specialities are also usually delicious and good value.

Food

French cooking varies greatly from region to region, making use of local produce and traditional cooking methods. Almost every part of France seems to have its own specialities – whether particular foods or methods of preparing them.

Fish is abundant in coastal regions, particularly in Brittany where shellfish and crustaceans are the speciality, and an assortment of Mediterranean fish can be tasted in Provence and Languedoc. Beef is good and plentiful in the north where the white Charollais cattle are bred, lamb is another speciality of Brittany, and pork is favoured in Lorraine. The specialities of Limousin and the Dordogne are fungi (not only the expensive truffles of Périgord), wild game, walnuts and vegetables, with goose fat often used to enrich inexpensive country-style dishes. In the Pyrénées also, goose fat is used in cooking, and Bayonne

Above: Garlic is one of the characteristic sights and flavours of Provence

Left: The chic student cafés of the Cours Mirabeau in Aix-en-Provence

ham and the Basque chickens are famous. The Alps are known for their many dishes *au gratin*. Garlic flavours the great dishes of Provence. In Burgundy red wine is used in many dishes, even for poaching eggs! Cream is used in Alsace and Lorraine in a lot of sweet dishes as well as the savoury Quiche Lorraine. Almost every area has its own cheeses, some well-known, but the others, produced on a smaller scale, are also well worth sampling. Wine is used in cooking all over the country but as this is usually the local wine, it may make a dish subtly different from the same thing cooked elsewhere.

Drinks

Some of the best wines and liqueurs in the world come from France and they have a whole bibliography of their own. Some of the more famous, such as champagne and brandy, are featured in the gazetteer sections of this book. It is not possible here to give anything other than general guidance.

Apéritifs are usually served at the restaurant table before the meal. Vermouths, Dubonnet and *pastis* – such as Pernod or Ricard – are some of the better-known apéritifs available.

The old rules concerning which wines to drink with a meal are generally no longer followed and most people follow their personal preference.

Apart from the well-known French liqueurs such as Benedictine and yellow and green Chartreuse (both herb-flavoured),

crème de menthe (peppermint) and Cointreau (bitter orange), there are local *alcools blancs*, usually made from fruits such as strawberry (*fraise*), golden plum (*mirabelle*) and pear (*poire*, or 'William's'), and also unusual herb and aromatic drinks such as *la tintaine* (flavoured with fennel) and *liqueur des pins* with an aroma which takes you straight into a pinewood.

An interesting way to buy wines by the bottle are the vineyard *caves*, many of which invite custom by roadside signs and offer tastings. Each wine region, and possibly even small areas within the region, has its good years and its poor years dependent on the weather, condition of the soil and incidence of pests and diseases, and these ups and downs are reflected in prices.

The labelling of wines is strictly controlled and the best wines are AC (*appellation contrôlée*). Next in quality are wines marked VDQS (*Vin Délimité de Qualité Supérieure*). To obtain these Government controlled classifications each wine must fulfil its specification, which, among other things, identifies the wine's place of origin. Next in line are *Vins de Pays* – good local wines – followed by *vin de table* and *vin ordinaire*.

Beer is generally sold in bottles in France and is usually chilled. The only draught beer comes from a keg and is not sold everywhere.

Mineral waters, still, slightly sparkling and fully sparkling, are widely available in France.

Shopping for food

If you are camping or in self-catering accommodation shopping for food can be a pleasure, particularly if there is an open-air market nearby. Here you will find the regional luxuries, locally grown fruit and vegetables, cheeses and poultry.

Bread is eaten with every meal and it is best to buy it fresh every day at the *boulangerie*. The most popular loaf is the long thin *baguette*. Fancy cakes and pastries are bought at the *pâtisserie*, and cooked meats, sausages, quiches and other ready-to-eat savouries come from the *charcuterie*. Uncooked meat and poultry is sold at the *boucherie* (the *boucherie chevaline* sells horsemeat), and fish is bought at the *poissonnerie*. Groceries can be bought from the *épicerie* and there is also, of course, the supermarket (*supermarché*) where you can buy almost everything.

Many shops are closed on Sunday and Monday but there are usually a few food shops open in the mornings of those days.

You may take 150 grams (5¼oz) of tea into France at any age, but you have to be over 15 to take coffee. The allowance is 750 grams (1lb 11oz) of beans or ground coffee, or 300 grams (10½oz) of instant.

Normandy and Brittany

There are many quaint fishing ports in Brittany – Douarnenez is a firm tourist favourite

Normandy and Brittany, both closely linked to Britain by geography and a common ancestry, differ in many ways one from the other. Normandy has a mild climate and lush farmlands which provide the rich dairy produce and superb fruit and vegetables on which the province's sumptuous cuisine is based. Brittany, exposed to Atlantic winds, has a wild beauty, especially in the rugged granite and sandy coves of her coast.

Lobsters, shellfish and salt-grazed lamb are culinary delights here. Even the people are different, Normans showing the hard-headedness to be expected of the descendants of Vikings, and the fervently-religious Bretons exhibiting the independent spirit of their Celtic ancestors. Of special interest to the British visitor is the evidence to be seen in both provinces of their lasting historical and cultural links with Britain.

NORMANDY AND BRITTANY

British visitors to Normandy are often struck by the 'Englishness' of the scenery. Apple orchards, lush pastures, peaceful lanes and carpets of wild flowers echo the best-loved features of our own countryside. Less obvious at a glance is our shared ancestry with the Norman people.

The Conqueror's Land Reminders of William the Conqueror are abundant in Normandy, from his statue at Falaise, his birthplace, to the world-famous Bayeux Tapestry. This powerful man encouraged the building of the awe-inspiring abbeys and cathedrals that are such an important part of Normandy's heritage. Visitors flock to the abbeys of the Seine valley, and magnificent cathedrals include those of Rouen, Evreux, Coutances and Bayeux. Caen boasts the Abbaye aux Hommes and the Abbaye aux Dames, great churches founded by William and his wife Matilda respectively and containing their tombs.

The Norman Countryside Normandy's great churches are among the finest in France and should not be missed, but it is in many ways the vernacular architecture that best captures the spirit of the province. Pretty little farmsteads seem almost to have grown out of the landscape. Some are small fortified farmsteads of stone, often with characteristic round towers, as in the Perche region or parts of the Cotentin peninsula, while others are picture-book half-timbered and often thatched cottages, or *chaumières*, as in the enchanting Pays d'Auge, a picturesque region to the west of Lisieux. A signposted 'route du cidre' takes visitors through some of the best Auge countryside, passing many farms where cider and Calvados (apple brandy) are made and can be tasted and bought. The farms of Normandy are generally smaller and less intensively farmed than our own. This may be less productive than in Britain but as a result Normandy's countryside is clad in a colourful mantle of wild flowers. Pastures, hedgerows and woodlands abound with carpets of lady's smock, cowslips, orchids, violets, primroses and bluebells. Many of these coincide with the apple-blossom, making Normandy in late spring a place of enchantment.

Although Normandy once possessed much more forest than it does today, large areas of woodland survive, providing a peaceful and shady haven for walkers and picnickers, and many miles of attractive driving for the motorist.

Cliffs, Bays and Beaches Contrasting with the varied delights of inland Normandy is its long and interesting coastline. To the west lies the great seaport of Le Havre, contrasting with the quaint old fishing port of Honfleur across the Seine estuary. Nearby are the smart resorts of Deauville and Trouville, with sandy beaches and all the trappings of jet-set holidaymaking.

The beaches of Calvados and the western Cotentin peninsula hold a very different significance, and will always be associated with the D-Day landings on 6 June 1944. The huge, dune-backed beaches have been taken over by holidaymakers again, but everywhere there are military cemeteries, monuments and museums that are sobering reminders of 'Operation Overlord'.

The north and west coasts of the Cotentin peninsula are something of a prelude to Brittany as the coast becomes more rugged, studded with lighthouses, wild headlands and fishing ports. A spectacular transition from the Normandy coast to that of Brittany is provided by the Bay of Mont-St-Michel. Officially now part of Normandy, it has been a place of pilgrimage for hundreds of years, and now attracts up to three-quarters of a million visitors every year.

The splendid chalk cliffs at Étretat are counterparts of our White Cliffs of Dover

Markets like this, full of colour and movement, can be found all over Brittany

The ancient land of Brittany is formed of rocks that are among the oldest in the world, and here lived some of the first permanent settlers in France – the stone-age peoples who erected the massive standing stones (menhirs) and burial chambers (dolmens) which are to be seen in many parts of the province. The most splendid are the gigantic alignments of menhirs near Carnac, the earliest of which were raised about 7,500 years ago.

The First Bretons A much later wave of settlers introduced the distinctive Breton culture and character that survive today. These were Celts, who migrated from Wales and Cornwall during the 5th and 6th centuries AD. When they crossed the Channel and settled in what came to be known as 'Little Britain', they not only gave Brittany the foundations of its modern name (*Bretagne* in French), but brought with them their language and religion, still an essential part of Breton life. Breton, which has much in common with Welsh and Cornish, is still spoken by many people in Western Brittany.

Christians, Past and Present Brittany's place-names offer a clue to the religious influence of the early Celtic settlers. As Christians, they founded numerous churches, and very often the church benefactors were canonised by the local people. It is said that Brittany has over 7,000 saints of this kind, and many of them are still remembered in town and village names. The Breton people have carried their faith with them down the centuries and are well known for their religious fervour, which shows itself in many ways. One cannot drive far, especially in Western Brittany, without passing signs to tucked-away country chapels, and there are numerous stone crosses by the roadside. These culminate in a unique Breton art form – the parish enclosure (see page 28). The religious festivals known as *Pardons*, which take place, usually during the summer months, in almost every town and village, are impressive manifestations of religious zeal. The *Pardon* involves a procession of local people, often dressed in traditional Breton costume, particularly the regional lace *coiffes* (head-dresses), carry-

ing banners, candles and statues of saints and accompanied by hymns and prayers. The festival also has a secular face, with a fair, music and dancing, and perhaps wrestling, a traditional sport of the Breton peasant.

Armor and Argoat These ancient Celtic words are used to describe the two faces of Brittany: 'Argoat', meaning 'land of the woods' – the word for the interior; and 'Armor', meaning 'land of the sea'. Much of the forest that once covered the Argoat has been felled to make way for farmland or to build boats for this race of seafarers, but inland Brittany can still offer the visitor vast areas of unspoilt and peaceful country-side, where room can usually be found in hotels and campsites even at the height of the season. A large area around the Monts d'Arrée in the north west is now the Armorique Regional Nature Park. Surviving forests include the Forêt de Paimpont, west of Rennes – interesting not only for its wildlife but also for its legends. It is said that this is the ancient Forest of Brocéliande, steeped in legends of Merlin,

King Arthur and Sir Lancelot, as well as rich in Druidic connections.

For all its delights, the Argoat will always take second place, for the holidaymaker, to the Armor. Brittany's jagged and deeply indented coastline is over 750 miles long. There are important naval bases at Brest and Lorient. Fishing ports range from Concarneau and Lorient, two of the most important in France, to numerous small harbours with fleets of little boats. Many Bretons work on large modern trawlers or tunny boats, while others are involved in inshore fishing, bringing in among other things the delicious lobsters, scallops, crabs and other shellfish for which Brittany is well known.

Perhaps the most important influence that coastal Brittany has had on the life of its peoples in recent decades is the prosperity brought by tourism. Visitors from all over Europe are attracted by Brittany's many miles of smooth golden sand and dramatic cliff scenery. The province has numerous resorts that combine modern facilities with all the timeless charm that this ancient province has to offer.

23

Places of Interest

ALENÇON (Orne)

Not immediately impressive but with unexpected attributes, Alençon is a market town for produce from the surrounding farms and for Percheron horses. The Place Foch by the bridge over the River Sarthe is a good place to start exploring, and across the bridge is the Promenade des Rosaires where there are animals and an aviary. Alençon is a good centre for excursions, too, the delightful scenery and picturesque valleys of the Perseigne Forest to the south east, the Écouve Forest to the north, and the heather-covered hills of the Mancelles Alps to the west all being within easy reach.

Since the 17th century Alençon has been famous for the making of lace, examples of which can be seen in the Art Gallery and Lace Museum. It has also become a renowned pilgrimage centre where many flock to see the house where Ste-Thérèse de l'Enfant Jésus was born in 1873 (see also Lisieux, page 31).

What to see Art Gallery (17–19c paintings by Courbet, Géricault, Mme Vigée-Lebrun, etc); former Castle (14–15c towers); Chapel and house of Ste-Thérèse; Church of Notre Dame (14–15c with 16c stained-glass windows); Forest of Perseigne; Lace Museum.

LES ANDELYS (Eure)

This little town consists of the twin settlements of Grand Andely and Petit Andely. The former is a shopping centre with a busy market, while the latter is a charming old town in a beautiful setting beside the River Seine, overlooked by the massive cliff-top remains of Château Gaillard. This great fortress was built by Richard the Lionheart in the late 12th century as a defence against the King of France. The castle was later dismantled but, although little remains of the outer defences, part of the original redoubt and most of the keep are still standing and the site provides a magnificent view over the Seine valley. Les Andelys is a popular tourist centre and has sporting facilities including a sailing school.

What to see Château Gaillard; Church of St-Sauveur (12–15c).

ARGENTAN (Orne)

This small town on the banks of the River Orne suffered severe war damage in 1944, when it was the site of the last battle for Normandy. It has since been almost entirely rebuilt. Not far away is Le Pin-au-Haras, with a château built in 1717–28 and stables which house 100 fine stallions. This stud is open to the public. Also nearby is the Château d'O, a building as strange as its name, built of rose-coloured brick, with steeples, turrets and steeply-sloping roofs reflected in the lake which fronts it. Neither the château nor its garden is open to the public but it can be admired from the road. Argentan is best known for the production of lace, a craft which is practised by the nuns of the Benedictine abbey, the sole exponents of Le Point d'Argentan. Examples may sometimes be seen on request at the abbey.

What to see Church of St-Martin (15–16c); Le Pin-au-Haras.

ARROMANCHES-LES-BAINS (Calvados)

The seaside resort of Arromanches-les-Bains became internationally famous as the site of 'Mulberry B', one of two artificial 'mulberry' harbours, which were towed piece by piece across the Channel and used for the landing of supplies and troops for the Allies during the period following the D-Day invasion. Evidence of this operation can still be seen on the beach, where some of the caissons of the old mulberry harbour are visible.

What to see Musée du Débarquement (Invasion Museum – contains various collections relating to the Allied forces).

AVRANCHES (Manche)

Although it is one of the oldest towns in Normandy, Avranches is best known for its proximity to Mont-St-Michel. The Jardin des Plantes (Botanical Garden) provides a fine view of this imposing fortified island, and the Avranchin Museum contains many early manuscripts relating mainly to the Abbey of Mont-St-Michel. Other interesting features include the skull of an 8th-century bishop of Avranches, St Aubert, which is on display in the treasury of St-Gervase and St-Protais Basilica. *La plate-forme* is a paving stone on the site of the former cathedral, marking the spot where, in 1172, Henry II received absolution and did public penance following the murder of Thomas à Becket two years earlier. A much more recent monument commemorates the spot where General Patton had his headquarters while planning his major offensive in 1944.

What to see Avranchin Museum; Botanical Gardens; Patton Monument; The Platform.

Petit Andely, seen here from Richard the Lionheart's Château Gaillard, lies where the Seine curves through wooded hills

BAGNOLES-DE-L'ORNE (Orne)

Together with neighbouring Tessé-la-Madelaine, Bagnoles-de-l'Orne is the largest spa resort in western France. It is notable particularly for its position on a delightfully wooded lake, fed by the River Vée. The spa contains a natural spring whose water rises at a constant temperature of 27°C and is especially beneficial to those suffering from circulatory disorders. Bagnoles offers good entertainment and sporting facilities, including a casino, and is a popular excursion centre.
What to see Couterne Castle; Roc au Chien (viewpoint); The Spa building, park, and lake.

BALLEROY (Calvados)

The village, about 16km (10 miles) south west of Bayeux, is dominated by a fine 17th-century castle, which stands at the end of the main street and is surrounded by moats and formal gardens. The interior is richly decorated and houses an interesting collection of portraits. The château is also the home of a museum devoted to hot air balloons.
What to see Château de Balleroy.

BARENTIN (Seine-Maritime)

This town, 17km (10½ miles) north west of Rouen, is mainly concerned with the manufacture of textiles and electrical equipment, but it has earned the name 'the town of the street museum' because of the number of works by well-known sculptors, including Rodin and Bourdelle, which can be seen in its streets. Just outside the town is a more offbeat sculpture – a 44ft-high reproduction of the Statue of Liberty, built for a French film.
What to see Museum of Local History; sculptures.

BAYEUX (Calvados)

Bayeux, an important town during both the Roman and Norman eras, achieved the more modern distinction of being the first French town to be liberated in June 1944. Surprisingly, it suffered no war damage and the old quarter, around the Cathedral of Notre Dame, has retained a distinctly medieval flavour. One of the finest old houses is now the tourist information office. The Cathedral itself dates from 1077. Bayeux's most famous sight is Queen Matilda's Tapestry (*Tapisserie de la Reine Mathilde*), a magnificent 231-ft-long work of

Home of a Royal William

Normandy's links with Britain begin with the Battle of Hastings in 1066, after which William, Duke of Normandy, became King of England. Born in 1028 at Falaise, William was the illegitimate son of Robert 'le Diable', son of the Duke of Normandy. Robert died when his bastard heir was only seven, and William was brought up by his mother, a peasant girl named Arlette. William was a direct descendant of Rollo, Viking leader of the 9th-century invasion by wild 'Northmen', who became a Christian in exchange for land which was the basis of Normandy. He and his descendants encouraged communities of Benedictine monks and financed the building of their abbeys, paving the way for the great Norman tradition of church architecture. The conquest of England is commemorated in the Bayeux Tapestry, a remarkable embroidered 'strip-cartoon' depicting the story from Harold's visit to William in Normandy to his death, and William's victory, at Hastings. It can be seen in the former Bishop's Palace at Bayeux.

At Bayeux Harold swears fealty to William – a detail from the Tapestry

embroidery which traces the history of the Norman Conquest of England in the manner of a modern strip cartoon. The tapestry is believed to have been worked in England, and is a delightful picture-book of 11th-century life, providing historians with an insight into the armour, means of transport, etc, of the period. The tapestry is displayed in the former Bishop's Palace.
What to see Queen Matilda's Tapestry; Botanical Gardens; Cathedral of Notre Dame.

The tower of Bayeux Cathedral, 15th-century with an added 'bonnet', glows austerely beautiful in the winter sunshine

LE BEC-HELLOUIN (Eure)

Founded in 1034, the Abbey of Le Bec-Hellouin, about 34km (21 miles) from Rouen, soon became one of the most important religious and intellectual centres of Europe, providing two consecutive Archbishops of Canterbury (Lanfranc and Anselm) during the 11th century. Most of the medieval buildings are now destroyed, apart from the column foundations of the old abbey church; St-Nicholas Tower, which stands nearby, dates from the 15th century and some of the rest from the 17th. There is a fine view from the top of the tower over the new abbey buildings and the surrounding countryside.
What to see Car Museum; Parish Church (part 14c).

BELLÊME (Orne)

This small town, about 17km (10½ miles) south of Mortagne-au-Perche, clings to a high cliff overlooking a forest of majestic oaks and the lovely countryside of Perche. A number of fine 17th- and 18th-century houses are to be seen in the rue Ville-Close and neighbouring streets of the old quarter. 'Le Porch' (a fortified gateway) and some towers now incorporated in houses are all that remain of the 15th-century ramparts which were built upon the foundations of an 11th-century fortress.
What to see Bansard des Bois Mansion, 26 rue Ville-Close; Bellême Forest.

BERNAY (Eure)

Bernay is an ancient town which developed rapidly around its abbey in the 11th century. There are several old churches, including the Basilica of Notre Dame de la Couture, which has a roof composed entirely of wood. 13km (8 miles) to the south east is Beaumesnil château, its elegant Louis XIII exterior mirrored in a lake. The gardens can be viewed and there are guided tours of the interior on some days.
What to see Beaumesnil Château; Museum (collection of Rouen and Nevers china, Norman furniture); Notre-Dame-de-la-Couture Basilica (15c).

NORMANDY AND BRITTANY

BREST (N Finistère)

Brest is a long-established naval port with one of the finest natural harbours in the world. During the Second World War it suffered extensive damage and has subsequently undergone major rebuilding. As a result it is the most modern town in Brittany. The naval base and dockyard cover a large portion of the town's waterfront, and the 12th-century castle is also Admiralty property. The Cours Dajot, an extensive promenade laid out during the 18th century on the site of the old town walls by convicts from the naval prison, provides a fine view over the harbour and the surrounding countryside.

What to see Castle (12–17c); Paradise Tower (houses a naval museum); Naval Dockyard; Palais des Arts et de la Culture; Recouverance Bridge (biggest drawbridge in Europe); Tanguy Tower (Middle Ages).

BRIONNE (Eure)

This small town was originally built as a strongpoint to command the Risle valley. The 12th-century castle ruins include a Norman keep, from the base of which there is an attractive view of the town and the surrounding countryside. The town is now involved in the textile trade.

What to see Keep (12c).

CAEN (Calvados)

This industrial port and university city on the River Orne retains numerous links with its medieval past despite suffering severe war damage in 1944. The town's importance during the 11th century is emphasised by the castle (which now contains the Fine Arts Museum, a major regional art gallery with works by Italian, French and Flemish masters, and the Normandy Museum) and the Abbaye aux Hommes, both built by William the Conqueror. The Abbaye aux Dames was founded by his queen, Matilda, whose tomb can still be seen there.

What to see Botanical Gardens; Castle (11–15c); Hotel d'Escoville (16c – contains Tourist Information Centre); Fine Arts Museum; Normandy Museum (local history).

CANCALE (Ille-et-Vilaine)

This holiday resort and picturesque fishing port lies on the Bay of Mont-St-Michel. Oysters from beds in the Bay have brought Cancale gastronomic fame for centuries past. The town has recently become also a water-sports centre.

One of the best views of the beautiful bay and coastline beyond is from Chaîne Point about 2.5km (1½ miles) away, which can only be reached on foot though cars can negotiate the road for 1.5km (about 1 mile).

What to see Chaîne Point (views); Fenêtre jetty; Jeanne Jugan's House; Pointe du Hock (viewpoint); Woodcarving Museum.

CARHAIX-PLOUGUER (N Finistère)

A former Roman settlement, this is now a cattle-breeding area and the main milk-producing centre of the region, known for its cattle fairs. Carhaix is a good centre for touring the Montagnes Noires, the real heart of Brittany where Breton is still spoken. The anglers' paradise of Châteauneuf du Faou, a village on the River Aulne about 20km (12¼ miles) to the south west of the town, is a very pretty and typically Breton village.

What to see Church of St Temeur (part 16c); House of the Seneschal (Renaissance).

CARNAC (Morbihan)

As well as being a popular resort, Carnac is famous for its wealth of megaliths. More than 3,000 of these are standing stones set in multiple rows known as *alignments* which stretch across the countryside around Carnac for several kilometres. The Lines of Ménac and megaliths at Locmariaquer are particularly worth seeing. The St-Michel Tumulus, a long-barrow containing Bronze Age burial chambers, can be explored under the supervision of a guide, but most of the finds from the tumulus are now in Carnac Museum. Neighbouring Carnac-Plage has grown up around a fine stretch of gently-shelving beach facing the Atlantic but sheltered by the Quiberon Peninsula. Though recently developed, it is not brashly new, its hotels and villas being scattered among pines beside the mile-long beach. The peninsula and off-shore islands (see Quiberon, page 33) give added interest to the seascape.

What to see J Miln and Z le Rouzic Prehistorical Museum; St-Michel Tumulus.

CAUDEBEC-EN-CAUX (Seine-Maritime)

Built in the form of an amphitheatre facing the river Seine, Caudebec was once the capital of the Caux Region. Not much of the old town can be seen now as most of it was destroyed by fire in June 1940, only the Church of Notre Dame and three old houses surviving intact.

What to see Church of Notre Dame (15–16c); Maison des Templiers (Templars' House (13c) – museum of local history).

CHÂTEAULIN (S Finistère)

Standing on a bend in the canalised River Aulne, just above the tidal reaches, this small town is one of the major salmon-fishing centres in the area. Overlooking the town is the Chapel of Our Lady, which provides fine views of the deep Aulne Valley.

What to see Chapel of Our Lady.

CHERBOURG (Manche)

The port of Cherbourg, built originally as a naval base, was completely destroyed in 1944. Subsequently reconstructed, it has become important in the handling of both trans-Atlantic and cross-Channel traffic. The Fort-du-Roule, overlooking the town, houses a Museum of the Second World War and Liberation, and affords extensive views over the town and harbour installations. The naval port and arsenal are not open to overseas visitors.

What to see Emmanuel-Lias Park (tropical vegetation); Fort-du-Roule; Natural History Museum; Outer Harbour; Thomas Henry Fine Arts Museum; War and Liberation Museum.

More than 1,000 prehistoric standing stones, some twice a man's height, form the Ménec Lines near Carnac

CLÈRES (Seine-Maritime)
Clères is noted for one of Normandy's great attractions – a zoo within the grounds of the 14th-century castle. Although animals are featured, the zoo specialises in birds and has a wide variety of species in its collection. Clères caters for the motor enthusiast too, with guided tours round the Normandy Car Museum.
What to see Castle; Normandy Car Museum; Zoo.

COMBOURG (Ille-et-Vilaine)
This little town is romantically sited by the edge of a small lake and is surrounded by wooded countryside. It is dominated by an 11th-century castle where, during the 18th century, the writer Francois-René Chateaubriand spent two years of his youth. His gloomy experiences here were later related in his 'Mémoires d'Outre-Tombe' ('Memoirs from beyond the Tomb'). Consequently admirers of his work have turned Combourg into a literary pilgrimage centre where, today, the castle houses a museum devoted to him.
What to see The Castle.

CONCARNEAU (S Finistère)
The daily life of Concarneau is based primarily around the fishing industry but it is also a popular seaside resort. It is one of France's largest fishing ports and has become a significant market for tunny. The importance of fishing is highlighted in the town by the presence of numerous fish-canning plants. Concarneau's other famous asset is its walled town – which covers a small area of only 350m by 100m (380 yards by 108 yards). Built on an island, it is linked to the mainland by two bridges.
What to see Fishing Museum; the Harbours; Ville Close.

COUTANCES (Manche)
Coutances, known as the religious centre of the Cotentin Peninsula, stands majestically on a hill top above the Bulsard Valley. Although much of the town suffered war damage in 1944, Coutances Cathedral remained unscathed and the rebuilding around it has done nothing to detract from this fine example of Norman–Gothic architecture. There are pleasant public gardens near the cathedral, affording views over the Bulsard Valley.
What to see Cathedral (13c); Hôtel Poupinel (local museum).

'Choice fish' says the sign over this Dieppe quay, where colourful boats unload their catch

DAOULAS (N Finistère)
A little town straddling the River Daoulas, with an interesting Parish Close. This is a good place from which to visit the old-world Plougastel Peninsula, an area of hedged lanes cutting through farmland divided into small fields and famous for strawberries.
What to see Plougastel Peninsula.

DEAUVILLE (Calvados)
This elegant and luxurious international holiday resort founded by the Duc de Morny in 1866, has wide avenues and a fine beach backed by a wooden promenade ('les planches') where models sometimes display the latest Paris fashions and the wealthy or notorious stroll. Deauville has a yacht club and a large yacht basin and is a centre for aquatic events. It is probably best known, however, for its equestrian season which includes the Deauville Grand Prix, regular meetings at La Touques and Claire Fontaine racecourses, show-jumping and international polo. There are good entertainment facilities including night-clubs and a popular casino; but Deauville is, as may be expected of a jet-set resort, an expensive place in which to stay.
What to see Casino; Marina; 'Les Planches'; People.

DIEPPE (Seine-Maritime)
Despite its prominent position as a major passenger and commercial port, Dieppe continues to live up to its reputation as France's oldest seaside resort, offering good beach, entertainment and shopping facilities; Grand'Rue is an outstanding shopping precinct which seems to sell everything. Dieppe also has a thriving fishing industry, specialising in turbot, sole and scallops, and regular fish auctions take place at the Port de Pêche. Dieppe's past is preserved in the shape of the castle built on the site of the town's medieval fortifications. The Square du Canada, below the castle, contains a monument to Dieppe men who explored Canada between the 16th century and the 18th century, and a plaque commemorating the Canadian Commando Raid of 1942, an exploratory landing which, despite heavy losses, provided valuable information for the subsequent Allied invasion.
What to see Boulevard de la Mer (viewpoint); Castle (15c).

DINAN (Côtes-du-Nord)
Both the town and its surroundings hold a great deal of interest for the tourist. The old quarter has streets of ancient houses with trees and attractive gardens, and is surrounded by ramparts dominated by a castle dating from the 14th century which stands on a plateau 74m (240ft) above the River Rance. There are some impressive views from the ramparts, and from the terraced English Garden (Jardin Anglais), which overlooks the Viaduct and the Gothic Bridge.
What to see Castle (14c – contains local history museum); English Garden; Old town (15–16c); St-Saviour's Basilica (12–16c).

DINARD (Ille-et-Vilaine)
This seaside holiday resort lying opposite St-Malo on the Rance estuary was made popular in the late 19th century by both British and American holiday-makers. Previously it had been a simple fishing village. As a resort, it owes its popularity to its entertainment facilities, its two large beaches and the splendid views of the surrounding coast which can be taken in from Moulinet Point. Further spectacular views of the coast and offshore islands can be seen from Étêtés Point and Port-Riou Garden, and a walk along the Clair de Lune Promenade provides a fine panorama of the Rance estuary.
What to see Aquarium and Marine Museum; Clair de Lune Promenade; Grand Plage (beach); Étêtés Point; Moulinet Point.

Fishing boats in the morning sun at Étretat, with the white cliffs of Falaise d'Amont behind

DOL-DE-BRETAGNE (Ille-et-Vilaine)

Dol, a former bishopric, is now known as the capital of the 'Marais' (marsh) district. It stands on the edge of a 19m (64ft) cliff which, until the 12th century, was washed by the sea. Dol's main attraction is its Cathedral (13th century) and attention should be given to the carved arm rests on the eighty 14th-century choir stalls. The Promenade des Douves, behind the Cathedral, offers good views of Mont Dol and the surrounding area.

What to see Cathedral of St-Samson; 'La Guillotière' Museum (local history); Promenade des Douves.

DOMFRONT (Orne)

Domfront stands on a steep-sided spur overlooking the Varenne River which flows here through the spectacular Valley of the Rocks. Although its fortress was razed, two impressive walls of the square keep have remained. An attractive public garden has been laid out on the site of the fortress, from where there is a splendid view of the river valley, and the Passais countryside.

What to see Church of Notre Dame sur l'Eau (11c); Town Hall (paintings by local artist Léandre, 1862–1934).

DOUARNENEZ (S Finistère)

The ancient town of Douarnenez is now linked to Tréboul by a bridge over the Port-Rhu estuary and these towns, together with Ploaré and Pouldavid, make up the modern community of Douarnenez. This is one of the busiest fishing ports on the Breton coast, and is noted particularly for sardines and lobsters. The harbours are lively and in particular Rosmeur Harbour is worth an early-morning visit to see the fish being auctioned. Look for countrywomen wearing traditional starched lace coifs. The town's chief industry, inevitably, is fish preserving but Tréboul is a popular seaside resort and there are fine beaches to both east and west of Douarnenez, which offers facilities for water sports and has two sailing schools. Many legends are connected with the town. The beautiful city of Ys, ruled in the 6th century by King Gradlon whose daughter was persuaded by the Devil to give him the golden key to the dyke which protected it, lies beneath the waves of the Bay of Douarnenez. It is said that the city will cease to be accursed when Good Friday Mass is celebrated in one of its drowned churches, the bells of which can sometimes be heard. Off-shore is Tristan's Isle, connected with the tragic love story of Tristan and Iseult and later the lair of the villainous La Fontenelle, a guerilla leader who ravaged the country during the religious wars of the 16th century.

What to see Boulevard Jean-Richepin; New Harbour; Rosmeur Harbour.

ÉTRETAT (Seine-Maritime)

A popular seaside resort noted for its unique cliff scenery. Two imposing chalk cliffs stand at either end of the beach, Falaise d'Amont (Downstream Cliff), surmounted by a small chapel, and Falaise d'Aval (Upstream Cliff) with a huge natural archway through its centre, and a 62m (200ft) tapered column which stands a short distance from the shore. An interesting restored covered market can be seen in the Place Maréchal Foch and a monument to the aviators Charles Nungesser and François Coli, who made an unsuccessful attempt to fly the Atlantic in 1927, stands on Falaise d'Amont near a museum dedicated to the two pioneers.

What to see Falaise d'Amont; Falaise d'Aval.

EVREUX (Eure)

An old-established town in the Iton Valley which has suffered repeated war damage over the last fifteen centuries but has managed to emerge as a pleasant market centre retaining a number of historical buildings. The cathedral, a mixture of many architectural styles, is still undergoing restoration but some of its early features have been preserved, notably the nave arches which date from the 12th century.

What to see Ancien Évêché (Bishop's Palace); Museum (in Ancien Évêché); Promenade des Remparts; Public Gardens.

Parish Art

Characteristic signs of the Breton's religious zeal are the parish enclosures (enclos paroissiaux) of north-western Brittany. Within a walled enclosure, entered through a grand arch, stands the parish church and a calvary, a stone crucifix usually ornamented with scenes from the life of Christ, or even from Breton legend; the calvary at Guimiliau has 200 carved figures. Often the church porch, also, is elaborately carved, and most of the *enclos* include an ossuary. These were used to store exhumed bones when graveyard space became short. Most *enclos* date from the 16th and 17th centuries, though the oldest, at La Martyre, near Landerneau, is 15th-century. There was often intense rivalry between neighbouring parishes, as at Guimiliau and St-Thégonnec. Together with

Detail of the enclosure at St Thégonnec

Lampaul-Guimiliau, these make up the *'Circuit des Trois Enclos'*, a signposted tour of the finest examples of this unusual art form.

FALAISE (Calvados)

An interesting little town in the rocky Ante Valley which suffered severe war damage during the German retreat of 1944. There has been extensive rebuilding but the town's dominant feature is still the huge ruined castle where William the Conqueror, the illegitimate son of Robert, Duke of Normandy, and Arlette, a Falaise tanner's daughter, was born in 1027. The Place Guillaume-le-Conquérant contains an equestrian statue of William, with the first six Dukes of Normandy; and a fountain dedicated to his mother, Arlette, stands near the river. Mount Myrrha, to the west of the town, provides a fine view of the castle and the surrounding countryside.
What to see Castle (12c); Church of Notre Dame de Guibray (part Romanesque); Church of St-Gervais (11–16c); Church of La Trinité (part 15c); Mount Myrrha.

FÉCAMP (Seine-Maritime)

A major fishing port, Fécamp is the most important centre for cod in France, the deep sea trawlers operating as far afield as Newfoundland. The town also has two other claims to fame – it is the birthplace of Benedictine Liqueur, and was the home of Guy de Maupassant, the 19th-century novelist. The Benedictine monastery was founded in the 11th century on the site of an earlier establishment and the liqueur was first distilled in the 16th century. Visitors may tour the distillery and the museum. The church of La Trinité, beautiful both inside and out, contains the Precious Blood relic, to which pilgrimages are made on the Tuesday and Thursday following Trinity Sunday.
What to see Benedictine Museum; Distillery; La Trinité Church (12–18c); Port.

LA FERTÉ BERNARD (Sarthe)

The original town with its *Ferté* (small fortress) was partly raised on piles above marshy land in the valley of the River Huisne, which, with its tributary the Même, flows through La Ferté Bernard today. The bustling market of the modern town contrasts with the tranquil section of old houses which lies beyond the medieval gatehouse (Porte St-Julien).
What to see Church of Notre Dame des Marais (15–17c); Folklore Museum; Old Houses; Porte St-Julien.

FLERS (Orne)

A town mainly concerned with light industry, situated in the picturesque area around the River Orne known as Suisse Normande (Norman Switzerland). The town itself is not very inspiring but the Château (now the Town Hall and Museum) is a fine building which dates from the 16th century and has an attractive moated garden. Eleven kilometres (7 miles) north west of the town is Mount Cerisi where spectacular views may be obtained from the castle on the summit.
What to see Château (15c); Mount Cerisi.

FOUGÈRES (Ille-et-Vilaine)

Fougères is set beside a forest on a promontory overlooking the

Nançon valley. It is an industrial town and concentrates, largely, on the manufacture of shoes. However its great castle is a fine example of medieval military architecture and has made Fougères a tourist centre. A good general view of the castle is obtained from the Place aux Arbres, a public garden on the former ramparts of the town. The castle, a vast fortress with thirteen towers which rate among the largest in Europe, is almost surrounded by the waters of the River Nançon. A walk is possible round the massive wall, from which there are good views.
What to see Castle; Fougères State Forest (beech woods – 3km (2 miles) NE); Place aux Arbres; Place du Marchix (old houses).

GISORS (Eure)

Gisors, the present capital of the Vexin region, was an important frontier town during the Middle Ages and still has considerable character in spite of World War II damage. The remains of the massive fortress, built by Robert of

Not a Gothic cathedral but a distillery! Behind this 19th-century façade, at Fécamp, Benedictine liqueur is made. The label (left) will show whether you have bought the real thing

Bêlleme at the end of the 11th century, provide ample evidence of the town's strategic importance, and there is an interesting old church with an unusual mixture of architectural styles.
What to see Castle (11–12c); Church of St-Gervais and St-Protais (12–16c).

GOURNAY-EN-BRAY (Seine-Maritime)

A busy dairy centre in the Epte Valley, famous for its cream cheese, in particular the well-known 'Petit Suisse'. The local church contains some interesting carvings and is remarkable for the varied ornamentation on the capitals of its columns.
What to see Church of St-Hildevert (11–12c).

GRANVILLE (Manche)

In the shadow of its rock, Granville has developed as a seaside resort and commercial port, known especially as an embarkation point for the Chausey Islands. Divided in two, the upper and lower parts of the town are significantly different from one-another. The Upper Town, founded by the English in 1439, has retained some of its rather grim but quaint character. Within its walls there are numerous exhibits hinting at Granville's military and religious past. In contrast, the more modern Lower Town is dominated by business and the tourist trade. Granville, as a whole, has good entertainment facilities including a casino.
What to see Aquarium; Christian-Dior Garden; Church of Notre Dame (15–17c); Old Granville Museum; Roc Point and Lighthouse; Waxworks Museum.

GUINGAMP (Côtes-du-Nord)

Lying in the Trieux valley, Guingamp is an important agricultural market. It was once a feudal city, indicated by the ruins of its 15th-century castle and ramparts. However, its fame is due to the revered statue of the Black Virgin in the Basilica of Notre Dame de Bon Secours. In her honour one of the famous 'pardons' of Brittany occurs on the Saturday night before the first Sunday in July. The candlelight procession, consisting of vast numbers of pilgrims and a presiding bishop, moves through the streets. After its conclusion three bonfires are lit by the bishop.
What to see Basilica of Notre Dame de Bon Secours.

NORMANDY AND BRITTANY

LE HAVRE (Seine-Maritime)

The second-largest port in France after Marseille, Le Havre is situated on the right bank of the Seine estuary. All the port installations are modern, due to the destruction of the docks in 1944. The old 16th-century town was destroyed at the same time, and a new town has been built, mainly in reinforced concrete. A huge new shopping centre is now open. The Place-de-l'Hôtel-de-Ville is one of the largest squares in Europe, and has a public garden in the centre. Leading off the square is a shopping concourse, the Rue-de-Paris, and the pleasantly shaded Avenue Foch leads from the square to the Porte Océane and the beach. The beach is approximately one mile long, and affords good views over the estuary. At the southern end of the beach is the pleasure craft harbour and the north breakwater, from the tip of which there is an extensive view of the outer harbour and the town. Outstanding above the town is the modern church of St-Joseph.

What to see André Malraux Fine Arts Museum (splendid galleries with paintings by Boudin and Dufy); Montgeon Forest; Old Havre Museum; Place-de-l'Hôtel-de-Ville.

HONFLEUR (Calvados)

Honfleur is an enchanting little port. It lies at the mouth of the Seine and was once more important than Le Havre which faces it across the river. The busy quays of the Old Dock (Vieux Bassin) are lined with tall, narrow, slate-roofed houses which are reflected in the water. The Church of St Catherine was built completely of wood by axe-masters from the shipyards, in thanksgiving at the end of the Hundred Years War (1453) and is one of the few surviving wooden churches in Europe.

Honfleur has, over the centuries, been an inspiration to writers (such as Baudelaire), musicians and painters, and in the 19th century saw the birth of the Impressionist School, members of which held their first meeting at the Ferme St-Siméon. It continues to attract artists from far afield.

The Côte-de-Grace, behind the town, provides fine views over the surrounding coastline.

What to see Côte-de-Grace; Church of Ste-Catherine (16–18c); Eugène Boudin Museum (paintings, 18c furniture); Old Honfleur Museum; (Musée du Vieux Honfleur – Maritime and Folk Art Museum); Vieux Bassin.

HUELGOAT (N Finistère)

An attractive town in a picturesque setting among the wooded glades, rocky hollows and waterfalls of the Forest of Huelgoat. The town is attractive for its beautiful surroundings rather than for its buildings. It is a favourite centre for anglers and there are numerous forest walks to local beauty spots. You have to be fairly agile to descend to the Grotte-du-Diable (Devil's Grotto), but the Allée Violette, a forest walk following the course of a stream which here roars below boulders before emerging into the open, is more easily negotiable.

What to see Grotte-du-Diable; Roche Tremblante (Trembling Rock); Allée Violette.

JOSSELIN (Morbihan)

Situated on the River Oust, this town contains one of the finest medieval castles in Brittany. The Basilica of Notre Dame du Roncier (Our Lady of the Bramble-bush) is well-known for its 'great pardon' which takes place on the second Sunday in September. There is a fine view from the top of the Basilica's tower.

What to see Castle (14–19c); Fountain of Notre Dame du Roncier.

LAMBALLE (Côtes-du-Nord)

A charming little market town on a hill overlooking the River Gouessant, Lamballe has a market dealing mainly in pigs and cattle. The Church of Notre Dame stands on a terrace which provides a panoramic view over the Gouessant Valley. Horse-lovers will enjoy visiting the stud farm (haras), which is open to the public between August and January. Also at the haras are a school of dressage and a riding club, and horse shows are held.

What to see Church of Notre Dame (mainly Gothic); Haras (stud farm).

LANDERNEAU (N Finistère)

This old town was once the capital of Léon. Situated at the head of the Elorn estuary amid beautiful farmlands, Landerneau has established itself as a port engaged in salmon and trout fishing. It is also the market for locally-grown vegetables and fruit. The town itself has a great deal of charm, with overhanging houses, an ancient bridge and a quaint market place, and is a good centre for touring. There are a number of Parish Enclosures (see page 28) in the vicinity.

What to see Bridge.

The Old Dock, its houses mirrored in still water, is typical of the delightful scenes which have made Honfleur loved by artists

LANDÉVENNEC (S Finistère)

Although situated near the mouth of the River Aulne on the Atlantic coast, Landévennec is so well sheltered that it has an almost Mediterranean feel, with lush vegetation around the settlement which lies at the foot of wooded slopes. As a result it is a favoured weekend retreat though it offers little in the way of entertainment. Its history is bound up in the abbey which was founded in the 5th century by St Guénolé, but only ruins of the abbey church are left as a reminder of Landévennec's monastic beginnings. Nearby is a Benedictine Abbey which was built in 1965 and is noted for the daily singing of Gregorian chant.
What to see Ruins of the former abbey; the Benedictine Abbey.

LANNION (Côtes du Nord)

Situated on the River Léguer, Lannion is both a port and a market town. Many of its streets are old and full of character, which has rendered it popular with tourists. The 12th-century church of Brélévenez overlooks the town and from its terrace there is a good view of the surrounding area. On the outskirts of Lannion is the famous research centre in tele-communications and electronics, the 'Centre de Recherches de Lannion'.
What to see The Bridge. Place Général-Leclerc.

LILLEBONNE (Seine-Maritime)

A small industrialised town which was a major port in Roman times. The Romans left a small theatre whose ruins can be seen, and there is an interesting Gallo-Roman museum.
What to see Castle (12–13c); Gallo-Roman Museum; Museum of Popular Art; Roman Theatre (2c).

LISIEUX (Calvados)

A thriving industrial centre which lost most of its old buildings during 1944. Lisieux's religious heritage, however, remained largely unscathed and the town contains one of the oldest Gothic cathedrals in Normandy.

In more modern times Lisieux has become famous as the home of Ste-Thérèse who was born in Alençon as Thérèse Martin. When she was only nine years of age she knew she had a vocation as a nun but the Church authorities thought she was too young and it was not

The Church of Le Pénity in Locronan square contains this coloured 16th-century carving of Christ's Entombment

until she made a pilgrimage to Rome and petitioned the Pope in person that she was allowed to take her vows. She was then 15. She entered the enclosed Carmelite Order and during her time as a nun wrote the story of her life, 'History of a Soul'. A few days after the book was finished she became seriously ill and died when she was only 24 years of age. She was canonised in 1925 and a basilica dedicated to her memory was consecrated in 1954. Lisieux becomes a gathering point for pilgrims on her feast day at the end of September.
What to see Basilica of Ste-Thérèse; Les Buissonnets (the family home of Ste-Thérèse); Carmelite Chapel (shrine of Ste-Thérèse); Cathedral of St-Pierre (12–17c); Diorama-de-Ste-Thérèse (showing incidents in the saint's life); Palais-de-Justice (Law Courts, Louis XIII style); Musée du Vieux Lisieux (local archaeology).

LOCRONAN (S Finistère)

A town once important for the manufacture of sailcloth, Locronan is set on the slopes of a hill 17km (10½ miles) north west of Quimper and is surrounded by forests. Although it has seen wealthier times it is still a little gem and retains a number of interesting Renaissance buildings.

Today it is famous for its 'pardon' processions in which the participants climb the Mountain of Locronan in memory of St Ronan, an Irish hermit who lived in the wooded hills nearby and for whom the town was named. The town's connections with the weaving trade are demonstrated in the St-Ronan Workshop and the weaving mill of the former India Company which also exhibits some sculptures.
What to see Museum (Breton life, art, etc); St-Ronan Workshop; Weaving Mill of the former India Company.

LOUVIERS (Eure)

Louviers is an attractive town situated in the Eure Valley near the forest. Since the establishment of contemporary light industries the town's former long-standing connection with the woollen textile industry has been broken.
What to see Museum (Rouen pottery); former Penitents' Monastery (17c).

MAYENNE (Mayenne)

Mayenne was partly destroyed by an air-raid during World War II. It has been rebuilt on the hills which slope down to the Mayenne River. The town's two halves are still linked by the old bridge, which fortunately was captured intact by the Allies during their 1944 advance. Climb up to the 11th-century castle for a good view of Mayenne from its walls, but the interior is not open to the public.
What to see Castle.

Land of Lace

Hand-made lace is one of the traditional crafts of Brittany and Normandy. In Brittany, especially, lace forms an integral part of the national costume, especially the lace *coiffe* (head-dress). Sadly, these days traditional dress is seen only at important festivals, which means that the demand from local people for hand-made lace is not what it was. However, the tourist boom has given a great boost to lace-makers, and Breton women sell hand-made lace in towns and villages. Important schools of lace-making were established in Normandy during the 17th and 18th centuries when the fashion for lace was introduced from Venice. They included those at Alençon, Bayeux and Argentan, which still produce fine lace today. Both needlepoint and bobbin lace are found, and each school has developed its own techniques and stitches. Examples of early lace can be seen in museums, notably at Alençon and Bayeux, and Breton lace is prominent in the costumes displayed in museums at Quimper, Dinan and Rennes.

NORMANDY AND BRITTANY

MONT-ST-MICHEL (Manche)
One of France's most famous sights, and certainly the best-known in Normandy, the abbey of Mont-St-Michel is built on an island about half a mile offshore. At this point the tidal range is quite substantial, up to 14m (45ft) between high and low tides. At low tide it is possible to walk round the island, but the tide returns very fast, so great care should be taken. The abbey stands on the site of an oratory founded by the Bishop of Avranches in 708, and buildings were added in various architectural styles, until the 16th century. From 1811 to 1863 the buildings were used as a prison, and relics of this period may be seen in the museums. Since the buildings were restored by the State, which took control of them in 1874, the abbey and ramparts have become one of France's most popular attractions; more than half a million people now visit the mount each year. Behind the outer ring of defences, the small town lies below the abbey, with its one street containing shops, cafés and hotels. Of particular interest among the abbey buildings are those on the north side called the 'Merveille', dating from the early 13th century, containing the Knights' Hall, the Almshouses, the Refectory and the old Romanesque Abbey. The West Platform, from which there is a splendid view over the bay, is well worth a visit.
What to see Abbey (13–16c); Abbey Gardens; Historical Museum; Mont-St-Michel Historical Museum; Ramparts (13–15c); Tiphaine's House; Truie qui File House.

MORGAT (S Finistère)
This is a small coastal resort with one of the best beaches in Brittany, very sandy and sheltered by a tree-covered promontory, the Beg ar Gador, which has a lighthouse that is open to the public. At the northern end of the beach there is a rocky spur which divides Morgat from its neighbour, Le Portzic. At the base of this spur, there are some small caves which can be entered at low tide. Nearby, south of Beg ar Gador, are some larger caves, popular with sightseers, including the Devil's Chamber and a grotto called the Altar, which has coloured walls.
What to see Les Grandes Grottes (big caves); Les Petites Grottes (little caves); Lighthouse (La Phare).

First a refuge from Vikings, later both monastery and fortress, Mont-St-Michel is reached by a causeway across the sands

MORLAIX (N Finistère)
The most obvious feature of Morlaix is the great viaduct which crosses the Dossen estuary. Built between 1861 and 1864, it is over 58m (188ft) high, 288m (944ft) long, and has two storeys. The best view of this impressive feat of 19th-century civil engineering is from the Place des Otages, near the railway station. The Grand'Rue contains several old houses and shops, and the Duchess Anne's House, a three-storey 16th-century mansion notable for its ornate façade, can also be seen in this vicinity. The once-important port is now commercially little used, but during the summer season large numbers of British-owned pleasure craft are to be found at anchor there.
What to see Kergos House (Renaissance); Museum (art and folklore of Léon); Viaduct.

MORTAGNE-AU-PERCHE (Orne)
Set on a hill above a luxuriant valley, this ancient town has retained some fragments of its medieval fortifications, notably the 15th-century Porte St-Denis. There is a fine view from the public gardens over the rolling Perche countryside. The Forest of Perche, a favourite excursion point, lies to the north.
What to see Forest of Perche; Hospice (16–18c).

MORTAIN (Manche)
An attractive town situated on a gorge of the river Cance. Although there was war damage in 1944, several interesting old buildings have survived, including the Gothic church of St-Évroult. Mortain is famous for its two waterfalls, the Grande Cascade which tumbles 25m (82ft) and Petite Cascade which falls 35m (121ft) to a rock amphitheatre. Both lie on the western outskirts of the town in attractive woodland settings.
What to see Blanche Abbey (12–13c); Church of St-Évroult (13c); Grande Cascade; Petite Cascade; Petite Chapelle.

NEUFCHÂTEL-EN-BRAY (Seine-Maritime)
Neufchâtel-en-Bray was once the capital of the Bray Region. The 'bondon', a small round cheese which has since made this part of Normandy a famous cheese area, originated here.
What to see J B Mathon-A Durand Museum (local history).

OMAHA BEACH (Calvados)
The operational code name, used to cover the American landings on the coast around St Laurent-sur-Mer on 6th June 1944, has survived as a semi-official location name for the beaches around St-Laurent, Colleville-sur-Mer, Les Moulins and Vierville-sur-Mer. The Omaha landings were extremely costly in terms of casualties and the area contains a number of monuments to those who fell. There is an American Military Cemetery near Colleville-sur-Mer with over 9,000 graves.
What to see American Military Cemetery; American National Guard Monument (at Vierville-sur-Mer); 5th Engineer Special Brigade Memorial (near Colleville-sur-Mer); Monument du Débarquement (near Les Moulins).

PERROS-GUIREC (Côtes-du-Nord)
A popular resort with safe beaches and a busy fishing harbour. A cliff path known as Sentier des Douaniers (customs patrol path), provides an enjoyable walk to nearby Ploumanac'h and there is a spectacular view of the surrounding coastline from the viewing table on the edge of the Boulevard Clemenceau.
What to see Pointe-du-Château (viewpoint); Table d'Orientation (viewing table); Town Hall (art exhibitions).

PLOËRMEL (Morbihan)

The small town of Ploërmel, once the seat of the Dukes of Brittany, is typically Breton. Much of its architecture, including a number of houses and the church of St-Armel, has survived from the 16th century. The church is renowned for its sculptured doorway and eight stained-glass windows. Another interesting feature is the statue erected in honour of Dr Guérin, a citizen of Ploërmel. He invented lint surgical dressings, which proved invaluable to the wounded during the Franco-Prussian War of 1870.
What to see Statue of Dr Guerin; 16c houses.

PLOUMANAC'H (Côtes du Nord)

Situated at the mouths of the Traouiéros Valleys, round the coast from Trébeurden, Ploumanac'h is both a small fishing port and a renowned coastal resort. Its striking blocks of rose and grey rock, formed into weird shapes by erosion of feldspar and quartz grains in the granite, are a major attraction of this coastline. They can best be appreciated from the platform of the lighthouse, usually open during July and August.

Another attraction at Ploumanac'h is found on one of the rocks in the Bay of St-Guirec. This is a granite statue of St Guirec, who arrived here in the 6th century. It replaced a wooden effigy which became the target of girls anxious to marry. They would stick pins into his nose!
What to see Lighthouse (viewpoint); Municipal Park.

PONT AUDEMER (Eure)

Pont Audemer, known for its leather-tanning, is a small town situated on the River Risle. It has managed to retain some of its former character despite the serious damage inflicted upon the town in 1944. Notable examples of its past include many charming half-timbered houses along the 'Cour Canel' and the church of St-Ouen which has some fine stained-glass windows. But one of the best features of Pont Audemer is the way the river divides here into a number of arms, a series of mirrors for the town's waterside buildings and bridges and providing many picturesque vistas. The Vieux Puits Inn has a quaint Norman-style interior.
What to see Church of St-Ouen (11c); Cour Canel; Vieux Puits Inn.

PONT-AVEN (S Finistère)

A small town lying on the River Aven at the point where the tidal estuary begins. The Bois d'Amour (Forest of Love) on the town's northern outskirts, has attracted many artists including Gauguin, whose Pont-Aven school of painters was inspired by the settings to be found there. Posts mark the places that have been painted and some canvases, including a few by Gauguin, may be seen in the museum.
What to see Bois d'Amour; Museum.

PONTIVY (Morbihan)

A town of architectural contrasts in an attractive setting on the River Blavet. The ancient overhanging houses around the Place-du-Martray are offset by the 'new town' constructed by Napoleon. 'New' buildings include the Town Hall, the Barracks and the Court House. For a time the town was known as Napoléonville.
What to see Old houses; castle.

PONT-L'ABBÉ (S Finistère)

Standing at the beginning of an estuary, the town is the capital of the Bigouden Region. Costumes of the region are very picturesque and examples may be seen in the Bigouden Museum. They are also worn for local markets, fairs and the annual 'pardon' ceremonies. A local industry is the manufacture of dolls in regional costumes. There is a Carmelite church, with fine large rose-windows.
What to see Bigouden Memorial; Bigouden Museum; Castle (14–17c); Carmelite Church (14–15c).

PORT-LOUIS (Morbihan)

An old fortified town, previously known as Blavet but renamed in honour of King Louis XIII, which has become a popular seaside resort with good beaches. The 17th-century ramparts are still in existence and tunny fishing boats continue to use the harbour although this trade is not as active as it was in years gone by.
What to see Citadel (16c); Naval Museum (in the Citadel).

QUIBERON (Morbihan)

The Quiberon Peninsula is famed for its exposed Atlantic coast, the Côte Sauvage, but the town of Quiberon, at its southern end, is sheltered and has a fine sandy beach and a very healthy climate. This is a good centre both for those who enjoy walking and those touring by car. Go westward to the Côte Sauvage whose wild grandeur is fascinatingly beautiful, or eastward to the Pointe de Conguel where there is a viewing table from which one can pick out the off-shore islands – Belle-Ile, Hoëdic, Houat. Boats run to the islands from Quiberon and a visit to Belle-Ile, whose name – Beautiful Island – is truly appropriate, is certainly worth while. The peninsula has had a war-torn history and the ill-fated landing in 1795 by Royalist emigrées is commemorated by an obelisk near Port-Haliguen, east of the town.
What to see Fishing port; Lighthouse (views); Islands; Pointe de Conguel.

Sheltered by wooded cliffs seen here over its rooftops, Ploumanach is both resort and port

QUIMPER (S Finistère)

A fascinating town threaded with narrow cobbled streets, well worth a visit for the atmosphere of old 'Breton' which lingers here. Through the centre of the town flows the stately River Odet, the pavements on either side lined with lime trees, the Cathedral to the north, the beech-clad slopes of Mount Frugy to the south. Traditional costume can still be seen on Quimper's streets, particularly in late July when the Great Festival of Cornouaille, one of the most popular folk festivals in Brittany, is celebrated. Many quaint old buildings have been preserved around the Place Terre-au-Duc but Quimper's crowning glory is the magnificent Gothic Cathedral with its ornate spires and towers and 15th-century stained glass. The Brittany Museum contains exhibits of Breton costume and also has a section devoted to Quimper pottery which has been a local industry since the late 17th century. Further examples of this art may be seen at the pottery on the Allées de Locmaria, where a workshop is open to visitors at most times of the year (closed weekends and holidays). A fine view may be obtained from Mount Frugy which rises above the Place de la Résistance.

What to see Brittany Museum; Cathedral (13–18c); Fine Arts Museum; Pottery.

The Quimper Museum shows Breton dress dating back 700 years

The spires of Quimper Cathedral soar over its elegant bridges

QUIMPERLÉ (S Finistère)

Quimperlé, a town well known to the painter Gauguin, is described thus in a local saying: 'If Quimper is the smile of Cornouaille, then Quimperlé is its kiss'. It lies at the point where the Rivers Ellé and Isole combine to form the Laïta. It is, in effect, two towns: the upper town, above the rivers; and the lower town, grouped round them. Each has its own church: that of Ste-Croix, with a fine Romanesque apse, in the lower town; and the Church of Our Lady of the Assumption in the upper town. There are some ancient houses with overhanging upper storeys in the Rue Dom-Morice.

What to see Church of Our Lady of the Assumption (13–15c); Church of Ste-Croix (12–19c).

QUINTIN (Côtes-du-Nord)

The town is built on a hill, overlooking the River Gouët, and a fine view can be had from the Castle of which only a 17th-century wing remains. The town was once fortified, and traces of ramparts can still be seen. There are several rows of old houses on the terraces of the hill, dating from the 16th and 17th centuries, and a charming 15th-century fountain. The Basilica is a centre for pilgrimages since it contains several religious relics, among them a piece of the Virgin's girdle, brought here in the 13th century. It is also the scene of an annual 'pardon' ceremony on the second Sunday in May.

What to see Basilica; Castle (17c); Old Houses (16–17c).

RENNES (Ille-et-Vilaine)

Rennes, situated on the Rivers Ille and Vilaine, is the seat of government and culture in Brittany. It is a thriving industrial and agricultural centre, with the largest cider-apple market in France. However, not much of the original city has survived due to the devastating effects of the fire of 1920 and damage inflicted during the Second World War. The section that did escape, known as 'Old Rennes', is well worth visiting. It is situated near the Cathedral of St-Pierre and contains 15th- and 16th-century houses in picturesque streets. Another feature is the 15th-century Mordelaise Gate which was part of the former ramparts, and other old buildings including 17th- and 18th-century houses and the Law Courts, which once functioned as the Houses of Parliament of Brittany, can be seen around the Place-du-Palais. The Cathedral contains one of the masterpieces of Rennes – a 15th-century Flemish altarpiece carved in wood, depicting the life of the Virgin, and one of the most famous of its kind. Rennes also has a variety of museums to browse through and the Thabor Garden, one of the city's finest parks, offers 25 acres of handsomely laid-out flower gardens.

What to see Breton Car Museum; Breton Museum (local history); Cathedral of St-Pierre (18–19c); City Hall (18c); Law Courts (17c); Market; Mordelaise Gate (15c); Museum of Fine Arts; Old Rennes; Thabor Garden.

The Inebriated Apple

The traditional drink of Normandy and Brittany is cider, either a rough, still cider, similar to Somerset scrumpy, or the better-known *cidre bouché*, a naturally sparkling cider sold in tightly corked bottles. Both are made on the farms where the apples are grown. The apple juice ferments naturally, clouding over and then clearing as it matures. The type of apple, the growing conditions and the way in which the juice is treated after pressing all affect the flavour of the finished product. The finest is reputed to come from the farms of the Pays d'Auge around Cambremer in the department of Calvados. This department is the home of apple brandy – one of France's classic spirits. To make Calvados, mature cider is distilled twice then left in oak casks for many years. Some of the best and mellowest may be up to 50 years old, but 10 to 15 years is the average. It is often drunk as a *digestif* between courses or at the end of a meal.

ROCHEFORT-EN-TERRE (Morbihan)

This small, picturesque town is set on a promontory encircled by valleys. It has retained much of its character, particularly in the 16th- and 17th-century houses along the Grande Rue. Rochefort-en-Terre was formerly a feudal stronghold, indicated by its castle ruins. Today Rochefort is recognised more as a religious centre, with an annual pilgrimage on the Sunday after 15th August. This originated, and is still based, around the revered Statue of 'Notre Dame de la Tronchaye' (Our Lady of La Tronchaye) kept in the church of the same name. There is a good view of the countryside from the castle terrace.

What to see Castle; Grande Rue.

ROSANBO CHÂTEAU (Côtes du Nord)

Situated some 7km (4¼ miles) west of Plouaret, the château stands on a rock above the river Bo, on the site of an earlier fortification. Constructed in stages between the 14th century and the 19th century, it now serves as a museum, and houses an interesting collection of furniture, tapestries and documents. Outside there is a landscaped French garden, with terraced lawns and a disused open-air theatre.

What to see Castle (14—19c); Gardens.

ROSCOFF (N Finistère)

A popular seaside town with its own form of spa, a seawater therapy centre frequented by the wealthy. Travellers from Plymouth find it a pleasant starting point for trips in Finistère or the western end of Côtes-du-Nord. In addition it is an important lobster-fishing port and is a famous market garden centre. The Church of Our Lady of Kroz-Baz, decorated with sculpted cannons and ships, is 16th-century and has a particularly interesting Renaissance belfry and altarpiece.

What to see Aquarium; Church of Our Lady of Kroz-Baz (16c); Great Fig Tree (planted around 1625).

ROUEN (Seine-Maritime)

Rouen, the administrative centre of Upper Normandy, is the fourth most important port in France, and has been completely reconstructed since the War, when it was destroyed by fire and bombing. The industrial and port installations are entirely modern,

Shattered in World World II, Rouen has been carefully restored, its ancient buildings and clock being among its treasures

but most of the famous landmarks and monuments have been skilfully restored. Reconstruction of the Cathedral of Notre Dame is still in progress, but services are conducted there nevertheless. It is world-famous for its massive but finely detailed west façade, originally built in the 12th century but rebuilt, altered, and added to over the centuries. The old town lies on the right bank of the Seine, and has been almost completely restored to its pre-war state, with narrow streets and half-timbered houses. Originally, industrial and residential areas were mixed, but now the factories, etc, have been removed to the left bank, leaving the right bank a masterpiece of 'medieval' architecture. Other interesting sights include the Gros-Horloge, the famous clock above the street of the same name, the Churches of St-Maclou and St-Ouen, which are both under restoration, the Place du Vieux-Marché where Joan of Arc was burned, and several museums. The most impressive view of the city may be had from the belfry next to the great clock.

What to see Antiques Museum; Corneille Museum (birthplace of the dramatist Pierre Corneille 1606–84); Fine Arts Museum, a major art gallery; Flaubert Museum (medicine); Gros Horloge (great clock); Joan of Arc Museum; Joan of Arc Tower; Law Courts; Natural History, Ethnography and Prehistory Museum; Place du Vieux-Marché; Le Secq des Tournelles Museum (jewellery, glass, ironwork, etc); tour of port installations.

ST-BRIEUC (Côtes-du-Nord)

A busy commercial and industrial centre lying between the valley of the Gouëdic and the Gouet, both of which are crossed by impressive viaducts. There are some interesting old buildings in the Rue Fardel and St-Brieuc has a fine fortified cathedral dating originally from the 13th century. The town is at its liveliest around 29th September when St-Michael's Fair is held.

What to see Aubé Hill (viewpoint); Grandes Promenades (walks around the Law Courts); Rond-point Huguin (viewpoint).

ST-CAST (Côtes-du-Nord)

A popular seaside resort flanked by two headlands, the Pointe-de-St-Cast in the north and the Pointe-de-la-Garde in the south, both of which provide extensive views. A column in the town commemorates the defeat of a raiding British fleet in 1758.

What to see Pointe-de-St-Cast; Pointe-de-la-Garde.

ST-GÉUNOLÉ (S Finistère)

A little resort and fishing port mainly concerned with the canning of locally caught fish. The local museum is a treasure house of all the prehistoric finds made in Finistère: Megaliths and Gallic lec'hs, or obelisks, outside the museum herald a marvellous collection of polished stone axe-heads, skilfully-shaped arrow heads, bronze weapons, and reconstructions of Iron Age cemeteries, housed in two halls.

What to see Finistère Prehistorical Museum.

ST-LÔ (Manche)

This busy modern town is situated on the banks of the River Vire. It is also the Prefecture of the Manche Department. In the Battle of Normandy 1944 St-Lô suffered severe bomb attacks and, consequently, became known as 'Capital of the Ruins'. How intense these raids were is emphasised by the now-strengthened façade and towers of the Church of Notre Dame. Inevitably large-scale rebuilding was undertaken which has, successfully, highlighted the character of the town by emphasising its rocky spur and ramparts. Another attraction at St-Lô is its stud which stables about 180 Norman, Percheron and English stallions.

What to see Museum of Fine Arts (late 16c tapestries); Stud.

ST-LUNAIRE (Ille-et-Vilaine)

This appealing seaside resort is composed of two contrasting beaches separated by the Pointe du Décollé – the smaller, popular one at St-Lunaire and the larger, more peaceful one at Longchamp. The Grotte des Sirènes (Sirens' Cave), is best viewed from the bridge, and from the Pointe du Décollé there is a good view of the rocky and picturesque Côte d'Émeraude (Emerald Coast). Another feature of St-Lunaire is its annual 'pardon', occurring in July, which is centred on the old church.

What to see Grotte des Sirènes; Pointe du Décollé.

NORMANDY AND BRITTANY

ST-MALO (Ille-et-Vilaine)

The fortified town of St-Malo is situated on the Rance estuary opposite Dinard. Renowned both as a popular tourist resort and a port, it is unique in possessing the only cod-fishing fleet in Brittany. The port handles a variety of imports including coal, wine and building material, whilst its major export is wheat. It is also busy commercially as the embarkation point for the Channel Islands. During World War II the town, excluding its ramparts, was severely damaged. However, the rebuilding which followed successfully restored St-Malo to its former character. Today its many narrow streets with their tall houses are a great attraction to the visitor. Within the walls the 14th- to 15th-century Castle has survived and now houses the Museum. This illustrates various aspects of the history of the town. To appreciate the town and its coastal location fully a tour of the ramparts is strongly recommended. An additional feature of St-Malo is that the French writer and statesman, Châteaubriand, was born here in 1768. The site of his birthplace is now occupied by the 'Hotel France et Châteaubriand'. There is a statue of him at the entrance to the Casino gardens.

What to see Aquarium; Castle (13–17c); Island of Grand Bé and tomb of Châteaubriand; National Fort (17c); Port; Quic-en-Groigne (gallery depicting historic scenes of town;) Ramparts (started in 12c); St-Malo Museum.

ST-POL-DE-LÉON (N Finistère)

A very important market town from January to September, when farm and market garden produce is brought in from the surrounding area to be sold – artichokes and cauliflowers are specialities here. The former cathedral was built between the 13th century and the 16th century and, although small in comparison with others in the region, is well proportioned and of architectural interest.

The 14th-century Kreisker Chapel, now the college chapel, is renowned in Brittany for the delicate construction of the slender belfry. If you can manage the 169 steps to the top, there is a fine view of the surrounding countryside and coast.

What to see Cathedral (13–16c); Kreisker Chapel (14–15c) and belfry.

ST-SAUVEUR-LE-VICOMTE (Manche)

A small town on the Cotentin peninsula, St-Sauveur-le-Vicomte was severely damaged in 1944, as was its castle. The church is 13th-century and houses a number of works of art, including a 15th-century statue of St-James of Compostela, and a 16th-century 'Ecce Homo'. Within the castle walls there is a museum, containing exhibits and relics of the writer Barbey d'Aurevilly (1808–1889), a native of the town.

What to see Barbey d'Aurevilly Museum.

ST-SERVAN-SUR-MER (Ille-et-Vilaine)

An attractive seaside resort adjoining St-Malo, noted for its pleasant gardens and for the Corniche d'Aleth (Aleth Coast Road), a walk which provides magnificent views over the coastline, the offshore islands and the River Rance estuary. Another good view may be obtained from the top of the Tour Solidor, a 14th-century tower which now contains a museum of Cape Horn vessels.

What to see Corniche d'Aleth; Fort de la Cité (18c); Musée International du Long-cours Cap Hornier (Cape Horn Vessels); Parc des Corbières; Tour Solidor (14c).

STE-ANNE-D'AURAY (Morbihan)

A town famous for its 'pardons' and pilgrimages centred upon Ste-Anne, who appeared before a local ploughman, Yves Nicolazic, in 1623. The church that he built, on her instructions, was replaced by the Renaissance style basilica in the 19th century.

The famous 'Pardon of Ste-Anne' on 25th and 26th July attracts visitors from all parts of Brittany, many of them in local costume. The town is about 10km (6 miles) from Auray.

What to see Basilica (19c); Historial de Ste-Anne (Ste-Anne Diorama); House of Nicolazic (17c); Museum (sculptures, dolls in local costume); Treasury (relics of Ste-Anne).

STE-MÈRE ÉGLISE (Manche)

A market town which was the target for the US 82nd Airborne Division's parachute drop on 5th/6th June 1944. There is a museum relating to this offensive, and the first milestone on Liberty Road (the route taken by the American forces as they moved inland) can be seen outside the town hall.

What to see Musée des Troupes Aéroportées (Airborne Forces Museum); Parish church (13c).

SÉES (Orne)

An ancient town on the River Orne famous for its Gothic cathedral, which is generally considered to be one of the best examples of Norman architecture in the region. It contains lovely 13th-century glass windows. Some later monastic buildings may also be seen near the cathedral, including the former Abbey of St-Martin and the old Bishop's Palace, but these are not open to the public.

What to see Cathedral (13–14c).

TRÉGUIER (Côtes-du-Nord)

Built on a hill above the estuary of the Jaudy and Guindy Rivers, Tréguier has a deep water port which has become a major anchorage for pleasure craft, particularly from Britain. The cathedral is one of the most magnificent in Brittany, built between the 13th and 15th centuries, with some later additions, and contains some interesting 15th-century carvings and frescos, and cloisters dating from the same period. The town stages the 'Pardon of the Poor' on 19th May every year, which includes a procession from the cathedral to the nearby town of Mindy-Tréguier.

What to see Trégor hand-weaving workshop.

TROUVILLE (Calvados)

Trouville is one of the premier holiday resorts in northern France. Here the Normandy Corniche gives way to a fine, long sandy beach and the famous promenade of wooden planking. It was a favourite place of Empress Eugénie, and this has given Trouville a rich legacy of buildings of architectural interest dating from the Third Empire. The town is situated opposite the other great resort, Deauville, across the mouth of the River Touques. There is a very impressive view of the towns and the beaches from the Bon Secours Calvary, on the Corniche road.

What to see Casino; Fishing harbour; Olympic-sized swimming pool.

The Solidor Tower at St-Servan, built to command the Rance estuary and now a Cape Horn museum, overlooks a quiet beach

A pastoral scene on the outskirts of Vernon, with the imposing Notre Dame Church on the skyline

VERNON (Eure)
One of the gateways to Normandy, this was a favourite place for English and French kings in the Middle Ages. It is in an attractive woodland setting beside the River Seine south of Les Andelys, with a number of half timbered houses, although much of the old town was destroyed in World War II. The bridge provides a splendid view of the river with its wooded islands, and Vernon has become a popular sailing centre.

5km (3 miles) south east of Vernon at Giverny is the recently opened home and garden where the painter Claude Monet lived from 1883 until his death in 1926. The waterlily pool has been reconstructed; this was painted as a vast decorative series which is at the Orangery in the Tuileries Gardens in Paris.
What to see Church of Notre Dame (12–15c); Claude Monet's house at Giverny; Tour des Archives (12c).

VITRÉ (Ille-et-Vilaine)
Vitré, an old fortified town retaining its medieval walls, stands on a promontory overlooking the Vilaine Valley and has been largely preserved in its 15th- to 16th-century state. Excellent views of the town and castle are obtained from all entrances to the town. The castle has been restored and contains a local history museum. The town ramparts retain the north and east walls in their original form.
What to see Castle (14–15c restored); Castle Museum.

UTAH BEACH, near Carentan (Manche)
The most northerly of the 1944 invasion beach heads, Utah beach was one of the two used to land American troops. It is situated between the villages of La Madeleine and Les Dunes de Varreville and was the scene of heavy fighting and casualties on 6th June 1944. At La Madeleine there is a museum, with equipment and displays, and several monuments to American forces.
What to see Musée-du-Débarquement (Landing museum).

VALOGNES (Manche)
A pleasant market town on the Cotentin peninsula which has been extensively rebuilt following war damage in 1944. One or two interesting old buildings have survived, however, notably the 15th-century Logis de Grand Quartier which contains the Cider Museum.
What to see Hôtel-de-Beaumont (18c); Musée Régional de Cidre (Cider Museum).

VANNES (Morbihan)
A popular tourist centre on the Gulf of Morbihan with a particularly well-preserved 'old quarter' – narrow alleyways and squares containing 16th-century gabled houses and surrounded by 13th-century ramparts. Gardens have been laid out around the base of the ramparts, and the Promenade de la Garenne, which was once the park belonging to the ducal castle, provides a fine view of the old town. Two of the best-known buildings are the Cathedral and the 19th-century Renaissance-style Town Hall.
What to see Château Gaillard (Archaeological Museum); House of St Vincent Ferrier (16c); Municipal Museum; Ramparts (13–17c).

Operation Overlord

6th June 1944 saw the start of Operation Overlord in which 200,000 troops were landed in Normandy. The British used Gold, Juno and Sword beaches, between the Orne estuary and Port en Bessin, including Arromanches (qv), site of a 'mulberry' harbour. The Americans landed on Omaha and Utah beaches further west (qv). Airborne landings began when troops from the American 82nd Airborne Division were parachuted into Ste-Mère-Eglise (qv). Fine planning and the great courage, despite heavy losses, of Allied troops assured a successful beginning to the campaign which freed Europe from the Nazis. Many people still visit the cemeteries and monuments to the fallen and several travel companies organise 'battlefield tours'. Another reminder is the modern appearance of many Norman towns which until the war were gems of medieval architecture. Over 500 towns and villages had to be rebuilt and many historic buildings have been painstakingly reconstructed – a fitting tribute to those who died.

A Normandy beach, alive with craft and tanks a week after the invasion began in 1944

The Loire and Central France

The lazy Loire, its languid nature typified by this stretch at Saumur's Pont Cessart, has a benign influence on the region

The Loire River, main artery of the area covered in this section, is best known for the 400-kilometre (250-mile) stretch that runs through the valley of the châteaux. Here, among some 150 famous palaces, is to be found the legacy of the French aristocracy—monuments to a monarchy's splendour, wealth and extravagance. Stretching from the Atlantic coast to the centre of France, this enormous expanse of farmlands, forests and mountains has many other attractions for the visitor.

To the east, in the centre of the country, is the Auvergne where one can still find unspoilt medieval towns and villages, with their reminders of the feudal past. In the west, the great plains of Poitou are dotted with large farms and small towns, revealing the gentle face of a peasant heritage. Here, too, the coastal marshlands of the Marais Poitevin provide for simple pleasures in food, drink and relaxation. Further south, the region also supplies Limoges porcelain and Aubusson carpets and tapestries; and hydro-electric power from the fast-flowing rivers of the Massif Central helps to make this part of France prosperous.

This region offers a wonderful diversity of scenery. Here the visitor can either join the tourist trail to the châteaux or explore out-of-the-way places that still cling proudly to their historic past.

THE LOIRE AND CENTRAL FRANCE

Like all great rivers, the Loire imposes its character and personality on the countryside. France's longest river, covering 1,115km (634 miles) from its source in the volcanic mountains of the Central Massif to its Atlantic estuary at St-Nazaire, is, for the most of this distance, a languid, lazy artery. Approximately it starts in the heart of the country, linking many parts that over the centuries have been vital in giving France its robust constitution. It has several lookalikes flowing into it, though each has its distinctive character. Le Loir, in particular, is often confused with its virtual namesake, yet it is a comparatively modest tributary of the great river; it loses its identity completely after 354km (218 miles) when it joins the Sarthe to the north of Angers.

Château Country The banks of both rivers, together with the Cher, the Indre and the Vienne which flow from the south to join the Loire west of Tours, share the area's most popular claim to fame – its magnificent châteaux. Many of these are ornate temples built for the Court's amusement.

After the Loire has curved north through Orléans, in the sweeping arc which begins at Sancerre and flows west, the onlooker is offered here and there a fairy-tale panorama of castles, châteaux, towers and manicured estates. The area around Tours – the Garden of France as the Province of Touraine is called – is the heart of the château country, where successive royal families indulged their whims. Amboise and Chenonceaux are among the best-known examples of châteaux from the late 15th- and 16th-century Renaissance period and, like the 16th- and 17th-century edifices of Valençay and Cheverny, stand on land where, centuries before, the Plantagenet kings ruled. Not all the palatial houses are châteaux. Many are the remains of castles built in the Middle Ages yet miraculously preserved.

At Chinon, Richard the Lionheart, most romantic of all the Plantagenets, is chronicled to have died in 1199 after being wounded by an arrow at Chalus about 240km (150 miles) away. In Chinon, too,

Joan of Arc, the inspired Maid of Orleans, had her fateful meeting at the Château du Milieu – one of the three fortresses of the castle – with the Dauphin in May 1429. It was to take her on a two-year military pilgrimage during which the army she led vanquished the English and her vision of the Dauphin's coronation came true.

Many of the châteaux are small places, built as late as the 19th century in imitation of the Italian Renaissance style. Of the older examples, the Court allowed several to fall into decay even before the 1789 revolution, but fortunately many were restored in the 19th century. Most of the châteaux have extensive grounds, often with well-kept gardens around the house.

In St-Aignan the present château – where the ramparts date back to the 15th century – is owned by a Count. Distinguished by the towers of the original fortress, the château, though overlooking the Cher Valley, is tucked away behind a busy main street but can be reached by a magnificent sweep of steps leading to the courtyard. The interior is barred to the public, but the gardens and the view from the terrace compensate for its limited access. There are other compensations in St-Aignan, particularly in the spring when this 9th-century former monks' settlement holds a hilarious moustache-growing festival.

Volcanic Auvergne Even more private is the 15th-century Château de Cordès, owned by a Paris lawyer and his family, at Orcival in the Auvergne. Compared to the great châteaux of the Loire, this is a mere weekend cottage. With the snow-covered peaks of the Monts Dômes in the Central Massif on the horizon, it is part of the necklace of two dozen little-known châteaux in the Auvergne. Behind the imposing, electronically operated wrought-iron gates, the wide wall-lined drive leads to gardens which are set out in the parterre style and were designed by the man who laid out the gardens at Versailles Palace outside Paris. Though the gardens can be inspected independently of the guided tour of the house, the attention of visitors is usually irresistibly drawn by the clamour of a large roped handbell signalling the start of the tour. Only certain rooms are open, including a small private chapel with an impressive altar made of Carrara marble. In the dungeons, the curiosities include an animated wooden statue of a monk with his dog and a torture chamber with all manner of medieval monstrosities on display.

Driving over the narrow, well-surfaced roads, the tourist in the Auvergne is con-

Left: Anglers cast over the Charente's trout at Châteauneuf, the edge of Cognac country

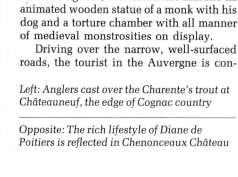

Opposite: The rich lifestyle of Diane de Poitiers is reflected in Chenonceaux Château

fronted by vistas reminiscent of Scotland only they are set in a stark and grim lunar-like terrain.

Approaching from the north, the landscape is at first dotted with small lakes. Then, as the roads twist and climb around extinct volcanoes – strange shapes as though sculpted by human hands – the views become progressively more spectacular and breathtaking. Cones, craters and pinnacles are strewn far and wide. Not surprisingly, with all that latent volcanic activity, the Auvergne is the most important health-spa centre in France, with several well-known resorts offering cures and a wide range of sports facilities, entertainments, and other diversions.

Reaching over 950m (3,090ft) at Salers, a truly magnificent feudal village built on a volcanic chimney, the road passes through a ring of white-flecked, snow covered ravines that yield only two passes through the rugged range of the Monts du Cantal. Both passes tend to be closed for much of the year, though the Col de Néronne at 1,242m (4,000ft) opens earlier than the Pas de Peyrol, 1,582m (5,140ft), which leads to the highest point in the range, the Puy Mary – a massive peak towering nearly 1,800m (5,850ft) high.

A wait for the warmer months when the snow has melted is well worth while. During most of the year traffic in much of the Auvergne is sparse, and though hairpin bends are numerous, there is little fast oncoming traffic to make the sharp, blind corners daunting. The main hazards to staying on the road are the riveting and distracting views on each side. In the villages the stone-tiled roofs, like the faces of gnarled old men, look on impassively at the passing scene. Occasionally, a shepherd with his dog can be found sitting on a fence or dry-stone wall. Wild daffodils and narcissi provide a carpet more colourful in springtime than some of the Aubusson tapestries which adorn the churches in this area. In September, autumn crocuses cloak the fields. Now and again a fighter plane swoops overhead, wrecking the timeless calm. The contrast between the affairs of centuries is brought starkly into relief in this corner of France.

Outside Bort-les-Orgues they have tamed three rivers, including the Dordogne (see pages 56–73) to construct a barrage of such gigantic proportions that the harnessed water produces enough power to feed most of the generators in the hydro-electric system of the Massif Central.

The Dordogne rises at Puy de Sancy, at 1,886m (6,133ft) the highest point in the Central Massif, while about 160km (100 miles) away among the crusty pinnacles of the Cévennes, the great Loire has its beginnings. A small field beside a drab house hides its birthpangs at Gerbier de Jonc, a 154m (500ft) volcanic cone which dominates the plateau of St-Agrève in the Ardèche. This is a smooth pudding-shaped rock reminiscent of the Sugarloaf Mountain in Rio de Janeiro.

The Marshlands The Loire is said to cut France into halves. Flowing westwards after the bulge of Orleans, the river makes a natural boundary between the thick wooded landscape of Maine with its famous motor-racing capital of Le Mans, and the Poitou Charente to the south where the province's rustic calm is expressed by its emphasis on dairy farming. In contrast, La Rochelle, once the provincial capital, is now a swinging seaside resort. A few miles inland, in the Marais Poitevin – sometimes called 'Green Venice' – punts ply the silent and leafy waterways on lazy summer days. The whole character of the region is epitomised by two attractive white cottages with blue shutters on the far bank of the Sèvre Niortaise river. These exquisite cottages make such an obvious picture postcard scene that they have been reproduced on linen calendars and tea-towels sold all over the world.

Many of France's rivers offer these delightful settings. The Loire has more than most. Yet, great river though it is, commercially it is a barren waterway – nobody has bothered to navigate it since the railways arrived. Which makes it much more attractive for the tourist!

Places of Interest

AMBAZAC (Haute-Vienne)

A small town in a hilly region 19km (11½ miles) north east of Limoges which has recently become a centre for uranium mining. Ambazac is well-known for its 'Treasure' (see Limoges enamels, page 48), which can now be seen in the local church.

What to see Ambazac Church.

AMBOISE (Indre-et-Loire)

An old-established town in a picturesque setting overlooking the River Loire. Amboise's principal attraction is the splendid château, built by Charles VIII on the site of a feudal fortress. It contains the beautiful Chapel of St-Hubert, set high on the ramparts, and the Minimes Tower with the usual feature of a ramp-type stairway which can be mounted by a horseman. Amboise has close associations with Leonardo da Vinci who lived at Clos-Lucé from 1516 until his death in 1519. The 15th-century mansion is open to visitors at most times and contains models of some of the machines Leonardo designed. The town has two museums and several interesting old churches. A more modern note is struck by the 20th-century fountain, designed by the painter Max Ernst, which stands near the river.

What to see Château (15c restored); Church of St-Denis (12c); Church of St-Florentin (15c); Clos-Lucé (15c – Leonardo da Vinci's house); Musée de l'Hôtel-de-Ville (works of art, etc); Musée de la Poste (postal history).

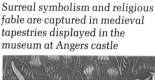

Surreal symbolism and religious fable are captured in medieval tapestries displayed in the museum at Angers castle

ANGERS (Maine-et-Loire)

Spread over both banks of the River Maine, Angers, the ancient capital of Anjou, is an important textile and wine-producing centre. The castle, dating originally from the 9th century, has a superb collection of old tapestries including the famous 'Apocalypse Tapestry', nearly 170 metres (551ft) long and dating from the late 14th century. The cathedral, built between the 12th and 13th centuries, contains stained glass of several different periods, and the Logis Barrault houses paintings and the works of the 19th-century sculptor David d'Angers. The former hospital of St John (Ancien Hôpital St-Jean) has a display of modern tapestries and also contains a small Anjou Wine Museum. For four weeks during June and July an arts festival attracts many visitors.

What to see Ancien Hôpital St-Jean; Château (13–15c); Cathedral of St-Maurice (12–13c); La Garenne Parc; Hôtel Pincé (Turpin-de-Crissé Museum – paintings, *objets d'art*, etc); Logis Barrault (Fine Arts Museum).

ANGOULÊME (Charente)

An old-established town set on a hill above the River Charente, Angoulême is an important industrial and commercial centre which has lost little of its medieval charm. The old town ramparts with their flanking towers have been converted into pleasant boulevards from which fine views may be obtained, and a number of elegant 18th-century mansions have been preserved in the town centre. Angoulême has an ornate cathedral, famous for its west front which is adorned with a scene of Judgement Day composed of some seventy sculptured figures. The town has two museums dealing with local archaeology and history and is a popular tourist and excursion centre.

What to see Cathedral of St-Pierre (12–19c); Chapel of Cordeliers (part 16c); Hôtel-de-Ville (Town Hall – 13–15c); Municipal Museum; Musée de la Société Archéologique.

ARGENTON-SUR-CREUSE (Indre)

A small picturesque town with many old buildings, situated on the banks of the River Creuse. The old bridge offers a splendid view of the river and the town, particularly the old quarter. This is a good centre for touring the delightful Creuse Valley, taking in beauty spots such as Gargilesse, Lake Chambon, and the ruined fortress of Crozant.

What to see Chapel of Notre-Dame-des-Bancs (15c).

AUBIGNY-SUR-NÈRE (Cher)

In the early 15th century, Aubigny was given to the Scottish Stuart family as a reward for their services against the English. Scotsmen started the glassworks and cloth mills which made the town prosperous. Notable sights include some early 16th-century houses, among which are the Maison du Bailli which bears the Stuart arms, and Maison St-Jean which is the only 15th-century house remaining. The best views of the old town are from the ramparts.

What to see Château des Stuarts (17c); Maison du Bailli (16c); Maison St-Jean (15c).

AUBUSSON (Creuse)

Lying in the pleasantly wooded Creuse Valley, Aubusson is famous throughout the world for the tapestries and carpets which have been produced there since the Middle Ages. Aubusson has retained a number of ornate 16th-century houses, and the 15th-century Tapestry-weaver's House is now a museum devoted to the history of this trade.

What to see Maison du Vieux-Tapissier (Old Tapestry-weaver's House); Hôtel-de-Ville (Town Hall) (tapestry and carpet exhibitions during the summer).

Francis I gave Azay-le-Rideau's fine château to his Captain of the Guard after its wealthy builder fled in disgrace

AURILLAC (Cantal)

This modern town, which grew up around its 10th-century abbey and ancient winding alleys, is the capital of the Haute-Auvergne district. Gerbert, who became the first French Pope (Sylvester II, 999-1003), was born near Aurillac and a statue of him can be seen by the River Jordanne. The town has retained some of its old buildings including the 14th-century Church of Notre-Dame-aux-Neiges with its revered statue of the black Virgin. A panoramic view of Aurillac is obtained from the Pont Rouge, and the town is the main centre for exploring the Upper Auvergne. The spectacular Route des Crêtes is too good to miss.
What to see Château St-Étienne (13c – contains local museum) and Maison des Volcans; Church of Notre-Dame-aux-Neiges; Place St-Géraud.

AZAY-LE-RIDEAU (Indre-et-Loire)

The outstanding feature of Azay-le-Rideau is its magnificent 16th-century Renaissance château, situated amid parkland on the bank of the River Indre. It was built by a wealthy financier who, involved in a scandal, fled. The King then gave it to the Captain of the Guard. It is now owned by the State. The defensive details of the building, in the Gothic style, are purely decorative – a 16th-century status symbol. A serene harmony pervades the jewel-like building and its setting. The interior has been laid out as a Renaissance museum.
What to see Château; Church of St-Symphorien.

BAUGÉ (Maine-et-Loire)

Situated on the River Couasnon, Baugé is the capital of the surrounding region. This market town is famous for the double-armed Cross of Anjou (later of Lorraine and, in 1940, the emblem of the Free French Forces) which was brought from the Holy Land in 1241. It is claimed to be part of the True Cross. A visit to Les Filles du Coeur de Marie Chapel, where the cross can be seen, is recommended. Baugé is twinned with Milngavie in Scotland; its château looks a bit Scottish, and Scottish masons may have helped to build it in the 15th century.
What to see Château (15c); Hôpital St-Joseph (17c); Les Filles du Coeur de Marie Chapel (18c).

BEAUGENCY (Loiret)

A small town with a long history, lying between Blois and Orléans in a pleasant rural setting on the banks of the Loire. The remarkable bridge of 22 arches is a reminder of the town's former importance both strategically and as a crossing-place for pilgrims. The Tour de l'Horloge was a gateway in the old city walls and the Tour du Diable on the quayside is part of the old bridge-head fortifications. Dominated by the massive shell of an 11th-century keep, the town retains much of its medieval appearance.
What to see Abbey Church of Notre-Dame (12c); Castle Keep (11c); Château (15c); Hôtel-de-Ville (17c Town Hall); Regional Museum (in the château – collections of costumes, furniture, etc, of the Orleans district); Tour du Diable (bridgehead fortification); Tour de l'Horloge (old city wall gateway).

BLOIS (Loir-et-Cher)

The ancient town of Blois is picturesquely located on the Loire, amidst rising hills. It is the hub of the farming community which surrounds it and has a little light industry, mainly concerned with chocolate manufacture.

During the Middle Ages the town was strategically important as a bridgehead and it was also the centre of a powerful county. Of its many historical buildings, pride of place must go to its château. What is extraordinary is the jumble of architectural styles and periods – 13th to 17th centuries – each one a richly creative contribution to the whole. Most original feature of all is the staircase in its octagonal openwork cage, which has been much copied. A fine arts museum is to be found in the Louis XII wing. On a hill to the north east of the château is the Cathedral of St-Louis with a crypt dating from the 10th century. The Old Quarter of the town, with its many interesting houses, stretches from the cathedral to the Loire.
What to see Cathedral of St-Louis; Château de Blois (dating from 13c); Church of St Nicholas; Fine Arts Museum (in the château); Hôtel d'Alluye (16c mansion); Hôtel-de-Ville (18c Episcopal Palace now serving as the Town Hall); Lapidary Museum (in the St-Saturnin Cemetery); Old Quarter; Poulaine Chocolate Factory (guided tours available); Robert-Houdin Museum (famous conjuror born in Blois).

The stone staircase is a memorable feature of the mixed architectural styles at Château de Blois

THE LOIRE AND CENTRAL FRANCE

An enduring example of the sculptor's art at Chartres

BOURGES (Cher)

This prosperous town lies to the south of Orleans at the junction of the Rivers Auron and Yèvre. It is a bishopric and administrative capital of the Department of Cher, and is an industrial, commercial and artistic centre. The town was the capital of the Duchy of Berry, and the timber-framed houses of its picturesque streets testify to its ancient past. The 15th-century Jacques Coeur Palace, built on the remains of the Gallo-Roman town walls, is one of the town's more remarkable mansions. (Jacques Coeur was a rich merchant, and treasurer of Charles VII).

Bourges grew up around the splendid Cathedral of St-Étienne, whose lofty tower now dominates it. Dating from the 12th century, the cathedral, with its exceptionally fine stained-glass windows, is one of the most beautiful in France. The town is rich in formal gardens and the Jardin des Prés-Fichaux, on the banks of the River Yèvre, is reputed to be one of the finest in France.

What to see Archaeological and Folklore Museum (in Hôtel Cujas); Cathedral of St-Étienne (12–15c); Collection of furniture (in Hôtel Lalemant 15–16c); Hôtel Cujas (16c); Hôtel Pellevoysin (15c); Hôtel-de-Ville (17c Archbishop's Palace, now Town Hall); Jacques Coeur Palace (15c).

BROUAGE (Charente-Maritime)

A former port, notable for its massive 17th-century ramparts which completely surround the centre of the town. Brouage's historic buildings include several old military installations and the birthplace of Samuel de Champlain, the founder of Quebec.

CHAISE-DIEU (LA) (Haute-Loire)

This small village stands at an altitude of over 1,000 metres (3,250ft) and commands an impressive view of southern Auvergne. It is dominated by the sober grandeur of its Benedictine Abbey, founded in 1043 and rebuilt in the 14th century by a local monk who became Pope Clément VI. Its interior is impressive, particularly the 'Danse Macabre' fresco depicting 15th-century life, the 16th-century Flanders tapestries, and the tomb of Pope Clément VI.

What to see Abbey; Historial de la Chaise-Dieu (waxworks museum).

CHÂLUS (Haute-Vienne)

The small hilltop town, in the Limousin countryside 33km (20 miles) south west of Limoges, is dominated by the ruined but massive tower of its medieval castle, Château Chabrol, which made Châlus famous. While attacking the castle, Richard the Lionheart was hit by the bolt from a crossbow; he died at Chinon from his gangrenous wound.

What to see Ruins of Château Chabrol.

CHAMBORD (CHÂTEAU DE) (Loir-et-Cher)

The largest château in the Loire Valley stands here on the banks of the Cosson to the west of Blois, in the midst of a huge wooded park which has been a rich hunting reserve since the early 16th century when Chambord was built. It has 440 rooms and 75 staircases, including the famous double-spiral stairway, and its design is attributed to Leonardo da Vinci. Started in 1519 by Francois I, it was completed by Henry II who made it the centrepiece of the Court circle. Always thereafter a favourite country seat for French Royalty, Chambord received particular patronage from Louis XIV whose protégé, the playwright Molière, wrote 'Le Bourgeois Gentilhomme' and 'Monsieur de Pourceaugnac' there. Most of the château's furnishings were destroyed during the French Revolution but this has done nothing to detract from the fine Renaissance architecture of the whole building; the central staircase and the Italian style terrace are particularly impressive.

CHARTRES (Eure-et-Loir)

Perched on a hill above the River Eure, Chartres, the administrative centre for the Department of Eure-et-Loir, is a delightful jumble of old gabled houses, cobbled streets and church spires. Soaring over all are the majestic towers of the Gothic cathedral, occupying a site which has supported a Christian church since the 4th century and ranking among the six most important French cathedrals. Rodin called Chartres Cathedral 'the Acropolis of France' and it is certainly worthy of that title, with its superb 12th-century west porch (le Portail Royal), and its enormous crypt, lofty arches, intricate sculptures and sumptuous stained glass. Chartres has been a place of pilgrimage since the 9th century when the relic believed to be the Veil of the Virgin Mary (La Voile de la Vierge) found its way into the cathedral treasury. This article is still preserved in the Chapel of St-Piat and pilgrims also gather to venerate the 16th-century wooden 'Virgin of the Pillar' (La Vierge du Pilier). The local museum, housed in the 17th-century former Bishop's Palace, contains paintings by 16th- to 18th-century artists including Holbein, Fragonard and Chardin, enamels by Léonard Limosin and a fine collection of weapons and armour.

What to see Cathedral of Notre-Dame (12–13c); Cellier-de-Loëns (13c cellar/underground hall); Chartres Museum.

CHÂTEAUBRIANT (Loire-Atlantique)

This old fortified town lies on the borders of Brittany and Anjou, within an area of woodland and ponds. The castle dates from the 11th century and has had additions made to it as recently as the 19th century.

What to see Castle (11–19c); Church of St Jean-de-Béré (11–17c).

Once a simple hunting lodge, the impressive Château de Chambord is now a national treasure

CHÂTEAUDUN (Eure-et-Loir)

This historical town is situated on the banks of the River Loir. It is the market town for the agricultural regions of Beauce and Le Perche and markets and fairs are held in the Place du 18-Octobre.

Châteaudun's most notable feature is its château. The round keep, dating from the 12th century, is important as one of the first and finest examples of its kind. In the Sainte-Chapelle there are fifteen 15th-century statues, evidence of the scope of local workshops at that time. The town's museum, where there is a splendid ornithological collection as well as other items of interest, is worth visiting. The town holds an annual horse show in mid-August.
What to see Château (part 12c); Museum (birds, fossils, prehistory, Egyptian pottery).

CHÂTEAUNEUF-SUR-LOIRE (Loiret)

This town acquired its name from its château, the surviving sections of which include the domed rotunda (now the Town Hall), the outbuildings and the pavilions. Châteauneuf also has a fine maritime museum devoted to navigation on the River Loire, and a delightful park containing giant rhododendrons.
What to see Hôtel-de-Ville (Town Hall); Musée de la Marine de Loire.

CHÂTEAUROUX (Indre)

Overlooking this busy town is the 15th-century Château Raoul, and 2km (1¼ miles) north are the remains of the former abbey at Déols. Châteauroux also has a museum containing exhibits of the Napoleonic period. From here a picturesque route takes you to Châteauroux Forest, a beautiful forest of oaks and other deciduous trees.
What to see Château Raoul; Déols Abbey (ruins); Forest; Musée Bertrand.

CHÂTELLERAULT (Vienne)

This flourishing town is situated on the River Vienne which is crossed by the delightful Pont Henri IV with its two stone towers. Châtellerault contains many old houses, the most famous being the 16th-century Maison de Descartes. The philosopher René Descartes spent his early life here and his house is now a museum.
What to see Maison de Descartes; Musée de l'Automobile et de la Technique (Car Museum); Musée Chéron de la Martinière.

CHÂTILLON-SUR-INDRE (Indre)

This small market town contains many old houses and winding alleyways. The remains of the town's medieval château include the 13th-century round keep from where there is a good view of the

Indre Valley. A similar view is obtained from the Place du Marché.
What to see Château; Church of Notre-Dame (part 11c); Place du Marché.

CHÂTRE (LA) (Indre)

This small town lies to the south of Châteauroux in a heavily wooded region called in some of her novels 'the Dark Valley' by French novelist George Sand, who spent much of her life there. It has several ancient little streets with some interesting 15th-century timbered houses. The keep of Château Chauvigny is now a George Sand museum.

CHAUMONT-SUR-LOIRE (Loir-et-Cher)

Situated to the south of Blois, the little town of Chaumont stands high above the Loire, providing fine views over the river valley landscape. The town itself is overlooked by an imposing 15th-century Gothic château whose fortress-like appearance is softened by purely decorative features. It is approached through a beautiful park planted with cedar trees. Its interior is very elegant, with fine Gobelin tapestries, faience tiling and good furniture. The stables, complete with saddle-room and carriages, are particularly well designed and worth visiting.

CHAUVIGNY (Vienne)

Chauvigny lies to the east of Poitiers in a picturesque setting overlooking the River Vienne. Dominating the upper town are the imposing ruins of five feudal castles, the earliest dating back to the 11th century. Also located in the upper town is the 12th-century Romanesque Church of St-Pierre.
What to see Castle ruins; Church of Notre-Dame; Church of St-Pierre.

CHENONCEAUX (CHÂTEAU DE) (Indre-et-Loire)

There are many who say this is the most beautiful dwelling in existence. It was built in the 16th century and given by Henry II to his mistress, Diana de Poitiers. After his death in 1559 his Queen, Catherine de Medici, wrested it from her in revenge. The château benefited from the tastes of both women – the evidence is to be found throughout the château and in the gardens which were laid out under their direction. Perhaps it is most famed for its gallery – 60m (65 yards) long – which spans the River Cher, but the interior of the house is also spectacular, incorporating Carrara marble statues, Gobelins tapestries, and paintings by distinguished artists such as Van Loo and Rubens. There is also a wax museum and Son-et-Lumière performances are given during the summer.

Both the mistress of Henry II and his queen influenced the design of the gardens at Chenonceaux, as well as the décor of the château

THE LOIRE AND CENTRAL FRANCE

CHEVERNY (CHÂTEAU DE) (Loir-et-Cher)

This aristocratic and peaceful 17th-century château, built of white stone, is set in a lovely wooded park on the edge of the Forêt de Cheverny 13km (8 miles) south east of Blois (Loir-et-Cher).

It differs from many of the famous châteaux of the Loire because, although it was completed on one year – 1634 – it was built on Classical lines more appropriate to 18th-century architecture. It has retained its original furniture and sumptuous decoration, including works by Mignard and Mosnier and some Flemish tapestries. There are also a number of tapestries in the Petit Salon, the King's Bedroom (no king ever slept there, he merely had the right to use it) and the Guardroom. Cheverny was designed as a stately home rather than as a palace and its present owners, descendants of the original Cheverny dynasty, maintain the family's hunting traditions by preserving more than 2,000 pairs of stag antlers in the trophy room and keeping a large pack of hounds in nearby kennels.

CHINON (Indre-et-Loire)

This town, on the banks of the River Vienne, has a distinctly medieval appearance. On the river's right bank is the second-largest ruin in France, a château which dates back to the Middle Ages and comprises three separate moated fortresses. These are the ruined Fort St-Georges, built by the English King Henry II and reputedly the scene of his death (1189); the Château du Milieu where Joan of Arc was received by the Dauphin in 1429; and the Château du Coudray where she slept during her stay.

Good examples of 14th- to 16th-century dwellings can be seen in the rue Haute St-Maurice and the rue Voltaire. A visit is also recommended to the Maison des États-Généraux (House of the States-General) where Richard the Lionheart died in 1199. It houses various collections including Joan of Arc's relics from 1431.

Le Croisic, on La Baule peninsula, is noted for shellfish

A good view of the town and its château is obtained from the Quai Danton, near the bridge (part 12th-century).
What to see Château (medieval); Maison des États-Généraux; Rabelais' House.

CLERMONT-FERRAND (Puy-de-Dôme)

Set in the heart of France, this large town is the capital of the Auvergne, known locally as 'the green county'. It is situated within a semicircle of hills and overlooks a fertile valley to the east, whilst to the west the rocky heights of the Monts Dômes dominate. A university town and bishopric, Clermont-Ferrand is also an important industrial and commercial centre.

The old part of the town is built on rising ground and is surrounded by modern suburbs whose coloured brick and red tiles contrast sharply with the black volcanic stone of the old town. Containing a number of ancient houses dating from the 16th century, its narrow streets, clustered around the cathedral, have retained much of their old-world character and contain a number of ancient houses. The twin spires of the Cathedral of Notre-Dame, one of the great Gothic churches of France, rise high above the houses of the old town. There is much of interest in the town, including a petrifying

fountain and the Musée du Ranquet which contains mementoes of Blaise Pascal.
What to see Cathedral of Notre-Dame (13c); Musée du Bargoin (Roman and prehistoric remains); Musée du Ranquet (Town Museum in the Maison des Architects – items of local interest including mementoes of Pascal).

COGNAC (Charente)

Lying to the north west of Angoulême in a traditional wine-producing area, astride the banks of the River Charente, Cognac is the centre of the brandy trade and has, of course, given its name to the famous French brandy.

It is an ancient town with an interesting Old Quarter which has a Romanesque church and many picturesque 16th- and 17th-century houses. On the eastern side of the town, overlooking the river, is a 13th-century château, birthplace of Francis of Angoulême who was to become Francis I of France. The château is now used as a storage cellar or 'chais' by a brandy firm.
What to see Brandy warehouses (some may be visited upon application); Château Francis I (13c); Church of St-Leger (14–18c); Hôtel-de-Ville (Town Hall situated in the 'Jardin Public', a landscaped park); Old Quarter; Town Museum (situated in the Jardin Public – contains a collection of Flemish paintings).

COLLONGES-LA-ROUGE (Corrèze)

This picturesque village lies to the east of Périgueux in a charming area notable for its forests, sloping hills and valleys, and owes its name to the rich colour of its buildings which are all constructed of a very red sandstone. Grouped around the 12th-century Romanesque Church of St-Sauveur are turreted manor-houses with mullioned windows, alleys, archways, covered markets, vine-clad balconies and charming views.

CROISIC (LE) (Loire-Atlantique)

A little seaside resort, mainly concerned with the catching of sardines and shell-fish. There are two good beaches and the port, overlooked by a number of 17th-century houses, is usually busy with fishing vessels and pleasure boats. Fresh fish is auctioned daily on the quay. Two hills rise above the port area: Mont-Esprit, man-made from ships' ballast; and, to the north, Mont-Lénigo which is a good viewpoint.
What to see Aquarium; Naval Museum (in the Town Hall).

CROZANT (Creuse)

This small village, situated in the Creuse Valley, is dominated by the 10th- and 13th-century ruins of its château. Set on a promontory where the gorges of the Rivers Creuse and Sédelle meet, the château, one of France's largest medieval fortress, became known as 'the key to the Limousin'. The terrace near the church gives a handsome view of the promontory and the Éguzon lake on which motor-boat trips can be taken.

DOUÉ-LA-FONTAINE (Maine-et-Loire)

This old town, built over a number of underground quarries, acquired its name from the natural spring discovered in the 18th century. Its main feature is its arena situated in the Douces quarter of the town. This was a quarry from Roman times until the 15th century, when seats were cut out of the rock. Today it is used for live entertainment and flower shows. Other attractions include the zoo and the carrion bird reserve, both in former quarries on the outskirts of Doué-la-Fontaine. A number of old houses and several cave dwellings are of interest.
What to see Arena; Zoo and bird reserve.

Spas of the Auvergne

Thanks to the mineral salts from the volcanic rock, the Auvergne is a thriving spa centre. Best known is Vichy, which is the fashionable mecca for those who suffer from digestive complaints and other common ailments, but there are at least ten other spas catering for various physical and mental needs.

Le Mont-Dore, for instance, offers not only curative springs but plenty of distractions, too. Here, in the spellbinding mountain setting of the Puy-de-Dôme, the remains of Roman baths and a temple can be seen. With 90,000 gallons of water spurting every 24-hours from eight springs, about 3,000 patients a day can be treated during the season (mid-May to the end of September). The treatment of respiratory disorders is particularly attractive to singers and public speakers.

An important medical spa centre specialising in heart disease is at Royat near Clermont-Ferrand, also in the Puy de Dôme.

DREUX (Eure-et-Loir)

A lively town, in the pleasantly wooded Blaise Valley, which has evolved from an ancient Gallic settlement into a thriving commercial and tourist centre. The Chapelle Royale St-Louis, the only remaining portion of Dreux's ducal fortress, contains the tombs of the Orléans family, including Louis Philippe who became King of France in 1830.
What to see Beffroi (former 16c Town Hall); Chapelle Royale St-Louis (19c); Church of St-Pierre (13–17c); Museum (local history).

FLÈCHE (LA) (Sarthe)

A charming market town on the banks of the Loir. La Flèche is nationally famous for its former military academy (Prytanée) now a school for the sons of army officers, civil servants, etc. Dating from the mid 17th century, the Prytanée contains an interesting Jesuit chapel and a small museum. Guided tours are available. La Tertre Rouge Zoo lies some 5km (3 miles) to the south west in a delightfully wooded setting.
What to see Château des Carmes (15–17c); Prytanée Militaire (17c); La Tertre Rouge Zoo.

FONTENAY-LE-COMTE (Vendée)

A town situated on the banks of the River Vendée which, in contrast to its violent early history, became during the Renaissance the home of poets and writers, including Rabelais.

The Quatre-Tias fountain bears a Latin inscription which translates 'The Fountain and Spring of Fine Minds', referring to the intellectual nature of the town. The Terre-Neuve Castle is 16th-century and contains some very fine ceilings, fireplaces and furniture. A great day out from here is a visit to the Vouvant Forest, where there is a zoo and much else of interest.
What to see Church of Notre-Dame (12–15c); Church of St-Jean; Terre-Neuve Castle (16c); Vendéen Museum.

FOUGÈRES-SUR-BIÈVRE (CHÂTEAU DE) (Loir-et-Cher)

Situated about 8km (5 miles) north west of Contres, this little château is a good example of feudal military engineering built in 1470, at a time when many other castles were being rebuilt or converted into more comfortable homes. The castle was built around an 11th-century keep and originally had a moat and drawbridge. Windows replaced arrow slits in the 16th century, and a roof was added to the keep, which had its battlements removed.

FOURAS (Charente-Maritime)

A small seaside resort at the mouth of the River Charente, Fouras commands a view of the Ile d'Oléron and the coastline from La Rochelle to Pont-d'Oléron, the best view being obtained from the Pointe-de-la-Fumée. There is a wooden board promenade, typical of French resorts, from which there are good views, and a château which houses a museum of maritime and local history. From here motor-boats run to Ile d'Aix.
What to see Château (12–17c); Pointe-de-la-Fumée (viewpoint).

Gien's fine château overlooks the Loire and the town, carefully restored after war damage. The château houses a museum of hunting and falconry

GENÇAY (Vienne)

A busy market town beside the River Clouère, Gençay is well known for its ruined 13th-century castle, where the French King, Jean-le-Bon, was imprisoned after his defeat at Poitiers. A slightly more modern note is struck by the 15th-century Château de la Roche-Gençay which stands a short distance to the south west.
What to see Château ruins (13c); Château de la Roche-Gençay (15c).

GIEN (Loiret)

This pleasant little town, situated on the banks of the Loire, is famous for its faience, a type of decorated pottery with a high glaze. Although heavily bombed during World War II, Gien has been tastefully restored to blend with the 15th-century château, which houses a museum of hunting and falconry. There are fine views of the château and town from the west bank of the Loire and from the old hump-backed bridge.
What to see Château; Hunting and Falconry Museum.

GIMEL-LES-CASCADES (Corrèze)

A picturesque area near Tulle, famous for the series of impressive waterfalls which are formed by the River Montane plunging into rocky ravines.
What to see Gimel Church (12–18c); Waterfalls (best seen from Vuillier Park).

GUÉRANDE (Loire-Atlantique)

Guérande, 6km (4 miles) north of La Baule, dominates the salt-marshes from its 49m (160ft) plateau. It is an old fortified town which has successfully kept its medieval character. Remarkably, the 15th-century circular wall is almost intact and water still fills the north and west sections of the moat. A little way north of the town there is a fine old stone windmill, the Moulin du Diable.
What to see Moulin du Diable; Ramparts (view of salt marshes and saltings); St-Michel or Castle Gate Museum (local history).

GUÉRET (Creuse)

Situated on a hill overlooking picturesque wooded valleys, Guéret is noted for its fine museum containing ceramics, tapestries, armour and weapons, and an extensive collection of dolls in traditional costume. There is also a 'Gold and Silver Treasure Gallery' devoted to painted enamel from the 12th to the 18th centuries.
What to see Hôtel des Moneyroux (15–16c mansion); Musée Municipal (museum).

Limoges Enamels

The jewel-bright colours of Limoges enamels have been renowned since the Middle Ages. Oxides of gold, silver, copper, cobalt, magnesium and pewter, all of which were once mined nearby, give a range of vivid colours which are mixed with a colourless base. This enamel is used to decorate metal – usually copper these days, though gold or silver can be used – as many as nine layers being applied. Each is separately fired at high temperature. An early masterpiece of enamel work is a reliquary which can be seen in the church at Ambazac 25 kilometres (15½ miles) north east of Limoges.

The same glowing colours are used to decorate Limoges porcelain, which has been made here for 200 years. It was an American, David Haviland, who made the ware famous. He came across Limoges in the mid-19th century and set up his own factory in the town. His high-quality porcelain soon reached the USA as well as Europe.

There are many opportunities to visit a porcelain factory or an enamel workshop.

ISSOUDUN (Indre)

This ancient town, many times a prize in battle, now manufactures leather goods. It is associated with the novelist Honoré de Balzac (1799-1850), a frequent visitor to nearby Frapesle Castle where he wrote some of his books.

Two of its historic buildings are particularly interesting. The 'Tour Blanche' (White Tower) was built by Richard the Lionheart at the end of the 12th century. From the top there is a fine view of the town and surrounding countryside. The 'Ancien Hôtel-Dieu' (former hospital), now a museum, contains pharmaceutical items dating from the 17th and 18th centuries.
What to see Ancien Hôtel-Dieu and chapel; Tour Blanche.

LANGEAIS (Indre et-Loire)

In this agreeable town are some delightful antique houses, though the castle is the main attraction. The original one, captured by the English in 1427, was sold to the French on condition that it was pulled down, save for the keep. So the 10th century stone tower – one of the oldest in France, stands alongside the 'new' château built quickly between 1465 and 1469.

LAVAL (Mayenne)

A busy industrial and market centre on the River Mayenne which has retained an attractive old quarter with pleasantly decorated 16th-century houses grouped around the castle and the cathedral. The best view of old Laval may be obtained from the Pont A-Briand and the 13th-century Pont Vieux which cross the Mayenne in the town centre.

The castle has two distinct parts: the new – a Renaissance building converted into Law Courts in the 19th century; and the old – dating originally from the 12th century. The old castle's main feature is the impressive three-storey keep, which contains a museum.
What to see Castle (12–19c); Cathedral (Romanesque – restored).

LAVARDIN (Loir-et-Cher)

A shattered 11th-century keep surrounded by remnants of its outer defences stands on a hill above the tiny, picturesque village, a constant reminder of Lavardin's medieval importance as a border fortress.
What to see Castle (11–15c); Church of St-Genest (12–15c).

Langeais Château, hardly altered since 1469, is built round a massive 10th-century keep

LIMOGES (Haute-Vienne)

This town, the capital of the Limousin region, has been an important settlement since the Gallo-Roman era, due to its position on a ford across the River Vienne, and today is a thriving industrial centre. It is internationally famous for the manufacture of porcelain, produced here for the last 200 years, and enamels which have been synonymous with the name of Limoges since the 12th century. Collections of Limoges chinaware, together with a history of the industry, can be seen in the Adrien-Dubouché National Museum; and the Municipal Museum, in the 18th-century former Bishop's Palace, contains examples of local enamels from their earliest conception until the present day. (See also page 48).

The 'old town' of Limoges contains some charming areas with narrow winding streets, and two well-preserved 13th-century bridges spanning the Vienne. Other notable buildings are the fine Gothic Cathedral and the crypt of St-Martial Abbey which dates back as far as the 4th century. Remnants of a Roman arena are in the Orsay Gardens.
What to see Adrien Dubouché National Museum; Cathedral of St-Étienne (13–16c); Church of St-Michel-des-Lions (14–15c); Church of St-Pierre-du-Queyroix (12–16c); Municipal Museum.

LOCHES (Indre-et-Loire)

An ancient town, once the stronghold of the Counts of Anjou and the Plantagenet Kings of England. The medieval city enclosed by 13th-century walls contains many varied and lovely old buildings including the massive 17th-century keep flanked by two 15th-century towers – the Tour Ronde and the Martelet. The town hall is charming. So too are the Porte des Cordeliers and Porte Picoys. Well-preserved underground dungeons, where Louis XI used to confine his prisoners in small cages, may be seen here. The Logis Royaux (Royal Residence) was the home of Agnès Sorel, Charles VIII's favourite, during the 15th century; and it was to this building that Joan of Arc came in 1429 to exhort Charles VII to go to Reims.
What to see Château (12–16c) containing Lansyer Museum (works of Lansyer) and Musée du Terroir (folklore museum); Donjon (keep – 11c).

Le Mont-Dore, high in the mountains, is a summer holiday resort, a well-equipped winter sports centre, and a spa

MANS (LE) (Sarthe)

A town has stood here, at the confluence of the Rivers Sarthe and Huisine, since Roman times. Today the town is a busy industrial and commercial centre with new estates around the medieval town, which is still partly enclosed by 4th-century ramparts. Features of the old town include the impressive cathedral and the late 15th-century Maison de la Reine-Bérengère – once a merchant's house and now containing the Museum of History and Ethnography.

Le Mans has a long association with the motor car. Local engineer Amédée Bollée developed some early automobiles here in the late 19th century and Louis Renault established his first decentralised factory close to the town in 1936. To the south of Le Mans lies the famous circuit where the twenty-four-hour race takes place, providing a severe test for both machine and driver. The same complex contains the Bugatti testing and training circuit and an automobile museum.
What to see Cathedral of St-Julien (11–15c); Motor Racing Circuits and Museum; Museum of History and Ethnography; Tessé Museum (works of art, exhibitions, etc.).

MARENNES (Charente-Maritime)

Standing at the mouth of the River Seudre surrounded by an area of salt marshes, Marennes is famous for its oyster beds and for the 'green' oysters which they produce. A fine view of the countryside is obtained from the church tower.
What to see Church of St-Pierre-de-Sales (15c).

MONDOUBLEAU (Loir-et-Cher)

Mondoubleau, on a hillside 28km (17 miles) north west of Vendôme, acquired its name from the castle built here at the end of the 10th century by Hugues Doubleau, only ruins of which remain. The town also contains a 15th-century house situated in the rue de la Basse-Ville as well as a number of 17th- to 18th-century dwellings. A good view of the surrounding countryside is obtained from the Grand Mail.
What to see Castle ruins (10c).

MONT-DORE (LE) (Puy-de-Dôme)

A busy tourist centre set in the mountains, Le Mont-Dore is famous both as a spa town and as a winter sports resort.

MONTLUÇON (Allier)

The oldest part of this mainly-industrial town lies around the castle, which contains a museum of folklore and another, rather unusual, museum devoted to the hurdy-gurdy (which traditionally accompanied the *bourrée* dance of Auvergne), with examples of instruments dating back to the 17th century.
What to see Castle (15c); Museum of Folklore; Musée International de la Vielle (Hurdy-Gurdy).

MONTOIRE-SUR-LE-LOIR (Loir-et-Cher)

A popular fishing centre whose old houses line the banks of the River Loir. The Romanesque Chapel of St-Gilles, which once belonged to a Benedictine priory, contains some fine 12th-century murals, and the town is overlooked by the impressive ruins of its 11th-century castle.

MONTRICHARD (Loir-et-Cher)

An interesting town with a number of 15th- to 16th-century buildings overlooked by the ruins of a feudal castle. Wine cellars have been established in the cliffs along the River Cher and some troglodyte dwellings may also be found there.
What to see Castle (11–13c); Chapel of Ste-Croix (Romanesque style); Nanteuil Church (12–15c).

MOULINS (Allier)

A busy town on the River Allier which was the seat of the Bourbon family until their fall from grace in the 16th century and is now a prominent commercial and industrial centre. Moulins is well endowed with buildings of architectural and historical interest including the impressive Flamboyant/Gothic Cathedral with its wealth of 15th- and 16th-century stained glass. Its masterpiece is a sumptuous triptych painted around 1500. Several 15th-century mansions have been turned into museums. The town's most unusual building is Le Jacquemart, a tall clock tower with the animated figures of a 17th-century family who strike the bells – the father and mother ringing the hours and the two children ringing the half- and quarter-hours.
What to see Cathedral of Notre-Dame (15–16c); Château (15c); Museum of Art and Archaeology; Musée de Folklore et du Vieux Moulins (old mills).

49

THE LOIRE AND CENTRAL FRANCE

NANTES (Loire-Atlantique)

A modern industrial town and busy seaport at the mouth of the River Loire, with maritime traditions stretching back to the Gallo-Roman era. Although best known today for its shipyards and refineries, Nantes has preserved an attractive 'old quarter' around the Place Royale and the former Island of Feydeau, where a number of 18th-century buildings may be seen. There is a fine cathedral, sadly damaged by fire in 1972, which contains the famous Renaissance tomb of François II, dating from the early 16th century. There are several museums dealing with local history; and Nantes Zoo, at La Jonelière 5km (3 miles) to the east, contains a good selection of animals and exotic birds.

What to see Botanical Gardens; Cathedral of St-Pierre-et-St-Paul (15–19c); Ducal Castle (15–18c); Fine Arts Museum; Maritime Museum; Museum of Local Popular Art and Decorative Art; Museum of Sacred Art; Musée-de-Nantes-par-l'Image (Pictorial history of Nantes); Nantes Zoo; Natural History Museum; Palais Dobrée (19c); Ste-Anne Belvedere (viewpoint).

NIORT (Deux-Sèvres)

An old town, a port until the River Sèvre silted up, which now has a variety of industries of which the most unusual is the making of preserves and liqueurs from angelica. The castle, once Niort's dominant feature, was begun by Henry II of England and completed by his son, Richard the Lionheart. The keep remains more or less intact and now contains a folk-lore museum with a section devoted to local costume. There are several other museums including the Musée du Pilori, the 16th-century former Town Hall, which houses a complete collection of coins from the Carolingian mint at Melle; and some fine Aubusson tapestries are on display in the Church of Notre-Dame.

What to see Castle (12c) Church of Notre-Dame (15–18c); Musée des Beaux-Arts (ivories, enamels, tapestries, etc); Musée du Pilori (antiquities and coins).

NOIRMOUTIER (ILE DE) (Vendée)

This attractive island is situated in the Bay of Bourgneuf, south of St-Nazaire and the Loire estuary, and is accessible by bridge, or by

The twin towers of Orléans cathedral rise majestically above the town roofs. The Loire is spanned by the Georges V bridge

causeway at low tide. Mimosa blooms in February, so gentle is its climate. The castle in the island's capital, Noirmoutier-en-l'Ile, has an 11th-century keep but most of the buildings and walls date from the 15th century. There is a spectacular view of the island and the surrounding area from the Tourelle de la Vigie. The castle also contains a museum of local history.

What to see Castle (11–15c); Church of St-Philbert (part 11c).

OLÉRON (ILE D') (Charente-Maritime)

The island is the second largest in France (after Corsica) being 30km (18½ miles) long and 6km (4 miles) across at its widest point. It is situated in the Pertuis d'Antioche, off Rochefort and south of La Rochelle, and is joined to the mainland by a high bridge.

The major town, St Pierre-d'Oléron, has a church with a lofty 18th-century belfry, from which there is an extensive view of the island, the Charente estuary and the surrounding area.

St-Trojan-les-Bains, in the south of the island, is a popular seaside resort with fine sandy beaches and there are good coastal views from the Pointe de Manson and the Pointe de Maumusson. Nearby at Château-d'Oléron, there are the ruins of a 17th-century fortress with a citadel which was destroyed by bombardment in 1945. The island also has areas of

pleasant woodland, and there are several other beaches and viewing points around the coast.

What to see

St-Pierre-d'Oléron: Church (18c); Museum.

St-Trojan-les-Bains: Fôret-de-St-Trojan (pine-woods); Pointe-de-Manson (viewpoint); Pointe-de-Maumusson (viewpoint).

Château d'Oléron: Citadel (ruins – 17c).

ORLÉANS (Loiret)

A busy market and industrial town standing at the most northerly point of the River Loire. Orléans suffered quite severe damage during World War II but its subsequent restoration has been carefully carried out to avoid detracting from its historical areas. Joan of Arc, an adopted daughter of the town following her deliverance of Orléans from the English, is commemorated in a variety of places. The cathedral is noted for its 17th-century organ and for the 18th-century woodcarving in the chancel. There is a 35-acre Floral Park, displaying more than a million species of plants, at the 'overspill' town of Orléans-la-Source.

What to see Cathedral of Ste-Croix (13–19c); Floral Park (Orléans-la-Source); Hôtel-de-Ville (Renaissance); Maison de Jeanne-d'Arc (museum); Musée des Beaux-Arts; Musée Historique et Archéologique; Salle des Thèses (15c bookshop)

PITHIVIERS (Loiret)

A small town to the south of Paris with tree-lined promenades on the site of its former ramparts, a few fragments of which survive. An ancient town, it grew up around the shrine of Salomon III of Brittany. There are two interesting museums and a château with some fine timber work.

What to see Château de l'Ardoise (16c); Church of St-Salomon and St-Gregory (11–12c, 16–17c); Musée Municipal (18c Hôtel-Dieu housing municipal museum including a South Sea Islands collection); Musée des Transports (at the station – a transport museum which includes a tourist steam train).

POITIERS (Vienne)

Situated on a rocky plateau at the confluence of the Rivers Clain and Boivre, Poitiers it is a university town and bishopric, but its economy is largely dependent on the agriculture of the surrounding area. An ancient town with Roman origins and many historical associations, it is one of France's leading art centres. Among its glories are five major Romanesque churches. Most renowned is the Church of Notre-Dame-la-Grande in the market place, once described as 'the richest Poitevin jewel'. The imposing Cathedral of St-Pierre is largely Gothic in style and contains choir stalls and stained glass dating from the 13th century. To the south of the cathedral is the Bapistry of St-Jean, probably the oldest Christian building in France as it dates from the 4th century and was built on earlier Roman foundations. It is now a museum. The Palais de Justice (Law Courts) incorporates the remains of the palace of the Dukes of Aquitaine including a fine 13th-century timber-roofed Great Hall and the 14th-century Maubergeon Tower. There are some striking old aristocratic houses and a spacious 19th-century Town Hall containing an art museum. The beautiful valleys of the Clain and the Boivre are within easy reach.

What to see Bapistry of St-Jean (4c, 7c,11c); Cathedral of St-Pierre (12c, 14–15c); Church of Notre-Dame-la-Grande (11–12c); Church of St Hilaire-le-Grand (11c); Hôtel Jean-Beucé (16c town house); Hôtel-de-Ville (19c Town Hall); Musée des Beaux Arts (located in the Town Hall); Palais de Justice (old Ducal palace).

Village Paper-mill

Many modest cottage industries flourish discreetly in the heart of France. The paper mill at the tiny hamlet of Laga, 6km (7½ miles) from Ambert in the Auvergne, is a remarkable example of how ancient crafts can survive.

In a picturesque house beside a stream, the 600-years-old firm of Richard de Bas has a museum. Here, where the quality of the water encouraged the establishment of the industry in the Middle Ages, hand-made paper is still produced commercially.

Visitors touring the factory can watch the paper pulp being poured into a frame by a man who, using a gentle shaking movement, evens out the layer and allows the surplus liquid to drain off. A second operator tips the mixture out of the frame on to a sheet of felt without making a crease or breaking the surface. The paper is then left to set before being hung up, just like a line of suburban washing, to finish drying.

In the museum is a copper-bound book claimed to be the smallest in the world and a 28mm by 14mm 900-page copy of the Koran.

POUZAUGES (Vendée)

The little town of Pouzauges lies to the south east of Nantes on the slope of a hill in a picturesque and heavily wooded area. The ancient church of St-Jacques dates from the 15th century and above the town stands the great square keep and outer wall of a 13th-century castle.
What to see Castle ruins (13c); Church of St-Jacques (15c).

PUY (LE) (Haute-Loire)

This town must be one of the most spectacular sights in France, set as it is around two gigantic lava plugs, the Rocher St-Michel and the Rocher Corneille.

At the centre of the town is the massive Cathedral of Notre-Dame. Much of the exterior is in 12th-century Romanesque style, but the majority of the interior decoration and the many works of art are much later, mostly 15th- to 17th-century. On the outskirts of the town, at the summit of the Rocher St-Michel, stands the very attractive Romanesque Chapel of St-Michel d'Aiguilhe, built in the 11th century. An outstanding feature of Le Puy is the huge statue of Notre-Dame-de-France on the summit of the Rocher Corneille. This is a good centre for excursions.
What to see Cathedral of Notre-Dame (12c); Chapel of St-Michel d'Aiguilhe (11c); Musée Crozatier (collection of regional lace); Notre-Dame-de-France (statue).

RÉ (ILE DE) (Charente-Maritime)

The island is situated off La Rochelle, north of the Ile d'Oléron across the Pertuis d'Antioche, and a considerable area of it is taken up by the famous Marais Salants (salt marshes). The landscape ranges from pine woods to vineyards and the island has become a popular summer resort. The island's capital, St-Martin, is a good example of a 17th-century fortified town, and the port and fishing boats are picturesque. South east of St-Martin are the ruins of the Abbey of Châteliers demolished in 1623 to provide building materials for the neighbouring Fort-de-la-Prée, a classic piece of 17th-century military architecture. In the north of the island there is a panoramic view from the Phare de Baleines (lighthouse) of the Vendéen coast.
What to see
St-Martin: Abbaye des Châteliers; Bastions (17c); Fort de la Prée; Phare des Baleines (lighthouse).

The 11th-century Chapel of St-Michel d'Aiguilhe perches atop a lava pinnacle at Le Puy. It is reached by 268 steps

RICHELIEU (Indre-et-Loire)

This town, situated on the River Mable 19km (12 miles) east of Loudun, owes its significance to Armand du Plessis, later to become Cardinal de Richelieu, who bought the estate in 1621 and over a ten-year period transformed a simple village and manor into the seat of a duchy. Richelieu was regarded as a masterpiece in planning and is laid out to a rectangular pattern. Most of the 17th-century buildings are preserved, notably the covered market and the Hôtel de Sénéchal which has a classical courtyard. The town contains a museum relating to the Richelieu family, and displays documents and works of art. At the southern end of the town lies the great park of over 1,100 acres, but the château was demolished for building material after the revolution.
What to see Church of Notre-Dame; Richelieu Museum.

RIOM (Puy-de-Dôme)

Promenades which are laid out on the site of the old ramparts and contain several ornate 17th- and 18th-century fountains encircle Riom. A number of well-preserved 16th-century mansions are open to the public, including the Palais de Justice (Law Courts) where the last remaining trace of the castle of the Dukes of Berry, a 14th-century chapel, may be seen. There are two museums, and the Church of Notre-Dame-du-Marthuret contains a splendid 14th-century statue, the 'Virgin and Bird'.
What to see Basilica de St-Amable (12–13c); Church of Notre-Dame-du-Marthuret (14–15c); Clock Tower; Hôtel Guimoneau (16c – works of art, etc); Hôtel-de-Ville (Town Hall – 16c); Musée Mandet; Musée Régional d'Auvergne.

ROCHEFORT (Charente-Maritime)

Established as a port in 1666, Rochefort has maintained its maritime tradition. Pierre Loti (1850-1923), the celebrated sailor and author of escapist novels set in exotic places was born, lived and died here. Loti's house is preserved as a museum and contains mementoes of his voyages, etc. The Naval Museum traces the development of the art of naval warfare with the aid of items which came originally from the old Rochefort Arsenal.
What to see Hôpital Maritime (18c); Maison de Loti (Pierre Loti's house); Musée Naval.

CENTRAL FRANCE

ROCHELLE (LA) (Charente-Maritime)

For many, La Rochelle is one of France's loveliest towns. It has the second-largest fishing harbour in the country and has now become a popular resort and yachting centre. The Tour St-Nicolas and the Tour de la Chaine, dating from the 14th century, still guard the harbour entrance along with the Tour de la Lanterne, an early type of lighthouse which was once the town prison. La Rochelle has a number of gaily decorated 17th-century houses, and the 18th-century 'porches' which cover some of the older streets are of interest. The fortified Hôtel-de-Ville contains exhibits relating to the Huguenot wars.

What to see Aquarium; Cathedral of St-Louis (18c); Harbour and quays; Hôtel de la Bourse (18c); Hôtel-de-Ville (15–16c); Maison Henri II (16c); Musée des Beaux-Arts; Musée Lafaille (natural history, etc); Musée d'Orbigny (local history); Palais de Justice (Law Courts – 18c); Tour de la Lanterne (13–14c); Tour St-Nicolas (14c).

ROCHE-POSAY (LA) (Vienne)

A thermal spa much loved by the Romans at the confluence of the Rivers Creuse and Gartempe. The alkaline waters contain, among other things, sodium bicarbonate and iron and calcium salts. They are said to be particularly beneficial to arthritis and skin disease sufferers. La Roche-Posay is a pleasant mixture of old houses and modern villas and its main features are its feudal castle and fortified church.

What to see Castle (12–13c); La Roche-Posay Church (11–15c). Views down Creuse Valley.

ROCHE-SUR-YON (LA) (Vendée)

This town, the capital of the department of Vendée, was laid out in its present rigid pattern by Napoleon. A fine equestrian statue of the founder stands in the Place Napoléon and there is a museum dealing with local history and archaeology. One of the largest stud farms (haras) in France, renowned for breeding trotting-race horses, is located in the town and visits can be arranged at most times of the year. The town suburbs have attracted a lot of industry including washing machine and tyre manufacturers.

What to see Haras (Stud Farm); Museum.

The medieval Tour St-Nicholas and Tour de la Chaine guard La Rochelle's colourful harbour, now a popular yachting centre

ROMORANTIN-LANTHENAY (Loir-et-Cher)

An industrial and market centre on the River Sauldre. Around the rue de la Résistance there are a number of picturesque old houses including the half-timbered Renaissance-style former Chancellery and the richly decorated Maison du Carroir-d'Orée which contains an archaeological museum. Romorantin-Lanthenay was once the capital of the Sologne, a region of woods and lakes which have traditionally provided the fish, venison and wild-fowl for local tables. The Sologne Museum, in the Hôtel-de-Ville (Town Hall), deals with the natural history, crafts and traditions of that area. A racing car museum and library are located in the Faubourg d'Orléans.

What to see Musée de la Course Automobile (Racing Cars); Musée de Sologne.

ROYAN (Charente-Maritime)

After suffering severe war damage in 1944/5, Royan has risen from the ashes to become the principal resort on the Côte de Beauté. The town has been rebuilt in a decidedly modern style and its wealth of accommodation has ensured its popularity as a conference centre. Its sheltered sandy beaches, backed by wooded slopes, and its fine entertainment facilities make Royan a favourite holiday resort.

What to see Church of Notre-Dame.

SABLES-D'OLONNE (LES) (Vendée)

An extremely popular resort with a thriving sardine fishing industry, well known for its long expanse of safe, sandy beach backed by the 18th-century promenade known as 'Le Remblai'. Though noted for its modern sports and entertainment facilities, a glimpse of the past may be obtained in the old quarter of La Chaume.

What to see Beaches; Church of Notre-Dame-de-Bon-Port (17c); Musée de l'Abbaye Ste-Croix.

ST-FLOUR (Cantal)

Dramatically perched on a rock escarpment above the River Lander, St-Flour has become a popular tourist centre for the Haute-Auvergne area with its mountains, lakes and hot springs. The rather austere Gothic cathedral is surrounded by some interesting old buildings. The 17th-century Hôtel-de-Ville (Town Hall) contains the Haute-Auvergne Museum with items of local art, folklore, etc, on display; and the A-Douet Museum has similar exhibits.

What to see Cathedral (14–15c); Musée A-Douet; Musée de la Haute-Auvergne.

ST-LÉONARD-DE-NOBLAT (Haute-Vienne)

Standing on a hill above rolling countryside about 30km (18 miles) east of Limoges, this small market town is locally famous for the 'Quintaine' ceremony which takes place each November in memory of St-Léonard, the patron saint of prisoners, and entails horsemen demolishing a symbolic wooden castle. A number of lovely medieval-style buildings cluster round the Romanesque church, which contains the tomb and relics of the gentle St-Léonard.

What to see Parish Church of St-Léonard (11–13c).

Cognac~best of brandy

'Brandy' is not a flattering name to give to a drink as it just means 'burnt', a name the English adopted from the Dutch 'Brande-wijn' (burnt wine). The wines of the Charente are sharp and lack body, yet when 'burnt' they make one of the world's best liqueurs – Cognac, named after the small town which is the centre of the brandy trade. Over 20,000,000 bottles are exported each year.

The best grapes for Cognac-making are grown in chalky soil – 'Fines Champagnes' on the label will tell you it comes from the right area.

To make Cognac the wine is heated and then twice distilled. It is matured for at least two years, in quiet, dimly-lit vaults, in barrels

An alembic, used for distilling brandy

made from heart oak grown near Limoges. During this time the spirit absorbs the wood essences and takes in oxygen.

ST-NAZAIRE
(Loire-Atlantique)

Situated on the Loire estuary, St-Nazaire's growth since the early 19th century has been due to its port facilities and shipbuilding industry. Three point of major interest are the entrance lock, scene of the famous Commando raid in 1942; the submarine pens built by the Germans during the war and now the site of various industries; and the covered submarine exit from which there is a good view of the town and port. Also of interest are the shipyards, the lighthouse, and Ste-Anne's Church.

What to see Church of Ste-Anne; Lighthouse; Port; Shipyards.

ST NECTAIRE (Puy-de-Dôme)

St Nectaire-le-Bas is a tiny spa set in pine-forested hills, where kidney disorders are treated. St Nectaire-le-Haut has a majestically simple 12th-century church, arguably the best example of Auvergnat Romanesque. Its tranquil beauty is enhanced by its setting on a narrow platform of rock which raises the church on high. The finely sculpted capitals within are low enough to be plainly visible, and the treasury contains a striking gold-plated reliquary-bust of St Baudime.

SAINTES
(Charente-Maritime)

The town began its history about 2,000 years ago when the Romans conquered the local Santones tribes. Witness to its Roman past are the arch of Germanicus and the amphitheatre, still used in summer for open-air performances. The Cathedral of St-Pierre is a massive 15th-century Gothic construction with an enormous bell tower surmounted by a steeple. The town was restructured after the revolution and only the area around the cathedral remains in its old form. Near the River Charente, on which Saintes stands, is a public garden; and horses including English Arabs and French trotters can be seen (from mid-July to February) at the haras (stud farm) on the outskirts of the town.

What to see Abbaye-aux-Dames (11–16c – restored); Amphitheatre (1c); Arc de Germanicus (1c); Archaeological Museum; Cathedral of St-Pierre (12–16c); Church of St-Europe (15c); Dupay-Mestreau Regional Museum; Education Museum of Prehistory; Fine Arts Museum; Haras.

SANCERRE (Cher)

Sancerre, very nearly a fairy tale village, sits on top of a hill. From its terraces, bordered with lime trees, a serene view of the Loire, its huge plain, and a handsomely curved viaduct, is laid out below. The village is as delightful as the famous white wine that bears its name. Steep, narrow, winding streets are lined with gabled and turreted old houses. Once fortified because of its strategic position, the town is dominated by an enormous keep, the Tour des Fiefs, which is all that remains of its castle.

What to see Beffroi (16c alarm tower now serving as a belfry); old town; Tour des Fiefs (15c keep).

SAULGES (Mayenne)

The village of Saulges is situated to the west of Le Mans. Small, quiet and attractively sited, it overlooks the Erve Valley. To the north of the village lie the Saulges caves providing interesting geological formations together with evidence of early human occupation. The Grotte de Rochefort on the north bank of the River Erve leads to a small underground lake.

SAUMUR (Maine-et-Loire)

Saumur, between Angers and Tours, looks its best from the River Loire. The clean white façades of castle and houses give it an air of compact neatness. It is at the heart of one of the oldest vine-yards in France. In addition to wine making, a traditional local activity is the manufacture of religious items such as rosaries.

This was an important crossing point of the Loire during the Middle Ages and was therefore strongly fortified. Even today Saumur is overlooked by its château which rises high above the town to the east, dominating the skyline. The proud Château de Saumur, with its four tall corner towers, dates from the 14th century and is regarded as one of the finest of the Loire châteaux. Restored early in the 19th century and again in the 20th century, it now houses two museums. Below the château in the old part of the town, around the 12th-century Church of St-Pierre, there are some fine town houses with stud work dating from the 15th and 16th centuries. Saumur is famous for the 'Cadre Noir' of the National Riding School, which is located just outside the town, and also the School of Cavalry.

What to see Cavalry Museum (in the School of Cavalry); Château de Saumur (14c); Church of Notre-Dame-de-Nantilly (12c); Hôtel-de-Ville (Town Hall – part 16c); Musée des Arts Decoratifs (Museum of Decorative Arts – in the Château); Musée des Blindés (Museum of Armoured Cavalry, Place du Chardonnet).

SELLES-SUR-CHER
(Loir-et-Cher)

A pleasant little town standing in a curve of the River Cher, Selles is a town of two châteaux – the mellow Renaissance façade of the later building fully exposed to casual view, and the stark defences of the 13th-century fortress almost obscured from sight. The former abbey church of St-Eusice is worth a visit for its friezes and decorations. At Meusnes, 6½km (4 miles) away is a museum explaining the craft of the locally-revived industry of flint-knapping.

What to see Châteaux (13–17c); Church of St-Eusice (12–15c – restored 17c); Local History and Folklore Museum.

One hill-top tower is a reminder that charming old-world Sancerre was once a formidable stronghold

THE LOIRE AND CENTRAL FRANCE

SOLESMES (Sarthe)

A village 3km (2 miles) east of Sablé-sur-Sarthe, dominated by the Abbey of St-Peter. The abbey church, dating partly from the 11th century, is open to visitors and contains some remarkable 15th- to 16th-century carvings – the 'Saints of Solesmes'. The abbey is well known for its Gregorian Chant – visitors may attend Mass there during the summer.

SULLY-SUR-LOIRE (Loiret)

The main attraction of this town is the 14th-century Château de Sully with its lovely riverside setting, moat and four round towers. A medieval fortress from the outside, a charming Renaissance dwelling within, it is noted for its connections with Joan of Arc, Sully (Henri IV's minister) and the young Voltaire. The château suffered damage in 1940 but its famous chestnut timber roof, in the upper hall of the keep, has survived. This dates from 1363 and is one of the finest medieval examples of its kind.

What to see Château de Sully; Collégiale de St-Ythier (Collegiate Church with two fine stained-glass windows – 16c).

TALMONT (Charente-Maritime)

This lovely old village has an interesting Romanesque church perched on the edge of the cliffs overlooking the Gironde Estuary south east of Royan. The famous church is not complete as the nave subsided into the sea many years ago, but the rest has been underpinned.

What to see Church of Ste-Radegonde.

THIERS (Puy de-Dôme)

Approached from the south, the houses of Thiers rise with panache up the steep hillside. Hardly the setting for a major cutlery manufacturing town, which Thiers has been since the Crusaders brought back from Palestine the technique of tempered steel. Thiers has also been an important paper-making centre. For centuries hundreds of artisans worked by (and actually over) the River Durolle, leaving a legacy of wooden workshops and fine half-timbered houses, some with carvings. Some have been restored, particularly the 15th-century Maison du Pirou. At 16 rue du Quatre-Septembre is the house where Daguerre, who perfected photography, lived from 1833 to 1846.

What to see Maison du Pirou (15c); old houses by river; Musée Fontenille-Mondière (history of steel artisans); views from ramparts; countryside of Monts du Forez and Livradois.

THOUARS (Deux-Sèvres)

This old and pleasant town stands above the River Thouet. It is overlooked by a very large 17th-century château which is built on the site of a medieval fortress. The château is not open to the public but access is permitted to the gallery. Amongst Thouars' ancient buildings are the Romanesque Church of St-Médard, the 12th-century Tour du Prince de Galles (Prince of Wales or Grenetière Tower) and a number of 15th-century houses in the rues St-Médard and du Château. There is a good view of Thouars and the Thouet Valley from the Chemin du Panorama.

What to see Château; Chemin du Panorama (viewpoint); Church of St-Médard; Old Houses; Sainte-Chapelle (part-Renaissance chapel); Tour du Prince de Galles.

TOURS (Indre-et-Loire)

During a long and varied history stretching back to Roman times, Tours has always been a town of local importance. It was a place of pilgrimage as early as the 6th century, when the tomb of St-Martin became a gathering point for the sick and needy, and it became a foremost producer of silk during the 15th and 16th centuries. Today Tours is a busy industrial, wine-producing, university town; and its position between the Rivers Loire and Cher ensures its popularity as a tourist centre.

The visitor to Tours will find a wealth of buildings of historical interest, ranging from the 15th-century gabled houses around the Place Foire-le-Roi, where medieval fairs were held, to the stately Renaissance Hôtel Gouin, now an archaeological museum and art gallery. The shrine of St-Martin still attracts pilgrims to the 19th-century Basilica which bears his name; and portions of the original 13th-century church, erected in his honour, can be seen in the vicinity. The Cathedral of St-Gatien, built over three centuries in an impressive French-Gothic style, contains some fine examples of medieval stained glass. There are numerous museums, including one devoted to wine-making in the Touraine and one which is concerned with traditional crafts. A single 12th-century tower (Tour-de-Guise) stands as a souvenir of the castle Henry II of England established here to command the Loire Valley.

What to see Basilica of St-Martin (19c); Botanical Gardens; Cathedral of St-Gatien (13–16c); Church of St-Julien (13c); Fine Arts Museum; Gemmail Museum (stained glass); Hôtel Gouin (medieval art collection); Maison de Tristan (15c); Musée du Compagnonnage (Craft Guilds Museum); Museum of Touraine Wines; Tour de Guise (12c).

Reflected in the tranquil Loire, Château de Sully looks forbidding but is exquisite inside

TRÔO (Loir-et-Cher)

An unusual little town set on a hillside and full of sloping alleys and stairways. The rock on which it stands is riddled with caves and passages and a few troglodyte dwellings still exist there. The church of St-Jacques-des-Guérets, which stands on the opposite bank of the Loire to the main town, is notable for its 12th-century murals. A well that gives out a remarkable echo is preserved in the Upper Town.

What to see La Butte (viewpoint); Collegiate Church of St-Martin (11c); Grand Puits (well); Grotte Pétrifiante (limestone cave).

TULLE (Corrèze)

A town which grew up around a medieval abbey in the Corrèze Valley and has survived a turbulent history, having been taken by invaders no less than five times since the 14th century. The 12th-century cathedral, with its 74m (240ft) belfry, is surrounded by an interesting old quarter.

What to see Cathedral of Notre-Dame (12–14c); Maison-de-Loyac (15c).

TURENNE (Corrèze)

An ancient town, 18km (11 miles) south of Brive-la-Gaillarde, which now consists mainly of some attractive old buildings grouped around the hill-top ruins of the 13th-century castle, from which there is an uninterrupted panorama.

USSÉ (CHÂTEAU D') (Indre-et-Loire)

A truly 'fairy tale' castle, with its turrets and chimneys towering above the River Indre 13½km (8 miles) north of Chinon, Ussé is said to be the model Charles Perrault used for the castle in his 'Sleeping Beauty'. Built between the 15th and 17th centuries, it is a mixture of Gothic, Renaissance and Classical styles. The 16th-century chapel is richly decorated; among other things, there is an Aubusson tapestry depicting the life of Joan of Arc.

UZERCHE (Corrèze)

A very attractive town, clinging to the hillside above the River Vézère, with a number of fine old buildings, many of them surmounted by towers and turrets. Fragments of Uzerche's medieval defences may be seen around the Porte Bécharie, a fortified gateway.

What to see Church of St-Pierre (12–13c).

Villandry Château's gardens are constructed to harmonise with the house, completed in 1536

VAL (CHÂTEAU DE) (Cantal)

A wonderfully romantic 15th-century castle, flanked by five round towers, seated on a rock in the artificial lake of Bort and joined to the shore by a causeway. Illuminated in summer, the castle holds annual art exhibitions. The lake has a beach and facilities for water-sports and motor-boat excursions. The River Dordogne is dammed by the Barrage de Bort whose belvedere permits the visitor to survey the huge construction. Bort-les-Orgues, just south of the dam, is so-called because of a high plateau of rock nearby from which one obtains a panoramic view. The château is about 6km (4 miles) north of Bort-les-Orgues.

VALENÇAY (Indre)

The main feature of Valençay is its 16th-century château which displays both Renaissance and Classical architectural styles. The west wing contains various collections including *objets d'art* and Empire furniture. There is a surrounding park which contains llamas, fallow deer and birds. Another attraction of the château is its 'Son et Lumière' displays.

VENDÔME (Loir-et-Cher)

This old town with its ruined château is situated on the River Loir. One of Vendôme's attractions is Trinité Church, originally part of the 11th-century Benedictine abbey. The adjoining monks' building now houses a museum which contains sections covering prehistory, antiquity and furniture. The old quarter of Vendôme has an impressive 14th-century gateway, the Porte St-Georges. From the Jardin Public there is a good view of Vendôme and it surroundings. A similar view is obtained from the Promenade de la Montagne, located near the château.

What to see Ancien Collège des Oratoriens (part Romanesque); Château ruins; Jardin Public; Museum; Old Quarter; Porte St-Georges; Trinité Church.

VICHY (Allier)

Vichy, situated on the River Allier, is one of France's most famous spas. Its curative waters, renowned since Roman times, are used today to treat digestive disorders and other complaints. The town is a major tourist centre. It has developed its cultural resources as a centre for festivals, conferences, exhibitions and concerts. Sporting facilities of every kind – especially aquatic – are available in a modern complex by the river, which has been widened to form the artificial Lac d'Allier. Vichy is a prestigious international venue and is also a good starting-point for trips into the hills south of the town.

What to see Church of St-Blaise (part 12c); Grand Établissement Thermal; Maison du Bailliage (16c – now a museum of local art and archaeology); Maison de Madame de Sévigné (17c); Parc d'Allier; Parc des Sources.

VILLANDRY (CHÂTEAU DE) (Indre-et-Loire)

The château was built in the 16th century, incorporating the keep of an earlier fortress. It lies about 16km (9½ miles) west of Tours on the D7 and is remarkable for its unique 16th-century-style formal French gardens which were reconstructed in the 19th century. The gardens are laid out in geometric patterns with shrubs, flowers and fruit trees, and may be viewed from the belvedere at the rear of the château.

What to see Château (16c); Church.

The Dordogne and South-West France

Dramatic Castelnaud Château clings to a sheer rock face overlooking the Dordogne and north to Beynac

Neatly framed between the Atlantic and the Massif Central, with the Gironde delta to the north and the Spanish border to the south, lie the provinces of Aquitaine and Midi-Pyrénées. Within these frontiers is a pot-pourri of snow-capped mountains, lush river valleys, arid plateaux and gorges, and huge dunelands and pine forests.

This southern land has attracted men since the Old Stone Age. Romans found it to their liking, and in the Middle Ages the French and English fought over it and left their fortifications to remind us of their struggles. Warm-stoned towns and villages provide the backcloth for what seems now to be an immutably tranquil way of life.

Aquitaine

The Romans gave the name Aquitaine – 'Land of Water' – to this area. It has a long coastline, with some étangs (lagoons) in the north, but the Romans may have been struck principally by the way the countryside is netted with rivers. They flow from the Massif Central in the east and the Pyrénées in the south, and almost all eventually reach the Gironde estuary via the Garonne or the Dordogne, or help to swell the waters of the Adour which enters the sea north of Biarritz.

The Dordogne The River Dordogne, which has given its name to this favourite holiday area, flows through a gently seductive landscape. Densely-wooded hillsides rise above pinkish limestone cliffs, fields red with spring poppies or thick-green with summer tobacco line the river banks, little villages claw into the hillsides, their terraced restaurants serving a local cuisine which is acknowledged as one of France's finest.

Perhaps the area was always known for its good living. Palaeolithic man lived here in rock shelters and caves, survived by hunting bison and deer, and left the world's first record of man the artist. A quite remarkable collection of cave paintings and engravings has been discovered in the valleys of the Dordogne and its tributary, the Vézère, the most famous of which are at Lascaux and Les Eyzies ('the capital of prehistory') (see page 65).

The hundreds of châteaux and many fortified towns here bear witness to the troubled Middle Ages when England clashed with France. English claims to Aquitaine can be traced to the famous marriage between Eleanor of Aquitaine and Henri Plantagenet (later Henry II) in 1152. Of the *bastides* (fortified towns – see page 68), built here during the ensuing struggles for sovereignty, Monpazier is the best-surviving example. Domme, however, is the most visited, mainly due to its clifftop location overlooking the Dordogne Valley.

The view from Domme's terrace also manages to encapsulate the long-running Anglo-French conflict. On the far bank of the river stands the imposing fortress of Château Beynac, a French stronghold during the Hundred Years War (1337–1453). Perched on the summit of a sheer outcrop, it looks out imperiously across the river (once the dividing line between opposing forces) to the soaring, almost fairytale towers of Castelnau.

A strong sense of the medieval also pervades the towns and villages strung out beside or near the river. Outstanding is Sarlat. The golden-bricked houses and courtyards of Old Sarlat, radiating haphazardly from the market square, form the nucleus of France's most authentically medieval town.

The towns around Sarlat are not large, for this is essentially farming country. Rich alluvial soils along the river valley and a warm – but not bakingly hot – climate support a bountiful, prosperous agriculture based on tobacco, fruit, maize, wheat and walnuts.

Further west, past Bergerac, the Dordogne Valley widens into a flatter landscape. Vineyards become increasingly common as the river joins the Garonne in the headwaters of the Gironde estuary just north of Bordeaux.

The coastal lands The Gironde estuary meets the Atlantic at the Point de Grave at the northern tip of Les Landes, a huge triangular area of pine forest, lake, sand dune and beach. The longest side of this triangle runs along the Atlantic coast, past the oyster beds, small resorts and yachting marinas of the Arcachon basin and almost all the way to the Spanish border. Inland are the highest sand dunes in Europe, backed by pine trees planted in the 19th century to arrest the advance of the sands.

The beaches, pounded by a vigorous Atlantic surf, are long and mostly deserted. They stretch some 150 miles to Biarritz,

Above: in a lush green valley in the Pyrénées, the small village of Conques has a well-known Romanesque church

Left: Dordogne's summer grape harvest – the crop that produces one of the Englishman's favourite tipples – full-bodied claret

58

sinuous near Cahors. Once an important Roman settlement, the town occupies a natural defensive site in one of the great loops in the river, its medieval fortifications including the formidably defended Pont de Valentré.

To the west of the town are the productive, but little-known, Cahors vineyards, whilst to the east the Lot flows through one of its most tortuous and scenic sections, especially around the dramatically sited cliff village of St-Cirq-Lapopie.

To the south lie the higher, stony lands of the Quercy Causse and the rocky gorges of the Rivers Aveyron and Tarn. These rivers emerge to join the Garonne west of Montauban, in a wide fertile plain which is France's most prolific fruit-growing area. Grapes, peaches, apples, pears, plums and vegetables are all on sale at the local markets.

In the towns and villages of the Garonne, a definite southern ambience and architecture begin to take over. Montauban, one of the most important market towns, is built largely from a pinkish brick. Toulouse, capital of the Midi-Pyrénées, is known as *la ville rose*; it has, at its heart, faded brick buildings which change colour from pink to mauve during the daily cycle from dawn to dusk. From here, on a clear day, the distant outline of the Pyrénées can be seen. This mountain chain, 400km (250 miles) long, may lack the sheer scale and grandeur of the French Alps but its fresh, green uplands boast a way of life relatively undisturbed by alpine tourism. The 60-mile-long Parc National des Pyrénées, rich in flora and fauna and criss-crossed with footpaths for summer hiking, covers a particularly beautiful area of over 125,000 acres.

The mountains are divided between Aquitaine and the Midi-Pyrénées. From the low slopes in the Basque Country to the central High Pyrénées and the Ariège highlands around Foix in the east, they are dotted with places of interest, some historic, some modern. A famous spot which has a bit of each is Lourdes, the heavily commercialised town which attracts both pilgrims and mixed feelings. Unequivocally attractive is nearby Pau, discovered by the English in the 19th century and much admired for its superb climate and lovely situation.

In the east, the little town of Foix, with its maze of steep, winding streets, is a convenient centre from which to explore the prehistoric caves at Niaux and the Aladdin's Cave of duty-free gift shops in the independent state of Andorra.

Although relatively undeveloped compared to the more fashionable – and expensive – Alps, winter sports are becoming increasingly popular here. Though of all the climates in which to end this tour of the sunny south-west, winter snow is the least appropriate!

where south-west France begins to show a few more of its many faces.

First and most obvious of these is a cosmopolitan little cluster of resorts, bays and rocky headlands running all the way to the Spanish border. This is Basque Country, a small pocket of France where a fiercely independent race shares with relatives across the Spanish border a culture which refuses to respect national boundaries. In the pretty whitewashed hill villages along the foothills of the Pyrénées, and in the town of Bayonne itself, the Basque influence and the flavour of Spain are strong.

Midi-Pyrénées

In shape and size, the Midi-Pyrénées roughly resembles its neighbouring region of Aquitaine. Again diversity is the keynote, from the gentle, wooded landscape watered by the Lot in the north to the severe profile of the Hautes Pyrénées which straddle the Spanish border.

The cultivated fields and cliffside villages beside the River Lot are reminiscent of the countryside around Sarlat, though in the 'causse' highlands, which have a chalky, dry soil, sheep-rearing is the main form of farming. The river is at its most

Places of Interest

Two bridges link the town of Albi, split by the broad waters of the Tarn
Inset: the ornate ceiling of the Cathedral of Ste-Cécile

AGEN (Lot-et-Garonne)

The chief town in the Department of Lot-et-Garonne, Agen is situated on the right bank of the River Garonne, and is well-known as a market town, specialising in vegetables and fruit, particularly plums.

In Renaissance times, the town was an important centre for the arts, including ceramics and pottery. The museum, housed in a group of Renaissance mansions, contains several valuable collections of ceramics and some fine works of art including paintings and etchings by Goya and other famous artists. The prize exhibit of the museum is the 'Venus of Le Mas' a Greek statue in marble which was discovered in 1876. A fine view of the town and surrounding countryside may be obtained from the tower of the museum.

An aqueduct on the north-western edge of the town carries a canal over the River Garonne.
What to see Cathedral of St-Caprais; Museum.

ALBI (Tarn)

The town is the capital of the Tarn region and lies across both banks in a loop of the River Tarn. Much of the town is built in pink brick which seems to glow when seen from a distance.

Toulouse-Lautrec, the artist, was born at Albi and his birthplace is open to the public. In addition, the town has a Toulouse-Lautrec Museum within the Palais-de-Berbie, the former episcopal palace, which was started in 1265 and added to until the 17th century. The museum contains the most substantial collection in existence of works by the artist. Exhibitions of works by present-day artists are also held.

Construction of the cathedral of Ste-Cécile began in 1282 and took another two centuries to complete; most of the present structure dates from the 15th century. Built from pink brick, its visual effect is one of power and grandeur. The interior is richly decorated and includes the huge 15th-century fresco 'The Last Judgement'. This theme is continued in the Great Vault which is decorated with paintings of saints and biblical figures.

Two bridges cross the Tarn within the town, the old Gothic bridge and the modern '22nd August' bridge, from which there is a good view along the river and over the town.
What to see Cathedral of Ste-Cécile (11–15c); Church of St-Salvy (11–15c); Palais-de-Berbie (13–17c); Toulouse-Lautrec Birthplace; Toulouse-Lautrec Museum;

ARCACHON (Gironde)

A very popular seaside resort with five kilometres of seafront overlooking the Bassin D'Arcachon, an inland lake which opens out into the Atlantic.

The town is divided into two distinct areas. The summer town with its beach, promenade and modern yacht marina provides a venue for all types of water sports in addition to golf and tennis. On the seafront there is an aquarium with many types of fish, and also a museum. The winter town is situated slightly to the south, among sand dunes and pines.

The Bassin D'Arcachon is a triangular area of water noted for its oyster beds (around the Île aux Oiseaux), and fish farms. There is a bird sanctuary north of Le Teich, in the south-eastern corner.
What to see Aquarium and Museum; Bird Sanctuary (Le Teich).

AUCH (Gers)

A charming old town, once the capital of ancient Gascony and now the administrative centre of the Department of Gers. Auch is a town of narrow streets and alleyways which wind their way down the hillside to the River Gers, passing through old gateways, and a 232-step stairway runs from the Place Salinis to the river bank. A fine statue of d'Artagnan, the Gascon immortalised in Alexandre Dumas' novel 'The Three Musketeers' stands on a landing of the staircase. The Place Salinis gives access to the Tour d'Armagnac, the 14th-century former prison, and to the Gothic Cathedral of Ste-Marie. Apart from its ornate façade, the cathedral is notable for its magnificent decorative carving.
What to see Cathedral of Ste-Marie (15–17c); Musée des Jacobins (Archaeology).

BAGNÈRES-DE-BIGORRE (Hautes-Pyrénées)

An ancient town in the Adour Valley which has become a popular holiday resort. It is also a spa town, and its waters, rich in calcium and sulphur, are reputed to have a beneficial effect on those suffering from arthritis or minor nervous disorders. Bagnères is an attractive town with a 15th-century church and an interesting fine arts museum.
What to see Church of St-Vincent (15–16c); Musée Salies (fine arts); Thermal Park.

BAYONNE
(Pyrénées-Atlantiques)
This old port at the confluence of the Rivers Nive and Adour was founded in the Roman era. Today, in addition to its maritime connections, Bayonne has become an important industrial and tourist centre. Bayonne is the principal town of the French Basque region and the folklore of this area is on display in the Basque Museum, which deals with every aspect of Basque life and history, and is also featured in the Bayonne Festival which takes place during August. Nearby is the important Bonnat Museum, with its collection of works by Rubens, Van Dyck, El Greco, Goya, Ingres and Murillo. The town is known for the succulent ham produced there (a Ham Fair is usually held shortly before Easter), and for its chocolate.

The remnants of Bayonne's defences mostly date from the 16th century, but parts of earlier Gallo-Roman walls can be seen skilfully incorporated into the later structure. On the right bank of the Adour, in the suburb of St-Esprit, is a huge, star-shaped citadel built by Vauban. The Cathedral of Ste-Marie, with its high spires and fine stained glass, is one of the best examples of Gothic architecture in the area and

Château de Beynac's clifftop site above the River Dordogne affords spectacular views of the valley

has fine 14th-century cloisters.
What to see Cathedral of Ste-Marie (13–16c); Musée Basque; Musée Bonnat (works of art etc).

Delicacies of Périgord

The black diamonds of Périgord are aptly named, as anyone who has priced a truffle will confirm. Looking not unlike a shrivelled, blackened walnut, the truffle is the great delicacy of Périgordian cuisine.

Specially-trained pigs or dogs sniff out the truffle, a type of underground mushroom which grows on the roots of certain oak trees. The *cavage* (picking) takes place in winter, when the elusive truffle is at its most fragrant.

Périgord is also famous for its *pâté de foie gras*, made from either goose or duck liver. This delicious, rich pâté may be served plain, with truffles, as a purée or mousse. The squeamish would be unwise to probe the secret of its preparation, a process which involves the force-feeding of the goose to produce a swollen liver.

BAZAS (Gironde)
An old town with arcaded squares and gabled houses which stands on a crag above the River Beuve. There is a shady walk along portions of the ancient ramparts and the fortified Porte-du-Gisquet can still be seen. Bazas possesses a fine Gothic cathedral with an intricately decorated façade, by the side of which is a garden from which one obtains a charming view of the Beuve Valley.
What to see Cathedral of St-Jean (13–16c).

BERGERAC (Dordogne)
Bergerac is an important tobacco- and wine-producing town on the River Dordogne. Its major product is tobacco, and the town contains the only Tobacco Museum in France, which is housed in the Hôtel-de-Ville (town hall). The town is associated with the big-nosed romantic, Cyrano de Bergerac, pathetic hero of Edmund Rostand's novel.

From Bergerac the Monbazillac vineyards, famous for their sweet dessert wines, may be visited. Many of the vineyard workers live at the village of Rouffignac-de-Sigoulès, where some of the houses have unusual circular tiles. Monbazillac Château, built in the middle of the 16th century, is

open to the public. The main building has a massive tower at each corner and is battlemented.

A spectacular excursion is to follow the River Dordogne eastwards as far as Badefols (26.5 km – 16½miles) where the river starts its great loops or *cingles*.
What to see Church of Notre-Dame (Gothic); Couvent des Recollets (12–17c); Monbazillac vineyards; Musée Municipal (local history); Musée du Tabac.

BÉTHARRAM (CAVES)
(Pyrénées-Atlantiques)
A subterranean aerial train travels for most of 3 km (1¾ miles) giving a bird's-eye view of the extraordinary galleries and eroded shapes which the River Gave de Pau has carved out over the ages.

The caves lie 11 km (8¼ miles) west of Lourdes.

BEYNAC-ET-CAZENAC
(Dordogne)
The castle here is a fine example of a feudal stronghold, standing on a cliff overlooking a sheer drop down to the River Dordogne. The keep dates from the 13th century but the rest of the castle buildings were added between the 14th and the 16th century. A magnificent view over the valley may be obtained from the south bastion.

Five magnificent beaches draw the crowds to the elegant 19th-century resort of Biarritz

BIARRITZ (Pyrénées-Atlantiques)

Once a fishing village, Biarritz has developed into a popular and fashionable resort. It has fine sandy beaches and is also a spa, with brine springs which are used to treat anaemia, metabolic and gynaecological complaints. One of Biarritz's main attractions is the Musée-de-la-Mer (Maritime Museum) which contains one of the best aquariums in France. The town has good entertainment facilities including two casinos, and surfing is just one of the many sports on offer.

Biarritz also has a number of folklore festivals and the Basque game of pelota should be watched for its speed and athletic grace. There are many spectacular views of the town and its coastline including those from the Rocher-de-la-Vierge, linked to the mainland by a narrow footbridge, and the lighthouse;
What to see Lighthouse; Musée-de-la-Mer; Old Port; Rocher-de-la-Vierge; Thermes Salins (brine springs).

BONAGUIL (CASTLE) (Lot-et-Garonne)

This proud and splendid example of military architecture reveals all the devices used by a feudal baron in the late 15th century to withstand attack and siege.

Bonaguil lies 8 km (5 miles) north-east of Fumel.

BORDEAUX (Gironde)

An industrialised seaport which is the fifth largest city in France, in addition to being the chief town of the region of Aquitaine. Bordeaux is also a famous wine-producing centre and a number of vineyards in the vicinity are open to visitors.

The history of the city stretches back to Gallo-Roman times and includes a period when it was held by the Black Prince, son of Edward III of England, but the overall architectural impression of the 'old quarter' is that of the 18th century. This is particularly so around the Place de la Bourse and the Place de la Comédie – the heart of Bordeaux – where the Grand Théâtre, a fine colonnaded building dating from 1780, reigns supreme. The Esplanade des Quinconces, near the river, is the largest square in Europe. The cathedral, with an imposing façade and richly decorated doorways, dates originally from the 11th century. Bordeaux has a large number of museums including the Centre Jean Moulin which is devoted to the French Resistance.

Bordeaux has excellent sporting and entertainment facilities and its location close to the Atlantic beaches, the forested Landes area, the classic wine *châteaux* and great vineyards, and the Dordogne Valley ensures its popularity as a tourist centre during the summer months.

Frenchmen playing boules – one of their favourite pastimes – in front of St-Croix Church, Bordeaux

What to see Cathedral of St-André (11–15c); Centre Jean Moulin (World War II); Grand Théâtre (18c); Hôtel-de-Ville (town hall – 18c); Musée d'Aquitaine (local history); Musée des Art Décoratifs; Musée des Beaux-Arts; Musée de la Marine (models of ships, etc) Musée Bonnal-Renaulac (Automobile Museum) in the suburb of Bègles; Musée d'Histoire Naturelle (Animals etc from the locality); Vineyards.

BOURDEILLES (Dordogne)

The castle at Bourdeilles, about 10km (6 miles) south-west of Brantôme, stands high above the River Dronne and consists of a 13th-century feudal castle and a Renaissance residence.

The 13th-century castle is known as the 'New Castle' because it was built on even older foundations. The elegant Renaissance building, which was begun because Catherine dei Medici, Queen of François I, was to pay a visit, but was left uncompleted when her visit was cancelled, contains some fine furnishings and sumptuous decoration. It is particularly noted for a series of wooden chests on display in the armoury.

In the village below there is a Gothic bridge and a 16th-century mill built in the shape of a ship.

BOURG (Gironde)

This old port, situated on the River Dordogne, is built in the form of an amphitheatre. Its medieval Château de la Citadelle, once the summer residence of the Archbishop of Bordeaux, was restored in the 18th century and again in 1944 after a fire. Some of the town's original ramparts are still visible and its old buildings include 15th-century houses and the 18th-century Hôtel de la Jurade (town hall).

Some prehistoric drawings, including mammoths, bison, and hunters, can be seen at Grottes de Pair-non-Pair 6km (3½ miles) to the east.
What to see Château de la Citadelle; Grottes de Pair-non-Pair; Hôtel de la Jurade.

BRANTÔME (Dordogne)

This charming town is set on an island in the River Dronne. It has grown up around the 8th-century abbey in which Pierre de Bourdeille, the 16th-century soldier, courtier and abbot now better known simply as 'Brantôme', wrote his celebrated chronicles which dealt with the lives of the rich and famous. He brought fame to the abbey which has since become a popular attraction. The 11th-century abbey belfry is rather unusual as it was built separately from the church. The monastery buildings are now occupied by the town hall and a museum.
What to see Abbey; Monastery buildings; Musée Fernand Desmoulin (local history and paintings).

CABRERETS (Lot)

A village in a romantic setting where the Rivers Célé and Sagne meet, Cabrerets is mainly visited for the Pech-Merle cave 3½km (2 miles) west.

It is one of the largest and most impressive of prehistoric painted caves. In addition to many mammal figures, there are outlines of human beings and stencilled hands which may represent some archaic magic ritual connected with hunting.

The 15th-century Gontaut-Biron manor house contains a museum of regional archaeological finds.

CADILLAC (Gironde)

An ancient town on the banks of the River Garonne whose economy is based on the local white wine 'Premières Côtes de Bordeaux'. It is dominated by the impressive Château of the Dukes of Épernon, starkly fortified on the outside but containing some beautifully decorated chimneypieces and a series of 17th-century tapestries.
What to see Chapel of the Dukes of Épernon (17c); Château (16–17c).

CADOUIN (Dordogne)

The Cistercian Abbey that was established here in the 12th century became famous for 'The Holy Shroud of Cadouin', a portion of cloth brought from Antioch which was believed to have been wrapped round the head of the dying Christ. It was not until 1934 that doubts were cast upon the authenticity of this relic following the discovery of 11th-century Arabian script on its surface. The abbey church dates from 1154 but was restored after the French Revolution. It is a building of simple design, in direct contrast to the Flamboyant-Gothic cloisters, constructed between the 15th and the 16th centuries. Cadouin lies about 36km (22½ miles) to the east of Bergerac, in a wooded valley.

CAHORS (Lot)

A town of distinctly medieval appearance, lying in a bend of the River Lot, which became exceedingly prosperous during the 13th century due mainly to an influx of bankers and merchants from Lombardy.

The tone of Cahors is set by the extraordinarily well-preserved 14th-century fortified Valentré Bridge – a mass of crenellations with three towers set along its length – and the whole town gives the impression of being crammed with belfries and fortified towers. The cathedral is notable for its magnificent Romanesque north door, ornamented with carved scenes relating to the Ascension. The Municipal Museum, housed in the former Bishop's Palace, deals with local history and archaeology. A fine distant view of the town and its surrounding countryside is obtained from Mont St-Cyr just outside Cahors.
What to see Cathedral of St-Étienne (12–16c); Church of St-Barthélemy (13c – restored); Municipal Museum; Roaldès Mansion (15c); Valentré Bridge.

Cahors
Clos la Coutale
APPELLATION CAHORS CONTROLÉE
1975
E. AYMARD & Y. BERNÉDE, Viticulteurs à VIRE, 46700 PUY L'EVÊQUE
TEL 47 DURAVEL (LOT)
73 cl
MIS EN BOUTEILLE À LA PROPRIÉTÉ

CARENNAC (Lot)

One of the most picturesque villages in the Dordogne, Carennac lies to the south of Tulle in a peaceful corner of Quercy. Its old houses are grouped around a 10th-century priory-deanery in which Fénelon (renowned in French literature for his story about Ulysses' son Télémaque), who became Archbishop of Cambrai, spent much of his early life. The deanery was severely damaged during the Revolution, but remains include the priory tower and a fortified gateway. The Romanesque Church of St-Pierre is notable for its beautiful 12th-century carved doorway.

CASTELNAU CASTLE (Lot)

The blood-red bulk of Castelnau rises high above the village of Prudhomat about 11km (7 miles) from St-Céré, and commands fine views over the surrounding countryside. A superb example of a feudal fortress, it has more than three miles of ramparts and towers. It dates from the 11th century and was abandoned in the 18th century but later restored. It now houses a lapidary museum and is richly furnished.

CASTELNAUD CASTLE (Dordogne)

The ruins of Castelnaud, command the beautiful countryside of the Céou and Dordogne Valleys. It was originally the home of the Cazenac family and later it was occupied by Simon de Montfort, father of the English soldier and statesman. During the 14th century the castle was substantially strengthened, becoming an English stronghold during the Hundred Years War.

CASTRES (Tarn)

An attractive town on the River Agout which has been an important cloth-producing centre since the 14th century. Castres has a fine 17th-century cathedral and the former Bishop's Palace, an elegant building of 1669, is set in fine gardens laid out by Le Nôtre. The palace contains two museums, one devoted to Goya.

A few miles to the east of Castres is Le Sidobre, a granite plateau whose eroded rocks have assumed fantastical shapes.
What to see Bishop's Palace (17c); Cathedral of St-Benôit (17c); Church of Notre Dame-de-la Platé (18c); Goya Museum.

On the banks of the Dordogne, amid lovely countryside, lies the delightful village of Carennac

THE DORDOGNE AND SOUTH-WEST FRANCE

CAUTERETS (Hautes-Pyrénées)

Cauterets is both a health and tourist resort. From it the Pyrenees National Park, created in 1967, can be reached. Rare plants, animals and birds are protected in the Park; if anyone has the good fortune to see a Pyrenean Brown bear it will have been a momentous experience, for there are very few left.

From Cauterets a variety of excursions into the Pyrenean valleys, with their lakes, waterfalls and lovely views, is possible. One of the best is via the Pont d'Espagne to the sparkling blue Lac de Gaube.

CAYLUS (Tarn-et-Garonne)

This attractive village beside the River Bonnette, about 44km (27½ miles) north-east of Montauban, has retained a number of medieval houses and a fine covered market. The church, which still bears traces of its 14th-century fortifications, contains an enormous wooden statue of Christ by the Cubist artist Zadkine (1953).

What to see Church (14c); Maison-des-Loups (13c).

CONDOM (Gers)

A busy town on the River Baise, in the Gascony region. Condom is famous for the manufacture of Armagnac brandy and there is a museum devoted to this trade in the old police station. There are a number of 18th-century buildings and the town also contains a fine cathedral with Gothic cloisters.

What to see Cathedral of St-Pierre (16c); Chapelle des Évêques (18c); Armagnac Museum.

CONQUES (Aveyron)

This old village is renowned for its magnificent Romanesque church of Ste-Foy which is claimed to be one of the best examples of its kind in southern France. It has a fine interior with a remarkable carving of the 'Last Judgement' above the west doorway. The church also contains a valuable religious art treasury (9th- to 16th-century) which includes a gold statue of Ste-Foy .

CORDES (Tarn)

This attractive medieval town is situated on the crown of a hill. Its walled fortifications still stand and are punctuated by various gateways. The majority of houses and buildings are Gothic, including the 'Maison-du-Grand-Fauconnier' (mayor's house, restored 19th-century) and the market hall with its timber roof. Today Cordes has become the home of artists and craftsmen.

What to see Church of St-Michel (Part 13c); Maison-du-Grand-Fauconnier; Market Hall; Musée Charles Portal (local history); Musée Yves Brayer (housed in the Maison-du-Grand-Fauconnier and containing a large permanent exhibition of works by Brayer, most popular of present-day Mediterranean artists).

DAX (Landes)

Dax, situated on the banks of the River Adour, to the south of the great pine forests of Les Landes, is a renowned health resort. Its curative hot water spring (*fontaine chaude*) has been used since the Roman era. The town was formerly a Gallo-Roman settlement and parts of the ancient fortifications may be seen in the Théodore-Denis park by the river.

What to see Cathedral (17c); Fontaine Chaude; Musée de Borda (local history); Théodore-Denis park.

Famous Wines of Bordeaux

The English were amongst the first to appreciate the fine wines of Bordeaux – they have been drinking claret since the Middle Ages. However 'claret' covers a structure and organisation of wine production that is as subtle and complex as the content of its most prestigious bottles. Most will agree that the finest wines come from the Médoc vineyards on the south bank of the Gironde but the unassailable quality is apparent in even the humble (and quite affordable) basic *appellation* of the Bordeaux region.

Also reasonably priced is the largely unknown wine from the vineyards west of Cahors. This is a full-bodied red, a robust, earthy drink, almost black in colour. Widely available to anyone on holiday in the Dordogne and Lot, Cahors red makes an interesting addition to any wine cellar, especially as its high tannin content gives longevity.

DOMME (Dordogne)

Domme is remarkable for its setting on a rocky promontory overlooking the River Dordogne and is a fine example of a *bastide*, a fortified town built during the Hundred Years War between the French and the English (14th to 15th centuries). From the Barre Belvedere there is a spectacular view of the river and the towns and countryside to the north. By walking along the cliffs it is possible to follow the outline of the old ramparts. Most of the fortifications have been destroyed but the 13th-century gateway, the Porte-des-Tours, is well preserved. Old houses built in honey-coloured stone, many with balconies and outside staircases,

Great craggy peaks, dense forests and blue waters dominate the Pyrenees National Park, near Cauterets

are vine-covered and gay with flowers in summer.

Beneath the covered market is the entrance to the caves (*grottes*), which were used as places of refuge for the inhabitants during the Hundred Years War and the 16th-century Wars of Religion. About 460 metres (500 yards) of these caves, with stalactites, stalagmites, and some remains of prehistoric creatures, are on view to the public.

What to see Barre Belvedere (viewing point); Les Grottes (caves); Porte-des-Tours (13c); Rampart walk.

EYZIES-DE-TAYAC (LES) (Dordogne)

This small village, situated at the meeting point of the Rivers Vézère and Beaune, is set among evergreen woods on top of steep cliffs.

The attraction to the tourist is not in the town itself, but in the prehistoric dwellings and remains which have been found in abundance in the surrounding area within the last hundred years and which have given the village the name 'The Capital of Prehistory'.

The National Museum of Prehistory is housed inside the castle, which was built between the 11th and 12th centuries and restored in the 16th century. Comprehensive collections of local prehistoric finds, photographs, diagrams and early works of art are on display. Good views of the village and the river valleys may be seen from the castle. The area around the village is richly endowed with prehistoric dwellings; these include the nearby Grand Roc cave, a series of small chambers opening from a tunnel, excavated in the side of a cliff and reached by a stairway. From here there is another fine view of the Vézère Valley. More than a dozen other prehistoric sites lie in the vicinity. Of these the most interesting, on account of the animal engravings, are the caves of Font-de-Gaume and Combarelles.

The many places of natural beauty in the area include the Gorge d'Enfer (gorge of hell) a forested area with waymarked paths where some of the animals drawn by Stone-Age men can be seen in large enclosures.

What to see Castle; Gorge d'Enfer; Grand Roc Cave; National Museum of Prehistory; Numerous prehistoric sites.

The broad, lazy waters of the River Dordogne stretch away from the hilltop medieval town of Domme to the Gironde estuary

FÉNELON CASTLE (Dordogne)

This castle, built in the 15th and 16th centuries, still has the appearance of a military fortification, despite later modifications such as the 17th-century entrance façade.

From the castle, which lies to the south of the River Dordogne between Sarlat and Souillac, there is a good view over the Dordogne Valley and the Périgord Noir.

FIGEAC (Lot)

An ancient town, on the River Célé, with some fine old houses, particularly around the rue Delzhens and the rue Gambetta. There are two medieval churches, both restored during the 17th century, but Figeac's most impressive building is the former Mint (Hôtel de la Monnaie), a restored Gothic mansion. The Mint now contains the town museum which is divided into the Lapidary Museum, dealing with sculpture from local buildings; a section devoted to old coins and seals; and the Champollion Museum, dedicated to Jean-François Champollion who was born in Figeac in 1790. Champollion was one of the first scholars to master the art of deciphering Egyptian hieroglyphics and the museum contains a cast of the Rosetta

Stone which provided clues to their meaning. Two 50-ft obelisks, known as the 'Needles of Figeac' (Aiguilles de Figeac) can be seen on the outskirts of the town. These date from the 12th century and are believed to have marked the limits of the local abbey's jurisdiction.

What to see Church of Notre-Dame-du-Puy (14–17c); Church of St-Sauveur (12–17c); Hôtel de la Monnaie (Museum of Figeac).

FOIX (Ariège)

An ancient town with some fine old half-timbered houses, dominated by its medieval castle which raises its three towers high above the Ariège Valley. The castle, once the stronghold of the Counts of Foix, contains the Museum of the Department of Ariège which traces the development of the region from prehistoric until modern times.

Foix is a good starting point for touring in the Pyrénées Mountains.

What to see Castle (12–15c); Church of St-Volusien (12c); Musée Départemental de l'Ariège.

GAILLAC (Tarn)

An ancient town in the centre of an important wine-producing area on the banks of the River Tarn. The principal building is the Château Foucaud which stands above the river in a landscaped

park and contains the local museum.

What to see Château Foucaud (18c); Church of St-Michel (11–14c); Local Museum; Philadelphe Thomas Museum (natural history, geology).

GAVARNIE (Hautes-Pyrénées)

At the approach to the tiny village is a statue of the eccentric Irishman, Count Henry Russel, who opened up the Pyrénées to climbers in the last century.

Behind the village, and dominating everything, is the great rock wall of the Cirque de Gavarnie, one of the most arresting sights in the Pyrénées, with its cascading waterfalls.

The traditional way to reach the Cirque from Gavarnie is by mule or donkey which can be hired in the village.

Gavarnie in summer is lively with visitors. Its church was once a priory which succoured pilgrims on their way to St James of Compostela in Spain.

GOURDON (Lot)

This small hillside town is the capital of the rolling Bouriane countryside. Avenues have now replaced the ramparts which encircled the castle that once stood above the town. Evidence of Gourdon's fortifications can still be seen in the Le Majou gateway and the protective battlements of the rose window in the church of St-Pierre. The town has also retained a number of old houses with projecting upper storeys. Fine views of Gourdon and the surrounding countryside can be obtained from the Esplanade, just outside the town.

Just north of Gourdon are the Cougnac Caves on some of whose walls are beautifully and seemingly freshly painted mammals, and human figures pierced by lances, dating from perhaps 25,000 years ago.

What to see Church of St-Pierre (part 14c); Rue du Majou.

HAUTEFORT (CHÂTEAU) (Dordogne)

This 17th-century château, set on a rock about 30km (18½ miles) north of Montignac, overlooks the medieval village of Hautefort and the Auvézère Valley. It has undergone restoration following severe damage by fire in 1968. The moat now contains flowers and there are relaxing gardens and terraces surrounding the château.

THE DORDOGNE AND SOUTH-WEST FRANCE

ISSIGEAC (Dordogne)
A small town in the Banège Valley, noted for its ancient houses and its proximity to the Monbazillac vineyards which lie to the north-west. There is a fine Gothic church and the turreted castle now contains the town hall.
What to see Bishop's Castle (Château des Évêques – 17c); Church (16c).

LABASTIDE-MURAT (Lot)
'Murat' was added to this town's name in honour of Joachim Murat, the daring soldier who married Napoleon's sister and became King of Naples. He was born in the town and is a local hero although he abandoned Napoleon in the dark days of the Empire and was shot in 1815 after an abortive attempt to retake Naples from the Bourbons.

Labastide-Murat, about 27km (17 miles) south of Rocamadour, stands high on the Gramat Causse, a bare yet impressive limestone plateau riddled with caves.
What to see Murat Museum.

LABRÈDE (CHÂTEAU DE) (Gironde)
This château dates from the medieval era although its front is Renaissance. It stands on an island in the centre of a lake amid parkland and is situated about 20km (12½ miles) south of Bordeaux. The château was the home of Montesquieu, 18th-century man of letters and wine grower, who loved the place and the countryside surrounding it. The domain has hardly changed since his time.

LACAVE CAVES (Lot)
The caves were discovered in 1902 at the foot of cliffs near the River Dordogne about 15km (9½ miles) north-west of Rocamadour. A lift and electric railway bring the visitor to a subterranean platform from which the tour of a mile of galleries begins.

Skilful use of light brings out the stalagmites and stalactites in a very effective manner, and underground rivers flow between the rocks to form pools and an underground lake. Prehistoric tools and weapons found within the caves are shown at the museum in Cabrerets (page 63).

LECTOURE (Gers)
The town overlooks the River Gers from a rocky crag, and is the capital of the Lomagne region. The cathedral was sacked and badly damaged in 1473 and again during the Wars of Religion and the tall spire had to be demolished. The interior was carefully restored during the 18th century, and retains its Gothic style.

The Municipal Museum is beneath the town hall and contains exhibits of local interest, the most significant being 20 stone altars found under the cathedral. They date from the Gallo-Roman period, and bear commemorative inscriptions and carvings of bulls' heads.

There is a spectacular view of the Gers Valley towards Auch, and good general views to the south and west of the town, from the Promenade du Bastion.
What to see Cathedral; Museum; Promenade du Bastion.

Massive torchlit processions of pilgrims (right) make their way annually along the Esplanade de Processions in Lourdes up to the statue of the Virgin outside the Church of the Rosary (above) which adjoins the grotto where Bernadette saw her visions

LESCAR (Pyrénées-Atlantiques)
Lescar, serving as a dormitory town for Pau 5km to the south-east, was built on its present hill-top site in the 12th century, and at one time was the regional capital.

The Cathedral of Notre-Dame testifies to the town's past importance. Construction began in 1120 with the choir and continued until severe damage by Protestants made extensive restoration necessary. This was carried out in the 17th and 19th centuries. The

chapter house is of particular interest, with scenes depicting the life of Daniel and the birth of Christ. The floor of the choir is paved with a 12th-century mosaic.
What to see Cathedral of Notre-Dame (12c).

Prehistoric Art

During the Old Stone Age south-west France was occupied by man the hunter. Our idea of prehistoric man as a savage concerned only with survival is now being largely revised, thanks in no small measure to the cave paintings and engravings discovered here. These paintings, mostly of animals, show that he was sensitive to line, colour, movement and mood. Most famous of all the French Palaeolithic art caves is that at Lascaux, outside Montignac, which contains pictures dating back some 17,000 years. It is now closed to all but accredited specialists in order to preserve the vivid frescoes from bacterial destruction, but an ambitious copy, Lascaux II, opens to the public in 1983.

It is still possible to see the real thing in the caves around Les Eyzies (multicoloured bison at Font-de-Gaume; a frieze of horses at Cap-Blanc). In the beautiful Pech-Merle Cave, east of Cahors, spotted horses are among the wall decorations.

Other cave systems in the region attract tourists not because of prehistoric drawings but for the stalactites and stalagmites, lakes and rivers, which make them places of fantasy.

MARTEL (Lot)
The town is named after Charles Martel, the 8th-century hero of Christendom who upon defeating the Saracens had a church built as an act of thanksgiving. Eventually, the town grew around this church. The present church of St-Maur is a fortified Gothic structure and has a buttressed bell tower which resembles a castle keep. Inside, the chancel windows have some interesting scenes in stained glass. The town hall is situated in the Hôtel de la Raymondie, a building completed in 1330, which has fine carved fireplaces and contains the local museum. An even older building is the Maison-Fabri, where Henry Plantagenet's eldest son died in 1183. Martel lies to the north-east of Souillac on the high limestone plateau, the Quercy Causse, and today is a market town, known particularly for nuts and truffles.
What to see Church of St-Maur (15c); Hôtel de la Raymondie (town hall); Maison-Fabri (12c); Museum (14c).

MAS-D'AZIL (CAVE) (Ariège)
An immense vault of rock is the entrance to the cave of Mas-d'Azil which has been used as a refuge by persecuted religious groups since Christians created a chapel in it during the 3rd century.
Inside is a museum displaying the many sculptures, skeletons, engravings and paintings and other prehistoric objects discovered in the Mas-d'Azil during excavations. It is about 32km (20 miles) north-west of Foix (page 65).

MILLAU (Aveyron)
Founded by the Romans in the 2nd century, the town became well known for its pottery. From the 12th century the town has also been an important centre for glove-making, today producing roughly one third of France's total output.
The old buildings are huddled in the centre of the present town and the Place du Maréchal-Foch, the old town square, has arcades dating from between the 12th and 16th centuries. The old pillory may still be seen and nearby is the museum with displays of pottery. Other areas of interest include the belfry, parts of which are 12th-century, and one of the fortified town gates, the Porte-des-Gozons.
What to see Church of Notre-Dame; Church of St Martin; Place du Maréchal-Foch.

LIBOURNE (Gironde)
A large *bastide* town situated at the confluence of the Rivers Dordogne and Isle. Libourne is a busy port, concerned mainly with the export of wine. An ancient tower stands guard over the quay, a remnant of the town's 13th-century defences. There are a number of old houses around the Grand-Place, including the town hall which contains a museum and art gallery.
What to see Chapelle-de-Condat (Romanesque/Gothic); Hôtel-de-Ville (15c town hall).

LOUBRESSAC (Lot)
A small fortified town on a cliff above the River Bave about 10km (6 miles) west of St Céré. Its picturesque old streets lead up to an impressive, turreted château which commands the Bave Valley. Originally a 15th-century mansion, the château was extensively renovated during the 17th century. It contains a fine collection of 18th-century furniture and prints, as well as various unusual mementoes of the French Revolution.

LOURDES (Hautes-Pyrénées)
Its delightful Pyrenean setting coupled with its world-wide fame as a Roman Catholic pilgrimage centre have ensured that Lourdes is never lacking in visitors. Each year millions visit the shrine where the Virgin appeared to Bernadette Soubirous in 1858 and revealed to her the whereabouts of the healing spring whose waters are now so eagerly sought after. The 'Cité-Religieuse' contains the famous Grotte de Masabielle where the vision occurred, and the pools where invalids bathe. The three churches which feature in the town's annual ceremonies and processions include an enormous underground basilica, constructed in 1958 to mark the centenary of the visions, which can accommodate a congregation of around 20,000. Museums, dioramas and houses used by the Soubirous family are also to be found in this area.
The secular part of the town, on the opposite bank of the Gave-de-Pau, contains Lourdes Castle, noted for its interesting Pyrenean Museum.

What to see Basilica du Rosaire (19c); Basilica Supérieure (19c); Basilica Souterraine St-Pie X (20c); Le Béout (mountain viewpoint); Cachot (Soubirous Family home; Castle (13–17c – contains Pyrenean Museum); Grotte de Masabielle; Pavillon Notre-Dame (Museum – Ste-Bernadette's life/sacred art); Pic-du-Jer (mountain viewpoint).

LUCHON (Haute Garonne)
Luchon, or Bagnères-de-Luchon as it is sometimes called, has evolved into a popular thermal spa and holiday resort. The springs, which have been used since Roman times, are particularly rich in sulphur and radioactivity and are much sought after by those suffering from respiratory disorders and rheumatism. The Thermal Establishment contains modern highly technical equipment and guided tours are available. The town is high in the Pyrénées and is a good centre for visiting beauty spots of the region such as Lac d'Oô.
What to see Musée du Pays de Luchon; Thermal Buildings.

MIREPOIX (Ariège)

Originally a *bastide* or fortified town, Mirepoix was built in 1279 by the family of a retainer of Simon de Montfort. Construction of the cathedral began in 1343 and the spire was started in 1506 when the church was consecrated, but some parts, such as the interior vaulting, were not completed until 1865.

There are many houses of the late 13th- to 15th-century period, particularly around the Place Général Leclerc which is the main square of the town. Here there are little shops and cafés around a public garden – a pleasant place to spend an hour or two.

What to see Cathedral (14–19c); Place Général Leclerc.

MOISSAC (Tarn-et-Garonne)

An attractive little town on the River Tarn surrounded by the green hills where fine table grapes are grown. The town grew up around a 7th-century Benedictine abbey, and the former abbey church of St-Pierre, a mixture of Romanesque and Gothic styles, stands as an impressive reminder of Moissac's former importance. The church is noted for its intricately decorated south doorway, portraying, among other biblical scenes, a 'Vision of the Apocalypse'. The building is adjoined by some of the finest 11th-century cloisters in the whole of France, also richly ornamented. A museum in the cloisters deals with religious art, and the Moissac Museum, in the 13th-century former abbot's house, is mainly devoted to regional folklore.

What to see Church of St-Pierre (11–15c); Claustral Museum; Cloisters (11c); Moissac Museum.

MONPAZIER (Dordogne)

A typical 'bastide' or fortified town, laid out by King Edward I of England in his capacity as Duke of Aquitaine. The original rigid pattern can still be observed, particularly around the Place Centrale, surrounded on all sides by arcades and covered galleries. This is the best-preserved *bastide* town in the Périgord region and has many picturesque corners. The massive castle of Biron, standing on a hilltop about 8km (5 miles) away, can be visited from Monpazier.

What to see Chapter House (13c); Church of St-Dominique (part 16c); Place Centrale.

Overlooking the Place Roosevelt at Montauban is the classical Cathedral of Notre-Dame, which dates from 1739

MONTAL (CHÂTEAU DE) (Lot)

The château stands in wooded surroundings above the Bave Valley 3km (2 miles) west of St-Céré. Built during the 16th century, its external appearance is an austere, warlike one, but the visitor needs only to enter the inner courtyard to be captivated by the softer Renaissance lines and abundance of decoration for which the château is famous.

MONTAUBAN (Tarn-et-Garonne)

A busy market town spread over both banks of the River Tarn, particularly concerned with the sale of local fruit and vegetables. Montauban was built as a fortified town in the 12th century and converted into a Protestant stronghold during the Wars of Religion. The present town has numerous 17th-century buildings, particularly around the arcaded Place National where most of the houses are built in the distinctive pink brick which may be seen throughout the town. The Pont Vieux, which spans the Tarn with seven arches, dates from the 14th century and was originally fortified. Near the bridge is one of the town's most important buildings – the Ingres Museum, housed in the former Bishop's Palace (17th-century). It contains drawings by Ingres (1780–1867) and works by the sculptor Bourdelle (1861–1929). Both artists were born in Montauban.

What to see Ingres Museum; Natural History and Prehistory Museum; Pont Vieux (old bridge).

Fortification of a Province

During the Middle Ages, Aquitaine was much fought over by England and France. Both sides built *bastides* (fortified towns) using a standard pattern, either rectangular or square in shape. The walls, with defensible towers and gateways, enclosed a street system of straight roads intersecting at right-angles – copied from the Romans and similar to the 'block' plan of many American cities. A main square, surrounded by covered arcades, would occupy the centre, together with a church (itself often fortified). This layout is incredibly well preserved at Monpazier, built in 1284.

Interestingly, Edward I, King of England (who built Monpazier), also used the *bastide* during his campaigns against Wales in the late 13th century, constructing fortified towns at, among other places, Conwy and Caernarfon.

Monpazier – a typical fortified town

MONT-DE-MARSAN (Landes)
Situated at the junction of the Rivers Douze and Midou, Mont-de-Marsan is the capital of the department of Landes, and the third most important town in the Armagnac region. It is a noted gastronomic centre and market town specialising in poultry and *foie gras* as well as fruit and maize. The area has a gentle climate and palms and magnolias flourish.

The town has two museums, the Dubalen and the Lacataye, both housed in 14th-century buildings. The former displays collections relating to prehistory and natural history, the latter contains works by two local sculptors, Charles Despiau and Robert Wlérick.

There are several old buildings in Mont-de-Marsan, from the Romanesque period to the Renaissance, and a good view of the old town is available from the river bridge, the Pont de Vue.

Mont-de-Marsan has a large arena where equestrian events and bullfighting take place. During late September and early October important dressage and show-jumping competitions are held there.
What to see Dubalen Museum; Hippodrome (equestrian events); Lacataye Museum; Pont-de-Vue (bridge).

NAJAC (Aveyron)
Najac is situated on a peak within a loop in the River Aveyron and an excellent view of the town and its setting is available from the D239 approach road to the east.

The 13th-century castle ruins are an impressive sight. The larger of the two protective round towers has a viewing platform from which one can see the castle, the valley and the 14th-century Gothic church. Many of the buildings in the town were constructed between the 13th and 16th centuries.
What to see Castle ruins (13c); Church (14c).

NÉRAC (Lot-et-Garonne)
The chief town of the Albret area, Nérac straddles the River Baïse at the point where the Gascon hills meet the open area of Landes.

The château is an elegant Renaissance mansion, and houses a museum containing many exhibits of the Gallo-Roman era. Two bridges span the river, the older of which is in the Gothic style. Either provides a good view of the town.

On the right bank of the Baïse, to

The medieval houses of Najac ramble up the steep slopes of the rocky outcrop to the striking 13th-century castle ruins

the south-east of the town, is the Promenade de la Garenne, a pleasant garden with trees, shrubs, fountains and a mosaic from the Roman villa which once stood on the site.
What to see Château (Renaissance); Promenade de la Garenne.

NIAUX (CAVE) (Ariège)
4km (2½ miles) south-west of Tarascon-sur-Ariège is the cave of Niaux. The prehistoric wall-paintings of black-outlined bison, horses, ibexes and reindeer are considered to belong to the finest examples of Magdalenian art.

OLORON-STE-MARIE (Pyrénées-Atlantiques)
A small town at the confluence of two mountain streams, the Gave d'Aspe and the Gave d'Ossau, with a picturesque old quarter

(Quartier Ste-Croix) perched on a hill surrounding the Church of Ste-Croix. There is a fine view of the valley and the surrounding mountains from the Promenade Bellevue, a walk on the line of the ancient ramparts.
What to see Church of Ste-Croix (part 13c); Church of Ste-Marie (13–14c); Promenade Bellevue.

ORTHEZ (Pyrénées-Atlantiques)
Capital of the ancient province of Béarn from the 12th to 14th centuries, Orthez today is an attractive market town which produces, among other things, the much admired Bayonne ham.

In the town centre is the 13th-century Pont Vieux (Old Bridge) with four arches and a defence-tower in the middle. All that remains of the medieval castle is the Tour Moncade whose interior

stairs lead up to a terrace and extensive views of the Pyrenean range.

The monument to General Foy is a memorial to his resistance at Orthez against the advancing troops of Wellington in 1814.

PADIRAC (CHASM) (Lot)
Padirac is one of the great natural wonders of France. It is one of the innumerable and varied underground caves created by water acting mechanically or chemically on fissured limestone rocks, and has been organised for comfortable sightseeing.

Lifts go down 338 ft. A punt glides for half a mile along the crystal-clear underground stream beneath its huge vault of rock. Lakes, waterfalls and extraordinary concretions of stalagmites and stalactites are seen, culminating in the Hall of the Great Dome whose roof is 300ft overhead.

Back again in the sunlight are restaurants, a zoo and an aviary.

PAU (Pyrénées-Atlantiques)
The capital of the Béarn region and a popular holiday resort, Pau has been a strategically and commercially important town since the 15th century when it came close to becoming the centre of an independent kingdom. The castle dates from this period, although it has undergone restoration. Henry of Navarre, later to become King Henry IV of France and to be instrumental in ending the bloody Wars of Religion, was born there in 1553 and the castle now contains a museum with some exhibits relating to that period. Since 1814, when the British army was based at Pau, British influence has been marked.

Another major attraction to tourists is the 2km long Boulevard des Pyrénées, laid out by the Emperor Napoleon, which provides magnificent views of the surrounding mountains. There are several museums, including one devoted to Marshal Bernadotte, who became King of Sweden in 1818, and Pau has fine entertainment and sporting facilities including a stadium where the Basque game of pelota is regularly played.
What to see Boulevard des Pyrénées; Château (14–19c); Musée Béarnais (Regional Museum); Musée des Beaux-Arts; Musée Bernadotte; Parc Beaumont (Botanical Gardens).

THE DORDOGNE AND SOUTH-WEST FRANCE

PENNE (Tarn)

The ancient village lies below the ruins of a feudal castle which stands on the edge of a sheer drop to the Aveyron Valley. The castle has survived a turbulent history since its 13th-century foundation and did not fall into disrepair until the 19th century. It now has a startling yet romantic appearance, its jagged walls clinging precariously to a rock pinnacle. The narrow village street is lined with picturesque houses, some of which have doors ornamented with carvings. Across the river are vineyards and orchards while upstream the river flows swiftly between high cliffs of limestone. Penne is about 36km (23 miles) east of Montauban.
What to see Aveyron Gorges; Castle (13c ruin).

PÉRIGUEUX (Dordogne)

Capital of the Department of Dordogne and the chief town of the Périgord region, Périgueux lies in a pleasant position beside the River Isle. Apart from its involvement with the tourist trade and light industry the town is internationally famous for its regional cookery, its specialities being truffles and pâté de foie gras.

The history of Périgueux stretches back to the Gallo-Roman era. This is recalled by the remains of the former arena and the Tour de Vésone which is the only surviving portion of the 2nd-century temple. The medieval period is also well represented, chiefly by the Cathedral of St-Front, one of the largest in the area and one of the most extraordinary with its five white Byzantine-style domes, turrets and lofty belfry revealing the architectural influences brought back by the Crusaders. There are a number of 15th- to 16th-century houses in the vicinity of the cathedral and the Périgord Museum containing prehistoric, Gallo-Roman and medieval sections is also located in the area. More ancient houses, dating from the same period, are to be found around the Pont-des-Barris. The remains of Château Barrière, which has an ancient keep and a strange staircase tower, lends a feudal flavour to the town's rich historical mixture. The countryside around Périgueux is well wooded, with small, hedged meadows.
What to see Arena (2c); Cathedral of St-Font (12–19c); Château Barrière (12c); Tour de Vésone (2c).

RÉOLE (LA) (Gironde)

An attractive little town set above the Garonne Valley. It is full of narrow, winding streets and elegant old buildings, notably a fortified town hall. Remnants of the ancient Benedictine abbey are preserved here including the abbey church of St-Pierre, dating from around the 13th century.
What to see Abbey; Hôtel-de-Ville (town hall); Signal du Mirail (viewpoint).

ROCAMADOUR (Lot)

A medieval fortified town in a remarkable situation set along the sides of a single street which winds its way up a rocky cliff face above the Gorge of Alzou. Rocamadour became an important place of pilgrimage as early as the 12th century, with the faithful from all walks of life making their way up the 141-step Great Stairway which leads from the main street to the Parvis-des-Églises where the Miraculous Chapel of Our Lady has been hollowed out of the bare rock.

Today seven churches are to be found around the Parvis (square), including the Romanesque/Gothic Basilica of St Sauveur and the 12th-century Chapel of St-Michel. The highest point of the cliff is crowned by the 14th-century castle from which there is a fine view over the surrounding area. Other areas of interest include the 15th-century town hall with a fine display of contemporary tapestries; and five fortified gateways which are the only remnants of the 13th-century defences.
What to see Basilica of St-Sauveur (11–13c); Castle (14c – viewpoint on ramparts); Chapelle Miraculeuse (12c); Chapelle St-Michel (12c); Musée Historical; Musée Roland-le-Preux (waxwork museum); Musée Trésor (religious relics etc).

Ever since the Middle Ages Rocamadour has been a famous place of pilgrimage. The village has seven churches

Wedged between the Dordogne and a sheer-faced cliff lies the pretty village of La Roque-Gageac

RODEZ (Aveyron)

Standing in an impressive position on a hill over 2,000 feet above sea level, Rodez has been a town of strategic importance since Gallo-Roman times and is today the capital of the Department of Aveyron. Its most prominent feature is the fine medieval cathedral, built of rose-coloured stone, which stands in the centre of the town. A mixture of Gothic and Renaissance, the cathedral has an outstanding belfry which is six storeys high. Rodez has preserved a quantity of old buildings, a number of which can be seen in the area around the Place-de-la-Cité near the cathedral.
What to see Cathedral of Notre-Dame (13–15c); Musée des Beaux-Arts; Musée Fenaille (archaeology, works of art etc).

ROQUEFORT-SUR-SOULZON (Aveyron)

A small town below the Cambalou mountain, famous for the Roquefort cheese which is matured in the humid atmosphere of the deep caves which are set in the mountainside. There is also an interesting prehistory museum.
What to see Caves of Roquefort; Museum.

ROQUE-GAGEAC (LA) (Dordogne)

Huddling at the base of a vertical cliff overlooking the Dordogne Valley, the village makes an extremely picturesque sight.

There are many old houses and mansions divided by narrow

streets and alleys, and the church provides good views.

Nearby is Malartrie Castle, a 19th-century copy of a 15th-century château. At the foot of the cliff is the interesting Tarde Manor.

What to see Malartrie Castle; Tarde Manor.

ROUFFIGNAC (Dordogne)

The only old building in the village is the church, all others having been built since World War II when they were burned by German troops. The church is early 16th-century, built in the Renaissance style, and the doorway is decorated with some fine carvings.

The cave for which the village is best known lies three miles to the south. An electric railway is used for the tour of the four kilometres of galleries available for viewing. Inside there is a series of prehistoric paintings and stone engravings depicting many animals including mammoths, rhinoceros and bison. Rouffignac lies to the north of Les Eyzies.

What to see Cave; Church (16c).

ST-BERTRAND-DE-COMMINGES (Haute Garonne)

Although its history can be traced back to a tribal settlement in 72BC the town, then known as Lugdunum Convenarum, first gained prominence under the Romans in the first century AD due to the thermal springs and marble quarries. Many Roman relics have been discovered including the forum, the baths, amphitheatre and basilicas, and the town has two museums devoted to material excavated from the Roman town.

The modern town lies on a hill above the Roman ruins and was founded in the early 12th century when work on the cathedral began. Originally the cathedral was built in the Romanesque style but many alterations were made between the 14th and 16th centuries, and much of the building is Gothic. The interior is richly decorated but the outstanding feature is the cloisters which are regarded as the finest in existence. In addition, the town contains several old houses, notably the two flanking the main gate to the town, the Porte Cabirole which dates from the first century AD. It lies about 33km (20 miles) north of Luchon.

About 7km (4 miles) north-west, by the little D26 road, are the Gargas caves which, in addition to the mammalian paintings, are intriguing because of the red stencilling of human hands. They were painted some 30,000 years ago and may have been connected with barbaric rituals.

What to see Cathedral (12–16c); Galerie du Trophée (Museum); Museum of Comminges; Roman excavations.

ST-CÉRÉ (Lot)

St-Céré is a small town situated in the Bave Valley. Its many houses dating from the 15th, 16th and 17th centuries, with overhanging upper storeys supported by wooden corbels and brown-tiled roofs, make the old part of the town very picturesque. The casino contains an interesting tapestry exhibition composed of designs by Jean Lurçat which were woven at Aubusson. St-Céré is a good base for walks and excursions in Haut-Quercy, the high limestone plateau to the west of the town. The fertile area lying between St-Céré and Carennac is especially well known for its strawberries and plums.

What to see Church of Ste-Spérie; Old houses; Tapestry exhibition (in casino).

The Perfect End to a Meal

No self-respecting *bon viveur* would contemplate a meal which came without a cheese course and a final, contemplative brandy. In south-west France he has something rather special to choose from. Roquefort cheese, made from ewe's milk, is so named after the limestone caves in Aveyron in which it ripens. A particular type of mould – *penicillium roqueforti* – thrives here, giving the smooth-textured, blue-veined cheese its characteristic piquant flavour when fully ripened.

Armagnac brandy also has an unmistakable taste. Produced in the areas around Auch, Condom and Eauze, this amber-coloured brandy is lighter-bodied then Cognac and is said to be more 'feminine', though it can be harsh if drunk too young. Its distinctive flavour is the product of a careful blend of grapes and a slow, single distilling process (Cognac is distilled twice – see page 52). A roundly-matured Armagnac from an oak cask is a smoothly delicate *digestif*.

THE DORDOGNE AND SOUTH-WEST FRANCE

ST-ÉMILION (Gironde)

This hill-top town and its fine walls have survived, almost in their entirety, from the Middle Ages. It overlooks the Dordogne Valley in an area which is famous for its red wine. St-Émilion contains one of France's rarest monuments – a 9th- to 12th-century subterranean church. It is entered by a fine 14th-century decorated doorway.

The town has a lovely market square and above this is the 13th-century Château du Roi.

What to see Chapelle de la Trinité; Château du Roi; Église Monolithe (subterranean church); Place du Marché (market square).

ST-GAUDENS (Haute-Garonne)

Situated in the upper Garonne Valley, this market town has a growing population following the discovery of natural gas in the area and the establishment of other industry nearby. The main feature of St-Gaudens is the Boulevard Jean-Bepmale which contains a monument dedicated to the three Pyrenean marshals – Foch, Joffre and Gallieni (monument des Trois Maréchaux). By the side of the monument is an orientation table which shows named silhouettes of the various Pyrenean peaks which can be seen from the boulevard. Other attractions in the town include the 11th- to 12th-century Church of St-Pierre and St-Gaudens, and the museum incorporating local history and Egyptian displays.

At Valentine, 2km (1¼ miles) to the south-west, are the ruins of a Gallo-Roman villa where a large bath complex and the stoke-hole of a hypocaust can be seen.

What to see Boulevard Jean-Bepmale; Church of St-Pierre and St-Gaudens; Monument des Trois Maréchaux; Musée Municipal; Valentine Roman villa.

ST-JEAN-DE-LUZ (Pyrénées-Atlantiques)

St-Jean-de-Luz is very much a Basque town and combines the diversions of a fashionable resort with the charm of an old fishing port. It is situated at the mouth of the River Nivelle and has been an important fishing port since medieval times; it still maintains a thriving trade in locally caught tunny and sardines. Apart from fishing, the town's claim to fame is the fact that Louis XIV married the Infanta Marie-Theresa, daughter of King Philip IV of Spain, in the church of St-Jean-Baptiste in 1660. The houses occupied by both the King and his bride have been preserved and the church contains fine decorations dating from that period. A number of old houses and an interesting 16th-century church are to be found in Ciboure, on the opposite bank of the river, the birthplace of the composer Maurice Ravel.

What to see Church of St-Jean-Baptiste (13c–17c); Church of St-Vincent (16c, at Ciboure); Maison de l'Infante (17c); Maison Louis XIV (17c).

ST-JEAN-PIED-DE-PORT (Pyrénées-Atlantiques)

A town in a delightful setting at the foot of the Roncevaux Pass and on a main route between France and Spain. It was the scene of the heroic defence in 778 against invading Muslims which was immortalised in the medieval 'Song of Roland'. The town is known for its double ramparts and for the 16th-century sandstone houses which can be seen around the rue de la Citadelle.

ST-SAVIN (Haute-Pyrénées)

Once the most important religious centres of the region, St-Savin still retains its former abbey church, dating from the 11th to 14th centuries. There is a museum in the old Benedictine chapterhouse and both this and the church contain fine collections of medieval religious works of art. From the terrace beside the main square there is a fine view of the broad Argelès Valley. The town lies about 16km (10 miles) south of Lourdes, just beyond the spa of Argelès-Gazost where circulatory diseases are treated.

SARE (Pyrénées-Atlantiques)

Sare is characteristic of the pretty villages in this region; some say it is the prettiest. It is full of old Basque houses, beflowered, painted and carved. The town hall is arcaded. There is a 17th-century church with three tiers of galleries within, and a sundial on the wall outside. Typical Basque tombstones – often devoid of Christian symbols – are to be seen in the churchyard. Adjoining the church is the inevitable pelota court.

In its main square Sare holds folklore festivals every Saturday during the summer months.

7km (4½ miles) from Sare, right on the Spanish frontier, are the caves of Sare where flat-bottomed punts take visitors for a trip along the subterranean lake.

SARLAT (Dordogne)

This town, the capital of the Périgord-Noir region, is one of the most attractive in south-west France. Its winding streets are filled with medieval and Renaissance houses, most of them built of distinctive golden-yellow stone. Sarlat consists of two quarters – the Clerics' Quarter to the east and the Western Quarter. They are separated by a 'modern' road, known as 'La Traverse', which dates from the 19th century. Both quarters are richly endowed with 15th- and 16th-century buildings but the larger Clerics' Quarter also contains the 16th-century cathedral and a Renaissance mansion, the maison de La Boétie, which has a finely sculpted stone façade.

What to see Cathedral (16–17c); Chapelle-des-Pénitents-Blancs (17c); Maison de La Boétie (16c).

Brightly painted fishing boats add to the charm of St Jean-de-Luz's attractive old harbour

Open-air street markets such as the one in Sarlat are a characteristic of most French towns

SOUILLAC (Lot)
Souillac grew up around its abbey in the 13th century and today is a little town which depends on tourism and commerce. It is situated in a fertile region on the north bank of the River Dordogne where it is met by a tributary, the Borrèze. The abbey was dissolved during the French Revolution and the abbey church has become the parish church. Its masterpiece is the great door-frame from the original church, which features intricately carved bas-reliefs and statues of the prophets and saints.
What to see Abbey (12–17c).

SOULAC-SUR-MER (Gironde)
Soulac is a small seaside resort on the Atlantic, near the Gironde estuary, situated among pine woods and sand dunes. From the seafront there is a fine view of the Cordouan lighthouse just off the coast. The Basilica of Notre-Dame-de-la-Fin-des-Terres is a remnant of a Benedictine abbey dating from the 12th century. It was buried for many years beneath sand and recovered at the end of the 18th century.
What to see Basilica of Notre-Dame-de-Fin-des-Terres (12c restored).

TARBES (Hautes-Pyrénées)
A busy market town with industrial and commercial interests, Tarbes is probably best known for its stud farm (Haras) established during the 19th century and specialising in Anglo/Arab cavalry horses. The town is also the birthplace of Ferdinand Foch, the famous World War I Marshal, and his house is preserved as a museum.
What to see Birthplace of Marshal Foch; Jardin Massey; Stud Farm (Haras).

TOULOUSE (Haute-Garonne)
One of the largest cities in the country, Toulouse, with its long-established university and industrial and commercial activities, has become the cultural and economic centre of southern France. An important Gallo-Roman settlement and a prominent stronghold in the Middle Ages, Toulouse has emerged as a popular tourist city, possessing a wealth of historic buildings, many of them constructed from the distinctive rose-red brick for which Toulouse is famous. One of the oldest is the large Basilica of St-Sernin which retains many 11th-century features. The cathedral and Les Jacobins, the old Dominican monastery, both date from the 13th century. Toulouse contains numerous mansions, built between the 16th and 18th centuries, notably the Capitole (town hall), a fine 18th-century building. The city is well endowed with museums. The Musée des Augustins, containing works of art from the 4th century until the present day, and the Museum of old Toulouse are particularly worthy of a visit.
What to see Basilica of St-Sernin (11–14c); Capitole (town hall – 18c). Cathedral of St-Étienne (13–17c); Church of Notre-Dame-de-la-Dalbade (16c); Church of Notre-Dame-du-Tour (16c); Les Jacobins (13–14c); Musée des Augustins; Musée Georges-Labit (19c – oriental); Musée d'Histoire Naturelle; Musée Paul-Dupuy (art); Musée St-Raymond (ancient art); Musée du Vieux Toulouse.

VILLEFRANCHE-DE-ROUERGUE (Aveyron)
Situated on the River Aveyron, this bastide town dates from the mid-13th century. Although the walled fortifications have disappeared, Villefranche-de-Rouergue, with its many straight streets lined with old houses, is still typical of this era. The heart of the town is its square, the Place Notre-Dame. Here stand the Church of Notre-Dame (part 13th century) noted for its 15th-century carved choir stalls. Another medieval building is the 15th-century Chartreuse St-Sauveur (Carthusian monastery) with its splendid Grand Cloître (great cloister).
What to see Chapelle des Pénitents-Noirs (17c); Chartreuse St-Sauveur; Church of Notre-Dame; Place Notre-Dame.

VILLENEUVE-SUR-LOT (Lot-et-Garonne)
Founded in the 13th century, Villeneuve-sur-Lot emerged as one of the strongest *bastides* in the area but only two gateways remain. Today it is a thriving market town concentrating on fruit and vegetables and is a regional market for plums. The Pont Vieux (old bridge) was built by the English in the 13th century. From here there is a lovely view of the River Lot and its immediate surroundings.
What to see Church of Ste-Catherine; Pont Vieux (old bridge); Town gateways.

The South of France

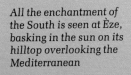

All the enchantment of the South is seen at Èze, basking in the sun on its hilltop overlooking the Mediterranean

The Côte d'Azur with its casinos and 'topless' beaches, its festivals, yachts, seafood and wine, is known world-wide in a way which brands the region as a whole. Yet this coastal strip is only a tiny part of a rich and beautiful area of France.

Bordering the Mediterranean lie Provence and Languedoc-Roussillon forming, with the Côte d'Azur, the most southerly belt of the country. Inland lies a region of mountains and fields rich in history and culture and blessed by an abundance of wildlife and fragrant flowers.

THE SOUTH OF FRANCE

From Cape Cerbère in the west to the Italian frontier just east of Menton stretch some 380 miles of coastline. The profile of this coastal arc varies greatly, but the sweeping belt of fragrant land has two common denominators – the fierce heat of the southern sun which warms the earth and the cool blue waters of the Mediterranean Sea that lap its fringe.

The Azure Coast Strung between the commercial capital of Marseille and the semitropical retreat of Menton are the glittering resorts, with their marinas, casinos and hot sandy beaches, the bustling ports and, inland, the tiny villages, which lie on the Côte d'Azur. Visitors can follow in the footsteps of the English aristocracy who, from the early 19th century, flocked to the Mediterranean to winter at Menton, Cannes or Nice and to adopt the Riviera as their playground.

Although its pebble-strewn beach is disappointing, Nice, the capital of the Riviera, typifies the elegance of the Regency era in its four-mile promenade, the Promenade des Anglais. Strolling through the pedestrian precincts, lined with exclusive boutiques, the glossy pages of the fashion magazines come to life.

Horticulture is a major industry, both to support the nearby perfume industry and to supply the flower markets of the world. The mild winter climate allows for early blooming of mimosa, jasmine, carnations and roses and each February Nice is transformed by blossom-decked carnival floats and beautiful girls during the Battle of Flowers. A similar festival in Menton reflects the quality of citrus fruits grown in the region. Between these two lies the Principality of Monaco, the tiny sovereign state known internationally for its casino, its prince and the late Princess Grace, and the Grand Prix car race through the streets of Monte Carlo.

Just as famous are the 'topless' beaches of St-Tropez where crowds of tourists gather to catch a glimpse of the 'beautiful people' at leisure. The tiny harbour, lined with tall houses colourwashed in shades of beige and apricot and sporting bright blue canopies, is alive with yachts – elegant floating palaces, resplendent in white paint and gleaming brass, flying the national flags of many countries. Just a street or so away are ice-cream stalls, souvenir shops and amusement parks.

Antibes has not noticeably suffered from the over-popularity which afflicts some other Riviera resorts. Its harbour is certainly lined with luxury craft but it retains a quiet dignity, its 17th-century ramparts towering above the beach where a small section of sand is set aside for the general public.

Public beaches are scattered and often small on the Côte d'Azur which, with its rocky and indented coastline, has few long stretches of sand. Many beaches are owned by hotels or cafés and it can be quite expensive to gain access to a beach and to hire a sunlounger (you will not be allowed to use your own chair).

The villages of the Loup Valley and Haute Provence, many of them perched high on hill tops, are a refreshing contrast to the brashness of the coast. Tall, narrow houses, their windows tightly shuttered, and with roofs of sun-baked terracotta tiles, encircle the village square where, as the day cools, the men gather and the metallic clank of *boules* fills the still air.

The gnarled trunks of olive trees line the hills, and north-west from Cannes, in the parched limestone fields around Castellane, grow fields of lavender, a blue haze of blossom in summer, destined to feed the perfume industry centred at Grasse.

Provence The mighty Rhône flows from the Massif Central south through Provence, absorbing the waters of the Eygues, the Nesque, the Sorgue and the Durance as they drain from the east. The river valleys provide natural routes through the mountain barrier, as the Romans recognised. Their influence is strong throughout the region, reminding one that this area was the first Province of Rome, which is why it is now called Provence. Roman monuments can be seen at Orange, St-Rémy and Vaison-la-Romaine, where a 2,000-year-old bridge is still in use.

Earlier still the Greeks had colonised the area around what is now the great port of Marseille and they, it is thought, introduced grapes. The most highly prized wine of the region comes from the area north of Avignon where the Popes set up their headquarters in the 14th century. Hence the wine, and the town on which the vineyards are centred, are called Châteauneuf-du-Pape (the new castle of the Pope). The vineyards of the south, although not among the most famous in France, are certainly prolific. From the region come not only the celebrated Châteauneuf-du-Pape but also sweet muscatels and the red wines of Ventoux and Luberon; while the Côtes de Provence wines include light rosés, dry whites and full-bodied reds.

The Camargue The Rhône divides above Arles into two arms which encircle the marshlands of the Camargue before reaching the sea. The wild white horses which gallop, manes flying, through the shallow waters of the delta are legendary, as are the ragged black bulls and the rose and white flamingos. But of recent years much land has been taken for rice-growing and salt production, and at the same time tourists have been attracted to the area. These changes have resulted in a great reduction in the numbers of animals and birds, and now, to protect the remaining wildlife, the French authorities have created a large reserve to which the public are not admitted. Some areas are still open but visitors wishing to see the fauna for which the Camargue is famous are likely to be disappointed. Something of the beauty of the area can, however, be seen by cruising along the Sète-Rhône canal which runs parallel with the coast through the étangs (lagoons), where one may sight heron and egret and watch silvery fish skimming the water.

Languedoc-Roussillon At the western end of the canal is Sète, a busy city much dissected by waterways. It is second only to Marseille as a commercial port and is also the biggest fishing port on the Mediterranean. Sète is famed for its oysters, but its open-air market is a dazzling display of a huge variety of seafoods.

Cannes, one of the fashionable resorts which draw sun-lovers to the Côte d'Azur

Guardians of the Camargue on their greys

The Languedoc's mineral resources are being exploited and there is substantial industrial development around Sète. Inland the great plain is a vast sea of vineyards backed by the less-productive mountains of the Cévennes.

Main attractions for tourists are its natural features – rivers, lakes and limestone caves with strangely-shaped stalactites. Roman influence is seen in towns like Nîmes, and in the three-tiered Pont du Gard, a masterpiece in stone which carried the Uzès to Nîmes aqueduct over the River Gardon and has survived the centuries almost unscathed.

Dominating an escarpment and with views to the mountains and the sea, the old hilltop 'Cité' of Carcassonne towers above the sprawling modern mass. The entrance through the mighty stone walls is by a drawbridge hung with heavy chains, then along a narrow uphill path and through a second defensive wall. Beyond, there is a further climb to the cathedral and fortified Château Comtal. Without shops and cafés to keep one in the mundane present, it would be easy to fall under the spell of Carcassonne and to imagine oneself back in the days of Chivalry.

Roussillon lies between the Mediterranean and the High Pyrénées. Places such as Canet-Plage and St Cyprien are developing along the same lines as Côte d'Azur resorts, with sporting clubs and casinos. Further south are the picturesque old fishing port of Collioure and, beyond the tamarisks and cork-woods of Cap Béar, the last seaside town before the border, Banyuls-sur-Mer.

Perpignan, once the seat of the Kings of Majorca and now the region's capital, is some 15km (9 miles) from the sea, surrounded by grasslands and market gardens. There are vineyards on the slopes of the Pyrénées foothills inland from Perpignan and in the coastal belt south of Collioure.

Here, where the people share their traditions and the Catalan language with their Spanish neighbours, the craggy summits of the mountains, rising ever higher and higher in the distance, serve both to link and divide the two nations.

Despite the vulgarity which occasionally mars the reputation of its most publicised area – the Côte d'Azur – the South of France is still, in many people's minds, associated with a kind of paradise on earth.

Places of Interest

Plump dolphins spout water in the fountains of elegant Aix

AIGUES-MORTES (Gard)

An historic town set amid lagoons and marshes on the edge of the Camargue, Aigues-Mortes is still enclosed by ramparts. It owes both its existence and its defences to Louis IX (St-Louis) who founded it in the 13th century as a port of embarkation for the Seventh Crusade in 1248. Thereafter it enjoyed some maritime prosperity until the port area became silted up during the 14th century. It is possible to walk round the walls of the rectangular town, starting in the area of the Tour de Constance, formerly used as a prison. From the summit there is a fine view stretching from the salt marshes to the mountains. There are organised tours of the marshes on some days during the high season.
What to see Ramparts (13c); Salt marshes; Tour de Constance (13–16c).

AIX-EN-PROVENCE (Bouches-du-Rhône)

The former capital of Provence, with a history dating back to its foundation in Roman times, Aix has retained much of its 17th- and 18th-century character and contains many buildings dating from that period. The town has now been developed as a spa and is noted for almonds, a speciality being the *calisson* – an iced, almond-flavoured biscuit. Aix is particularly busy during the summer when several festivals are held, including the International Music Festival (July–August).

The essence of Aix may be seen around the Cours Mirabeau, a spacious tree-lined avenue with elegant 18th-century mansions on one side and busy pavement cafés and shops on the other. Three ornate fountains stand at intervals in the centre of this thoroughfare. The Romanesque/Gothic cathedral contains some fine 15th-century Flemish tapestry and a splendid 15th-century painting 'The Burning Bush'. There is also a Tapestry Museum in the old Archbishop's palace. Other museums include the Cézanne Studio where the famous painter, born in Aix in 1839, did much of his later work.

A scenic trip from Aix is to the Roquefavour Aqueduct below Ventabren.
What to see Cathedral of St-Sauveur (5–16c); Granet Museum (fine arts and archaeology); Museum of Old Aix; Paul Cézanne Studio; Roquefavour Aqueduct, Ventabren; Tapestry Museum; Vedôme Pavilion (17c mansion).

ALÈS (Gard)

Alès, situated on the River Gardon, is a mining and industrial town and a centre for the silk trade. It has an old quarter built by the fortifier Vauban (17th century) which encompasses the former Cathédrale St-Jean which dates mainly from the 18th century. From the terraces of Fort Vauban there are good views of Alès and its surroundings.
What to see Cathédrale St-Jean; Fort Vauban; Jardins du Bosquet; Old quarter.

ANDUZE (Gard)

This small, picturesque town lies in a valley about 10km (6 miles) south-west of Alès and is known as the Gateway to the Cévennes. Much of the town is medieval, with winding streets and a clock tower, once part of the Château d'Anduze, which dates from 1320. It also has a park (Ancien parc du couvent des Cordeliers) where, from the terrace, there is a fine view of the Gardon Valley. On the outskirts of the town is an arboretum, the Parc de Prafrance, which specialises in bamboos and has been used as a set for a number of films.
What to see Ancien parc du couvent des Cordeliers (exotic trees); Parc de Prafrance (arboretum); Tour de l'Horloge (1320).

ANSOUIS (Vaucluse)

The fine château, Sabran Castle, has been owned by the Sabran family since medieval times and, though it presents the visitor with a gentle 17th-century-style

Carnival Time

Traditional celebrations and modern festivals provide the south of France with a year-long calendar of glittering events.

February is brightened by the Nice Carnival when flower-decked floats pour through the streets and fancy-dress balls, flower battles and fireworks add to the gaiety. Menton's Lemon Festival and the Mimosa Festival at Cannes also involve decorated floats.

Strangely, Arles celebrates Easter with bullfights. In May the International Film Festival takes over Cannes, and St-Tropez stages its own drama with the *Bravade*; the Monaco Grand Prix draws huge crowds.

There are nautical jousts on the Rhône to Sète canal, a jazz festival at La Grande-Motte, and folk dancing in the amphitheatre at Arles in July; and August sees the Lavender Festival at Digne and a firework display at Monteux. Winter brings many religious festivals, especially around Christmas when *santons*, painted clay figurines of Provençal characters, are placed around the crib.

The 1880s way of frolicking with flowers at Cannes

exterior, has retained one or two earlier features such as its Romanesque chapel. It lies on the D56 south of Apt and is open most days of the year.

What to see Château (17c); Musée Extraordinaire (marine life and Provençal furniture).

ANTIBES (Alpes-Maritimes)

A popular resort in an ideal situation between two small bays, Antibes is also the centre of the local flower-growing trade, specialising in anemones, carnations and roses. The history of the town stretches back to Greek times and the remains of the fortifications erected by the celebrated military engineer, Vauban, during the 17th century can still be seen around the Avenue Amiral-de-Grasse. Pablo Picasso spent some months in 1946 in Antibes and a skilfully laid-out museum devoted to his work has been established in the 16th-century Grimaldi Château where he set up his studio. The town also has associations with Napoleon who was imprisoned for a time in the nearby Fort Carré.

What to see Archaeological Museum; Grimaldi Château (16c – Picasso museum).

APT (Vaucluse)

The foundation of Apt stretches back to Roman times but it is known today for its fine medieval cathedral, dedicated to Ste-Anne. It is a good centre for touring the Luberon range (where there is a large nature reserve), and the Vaucluse Plateau. For the energetic a visit to Rustrel, 9.5km (5½ miles) to the north-east, followed by a walk to the Rustrel Colorado, a huge ochre quarry, is rewarding.

What to see Archaeology Museum; Cathedral of Ste-Anne (11–17c).

ARLES (Bouches-du-Rhône)

Once the most important city in Roman Gaul, Arles stands on the River Rhône at the gateway to the wild Camargue and plays a prominent part in the economic and tourist activities of the region. The city is rich in Roman relics including the huge arena (dating originally from the 2nd century and unusually well preserved despite being incorporated into the city defences during the 12th century), and a 1st-century theatre. Medieval architecture is well represented by the exquisitely decorated

The 14th-century fortified palace built by the Popes at Avignon rises above the modern town

Romanesque Church of St-Trophime and the remains of the town walls. Arles is well endowed with museums. It was in Arles that Van Gogh painted many of his best-known paintings and the scintillating colours which he used can be seen all around, though his paintings have been dispersed to the world's great art galleries. The city is the scene of various fairs and artistic events during the summer months and even stages bull-fighting in the Roman arena.

What to see Arena (2c); Church of St-Trophime (11–15c); Les Alyscamps (burial ground – 4–13c); Museum of Christian Art; Museum of Pagan Art; Museum Réattu (fine arts); Theatre (1c).

AVIGNON (Vaucluse)

Despite its position as the commercial centre of the Department of Vaucluse, Avignon is still a city of truly medieval aspect. Completely encircled by stout ramparts and dominated by the huge Palace of Popes, the city presents a somewhat warlike exterior. Most of its fortifications date from the 14th century when the Popes established their official

residence there in preference to Rome. An even older feature is the famous Pont d'Avignon (or more correctly Pont St-Bénézet) which once joined Avignon to Villeneuve-lès-Avignon via an island in the River Rhône. Everyone danced in a ring on the bridge, according to the song, but as it is – or was – a packhorse bridge there would not have been room for a circle of people. It is more likely that they danced on the island 'sous le pont' – under the bridge. The bridge, dating from 1177, is now incomplete but a few arches still lead out from the Avignon side, on the second of which is an ancient chapel. The Palace of Popes (Palais des Papes) is said to be one of the most tasteful mixtures of medieval military and civil architecture in the country. It stands, near the 12th-century Romanesque cathedral, at the foot of the Rocher-des-Doms, a hill containing a public garden from which there is a lovely view of the city and its surroundings.

Avignon has several interesting museums and its medieval appearance lends itself admirably to the Festival of Dramatic Art and

Dance which takes place annually in the city during July and August. It is also a good excursion centre and makes a good base for a holiday.

What to see Cathedral of Notre-Dame-des-Doms (12c); Musée Calvet (fine arts); Musée Lapidaire; Palais des Papes (14c); Pont d'Avignon (12c bridge); Ramparts (14c).

BARBENTANE (Bouches-du-Rhône)

A market town amid hills where olives, apricots and herbs grow and where wild flowers strew the sunny slopes. It stands near the confluence of the Rivers Rhône and Durance south-west of Avignon, and vestiges of the town's medieval defences, including a 14th-century tower and two fortified gateways can still be seen. It has an imposing 17th-century château noted for its Italian style 18th-century decoration and furnishings. The Montagnette, hills which run parallel to the Rhône below Avignon, can be explored from here.

What to see Château (17–18c); The Montagnette.

THE SOUTH OF FRANCE

BAUX-DE-PROVENCE (LES) (Bouches-du-Rhône)

This village with its ruined château occupies a prominent position upon a large rocky spur. It is a popular tourist attraction, its setting being one of the most breathtaking sights in Provence.

During the Middle Ages Baux was a thriving town and in the 13th century became the home of numerous troubadours, gaining recognition for its famous 'Court of Love' where musicians vied with one another in songs about their ladies' charms. The Lords of Baux were among the most powerful feudal houses in Provence. When the line died out (1426) Baux was incorporated into Provence and then into France. It was then in the king's gift but proved to be a bit of a thorn in the side of succeeding monarchs, especially after it turned Protestant. In 1632 Louis XIII had the fortifications destroyed. The citizens were fined a huge amount – and moved out!

There is now an inhabited section with shops, houses and churches, but the old abandoned village, with its steep cobbled streets, can be reached only on foot. Many of the surviving houses and chapels are partly hewn out of the rock, which gives the village an unusual appearance. There are several ruined Renaissance mansions too, including the Hôtel des Manvilles and the Hôtel des Porcelets. The 14th-century Tour de Brau remains intact and today contains the Musée Lapidaire (lapidary museum).

Another old building is the small Romanesque church of St-Vincent. This is noted for its Christmas Midnight Mass which observes the traditional Provençal custom of the offering of a lamb. From the church there is a fine view into the scenic Val d'Enfer with its contorted rocks.

What to see Château (13c); Hôtel des Manvilles (Renaissance); Hôtel des Porcelets (Renaissance); Musée d'Art moderne; Place St-Vincent; Rue du Trencat (Roman); Tour de Brau (14c) and Musée Lapidaire.

BEAUCAIRE (Gard)

This old town is set on the bank of the River Rhône opposite Tarascon. One of its main attractions is the site of the great fair which made Beaucaire famous. From the 13th to the 19th century the fair was held every July and attracted many thousands

Through spring and summer the golden stone buildings of Bormes-les-Mimosas are bright with flowers

of visitors. Documents describing these events are housed in the Musée du Vieux Beaucaire (local history).

Beaucaire also has an interesting ruined medieval château which was destroyed by Richelieu in the 17th century. Its walls enclose a Romanesque chapel (restored in the 19th century), courtyards, and a most unusual triangular tower. From the top of this tower there is a splendid view of the surrounding area.

What to see Château (11–13c); Musée Lapidaire (lapidary museum); Musée du Vieux Beaucaire; Site of fair.

BEAULIEU (Alpes-Maritimes)

Beaulieu has a favourable sheltered position, making it one of the Riviera's warmest resorts. This has made it popular during winter and has earned it the title of 'Little Africa'.

Above the lovely Baie des Fourmis (Trembling Bay) is a replica of a Greek villa, known as Kerylos. In particular the library is

interesting with its collection of ancient art objects.

There is a selection of hotels at Beaulieu including one of the most renowned on the Riviera – La Réserve. The town also has a casino. For magnificent views of the surroundings it is worth going to St Michel Plateau, though the climb up the Riviera escarpment takes about an hour each way.

What to see Alsace-Lorraine Boulevard; Baie des Fourmis; Villa Kerylos; Promenade Maurice-Rouvier; St-Michel Plateau.

BÉZIERS (Hérault)

The wine capital of Languedoc, Bézier's one-time 13th- and 14th-century cathedral crowns a hill over the River Orb, and its terraces offer distant views. The tree-lined promenade of the Allées Paul-Riquet has a statue to Riquet who built the Canal du Midi in the 17th century in the face of enormous technical difficulties; 2km south-west are the Fonséranes locks and canal bridge. 13km (8 miles) away

on a hill is a site, the Oppidum d'Ensérune, which was occupied successively from the 6th century BC by Iberians, Greeks and Romans. It is a remarkable open-air museum with views as far as the Pyrénées.

What to see One-time cathedral of St-Nazaire (13–14c); terrace; Musée du Vieux Biterrois et du vin (archaeology and wine museum); Fine Arts Museum (modern and older painters); canal bridge; Oppidum d'Ensérune.

BORMES-LES-MIMOSAS (Var)

An attractive resort, noted for its pleasant climate, situated on a steep incline at the entrance to the Dom Forest. Its streets are bright in spring and summer with potted flowers, agaves, eucalyptus and the mimosa from which it has taken its name. The older part of the town has sharply sloping streets, but a climb to the terrace of the Chapel of St-Francis is rewarded by a fine view of the coast.

What to see Town Hall Museum (local artists); St-Francis Chapel.

BRIANÇON (Hautes Alpes)

An intriguing old town and one of the highest in the country, standing approximately 1,321 metres (4,334ft) above sea level. Its strategic position near the Italian border prompted the defensive work which turned it into a star-shaped citadel. This work was engineered by Vauban during the 17th century and his ramparts still encircle the older part of the town or 'Ville Haute', where narrow streets cluster around the Church of Notre-Dame. From the old fort, at the highest point, there is a magnificent view of the surrounding mountains and forests. In the gorge below, the River Durance flows under the 200-year-old Pont d'Asfeld, which soars in a single span 56m (183ft) above the water. A truly spectacular place, best explored on foot.

What to see Bridge; Old fort; Ramparts.

BRIGNOLES (Var)

The old town, with its narrow, twisting street, clings to the slopes of a low hill, while new development has spread over the verdant plain below. Brignoles, an important bauxite producing centre, is well known for its marble quarries, and is the wine capital of Provence.

What to see Marble quarries; Museum of Brignoles (contains oldest known Christian sarcophagus).

CAGNES-SUR-MER (Alpes-Maritimes)

Orange trees, olives and carnations – what more exotic and perfumed surroundings could one find for a resort? Cagnes, set among wooded hills, is popular all the year round. It consists of a fishing village, Cros-de-Cagnes, and the ancient town of Haute-de-Cagnes which, with its old houses and narrow streets huddling around a medieval castle within the old town ramparts, attracts many artists. Renoir spent the last 12 years of his life there in a house which is now the Renoir Memorial Museum. The castle contains another comprehensive museum with pictures by 20th-century artists who worked locally. Sporting attractions include a fine racecourse. A trip can be made to Villeneuve-Loubet, 4km (2½ miles) away, where there is a Museum of Culinary Art.

What to see Castle Museum; Horse racing; Renoir Memorial Museum.

CANNES (Alpes-Maritimes)

One of the oldest of the Riviera resorts, Cannes owes much of its popularity to its superb setting below the Esterel mountain range and to its exceptionally mild climate. These were the factors which attracted Lord Brougham to spend the winter there during the mid-19th century, and the English aristocracy who followed his example assisted the little fishing village to begin its development into today's modern complex. The essence of the new Cannes may be found around the Boulevard de la Croisette, the seafront promenade bordered by renowned palace hotels and dotted with gardens and palm trees. Such events as the glamorous International Film Festival, which takes place each May, ensure the resort's continued prosperity.

In complete contrast the 'old town', overlooking the harbour, is a jumble of steep streets containing traces of the old town walls, a 12th-century tower (Tour du Mont Chevalier), and La Castre Museum which contains archaeological finds from all over the world and is surrounded by grounds from which there are magnificent views of the town and coast. Even more spectacular views are obtained from the Super-Cannes Observatory about 4km (2½ miles) away, which really should not be missed. Boats run from Cannes to the Lérins Islands, either to Île Ste-Marguerite in whose fortress the 'Man in the Iron Mask' was said to have been incarcerated, or to Île St-Honorat and its monastery. These trips make enjoyable half-day trips for those who enjoy the sea and sun.

What to see Boulevard de la Croisette; La Castre Museum; Lérins Islands; Super-Cannes Observatory; Tour du Mont Chevalier (12c).

CARCASSONNE (Aude)

La Cité, the marvellously well-preserved medieval part of Carcassonne, raises its towers and turrets above a double line of outer defences by the River Aude. It is said to be the finest example of a medieval fortified town in the country and certainly has a distinctly fairy-tale quality, especially at night when the whole area is floodlit. The fortifications were originally laid out around the 13th century but we owe their modern preservation to Viollet-le-Duc, the 19th-century architect and restorer, who was determined Carcassonne should lose nothing of its former glory. Across the river lies the Ville Basse (lower town) encircled by shady boulevards on the site of its old walls, and with narrow streets which make walking the best way of getting about.

The whole of La Cité is of interest, with its narrow streets, wall towers and old buildings, including the castle (almost a small town in itself) and the Basilica St-Nazaire, but it is so popular with tourists that it is perhaps best visited out of season. There are fully 3 kilometres of defensive walls and a walk between the inner and outer rings is reminiscent of a journey into the past.

What to see
La Cité: Château Comtal (13c); Château Museum; Fortifications.
Ville Basse: Cathedral of St-Michel (14c); Musée des Beaux Arts.

CARPENTRAS (Vaucluse)

Carpentras retains a small triumphal arch dating from the Roman occupation, but is now known for its wide boulevards built on the site of its old walls, and its fine houses and 18th-century public buildings. Irrigation of the surrounding countryside has made it a prosperous and bustling agricultural centre. On a clear day it is worth while driving to the summit of Mont Ventoux (at 1,912m (6,273ft) the highest peak in Provence) for the panoramas are spectacular.

What to see Bibliothèque; Cathedral of St-Siffrein (15c); Hôtel-Dieu (18c mansion including an old pharmacy); Museum of Archaeology; Museum (regional history/works of art); Musée Sobirats (18c mansion); Synagogue (18c – the oldest in France).

La Cité at Carcassonne, once a vital stronghold and marvellously preserved, has a medieval ruggedness loved by tourists

THE SOUTH OF FRANCE

CASSIS (Bouches-du-Rhône)
A small, popular resort and fishing port worth visiting for its fine seafood. Cassis' position makes it an ideal centre for visiting the famous Calanques, a series of deep natural harbours which run inland between towering cliffs along the coastline south east of Marseille. Approaching Cassis from Marseille is a layby which provides a glorious view of the port and the cliff of Cap Canaille, at 362m (1,188ft), the highest in France.

CASTELLANE (Alpes-de-Haute-Provence)
This tourist attraction, situated on the Route Napoléon and the River Verdon, has one of the most splendid locations in Upper Provence. It is dominated by a huge limestone cliff, known as the Roc, which rises to 184m (604ft). The nucleus of the town is the Place Marcel-Sauvaire where the pentagonal tower, a survivor of the former ramparts, may be seen. Although it is a full day's excursion, a visit to the spectacular Verdon Grand Canyon is something which really should not be missed – its wild immensity really has no parallel in Europe. A shorter trip is to the Castillon and Chaudanne reservoirs.
What to see Annonciade Gate; Chapel of Notre-Dame-du-Roc; Place Marcel-Sauvaire; Tower; Verdon Grand Canyon (about 60km (37 miles) away).

CHÂTEAUNEUF-DU-PAPE (Vaucluse)
A small town in the Rhône Valley famous for its local vineyards and the wine they produce. Châteauneuf is overlooked by the remains of the fortress built by the Avignon Popes to command the valley during the early 14th century. The Musée du Père Anselme deals with the history of wine making.
What to see Château-des-Papes (14c); Musée du Père Anselme.

COLLIOURE (Pyrénées-Orientales)
One of the most picturesque and ancient of the smaller fishing ports in the area, Collioure attracts many artists anxious to catch the vivid colours of sea and sail, and has now become a popular holiday resort. The Château Royal stands guard over the port and Collioure church, whose red-roofed tower, once a lighthouse, makes every photograph and painting of Collioure instantly recognisable, on the opposite side of the bay, has a distinctly Spanish flavour.
What to see Château Royal (15c); Harbours.

DIGNE (Alpes-de-Haute-Provence)
A popular, but peaceful, tourist resort on the left bank of the River Bléone. Little remains of the old town except the fine Provençal Romanesque cathedral, and the town's main attractions are its beautiful climate and the fields of lavender which surround it. The museum deals with the natural history of the area and the works of two 19th-century Digne painters, Paul and Étienne Martin.
What to see Cathedral of Notre-Dame-du-Bourg (13–14c); Grande Fontaine; Lavender; Museum.

DRAGUIGNAN (Var)
A former Roman settlement which has retained a medieval appearance and is a well-known market centre. The Tour de l'Horloge (clock tower) marks the spot where a Roman fort and a feudal castle once stood.

To the east of Draguignan, on the D59, is an Allied Military Cemetery containing the graves of British and American troops who fell during the airborne invasion in August 1944.

There is some spectacular scenery nearby and trips to the Châteaudouble Gorges or to the waterfalls on the Nartuby River are well worth while.
What to see Library and Museum (archaeology, natural history); Allées d'Azémar (old plane trees, Rodin's bust of Clemenceau).

ELNE (Pyrénées-Orientales)
A quiet country town which was an important settlement in Roman times. Elne is best known today for its fine 11th-century cathedral and for the magnificent Romanesque 12th-century cloisters that adjoin it. They contain an archaeology museum.
What to see Cathedral of Ste-Eulalie (11–14c); Museum (archaeology of Elne).

EMBRUN (Hautes Alpes)
An ancient town perched high above the River Durance near the Serre-Ponçon Lake, whose beautiful surroundings make it a popular year-round resort.
What to see Mountains; Serre-Ponçon Lake; Tour Brune (12c).

ENTREVAUX (Alpes-de-Haute-Provence)
This is a strikingly complete fortified village of the 17th century clustered about a rock over the River Var, which once formed the boundary between France and the neighbouring dukedom of Savoy. The seat of a bishopric until the late 18th century, Entrevaux has a one-time cathedral, and from the citadel a magnificent view of the valley is spread below.

ÈZE (Alpes-Maritimes)
One of the 'perched villages' for which Provence is famous, the village of Èze stands high above the resort of Èze-Bord-de-Mer between Nice and Menton. Its winding passages and stairways, containing a good selection of craft and gift shops, are ever popular with both tourists and painters. Fine views along the breathtaking coastline may be obtained from the Jardin Exotique (Tropical Gardens) which have been established around the remains of a 14th-century castle. A steep path winds down to the resort on the Lower Corniche road.
What to see Chapelle-des-Pénitents-Blancs (14c); Jardin Exotique.

Cap Canaille towers over the colourful harbour of Cassis
Below: Massed cacti at Èze

82

FLORAC (Lozère)

This agreeable little town on the right bank of the Tarnon and at the foot of the desolate yet fascinating uplands of the Causse Méjean, makes an excellent excursion centre. From it can be explored the dramatic Gorges of the Tarn; the varied scenery of the Corniche des Cévennes road to St-Jean-du-Gard; Mont Lozère, the highest mountain of the Cévennes, and the Runes waterfall.

FONTAINE-DE-VAUCLUSE (Vaucluse)

A village south of Cavaillon, overlooked by a ruined castle and famous for its 'Fountain'. From a cave the underground River Sorgue surges spectacularly in winter and spring, but in summer it tranquilly accompanies the *Son et Lumière*.
What to see Château (13c); La Fontaine-de-Vaucluse; Le Monde Souterrain (underground world) de Norbert Casteret (cave explorations).

FONT-ROMEU (Pyrénées-Orientales)

Font-Romeu, high in the Pyrénées, is popular both in summer and for winter sports. It has a hermitage with a chapel containing a 'miraculous' statue of the Virgin but its main attraction is its location.
What to see Calvary; Hermitage; Ski-runs.

FORCALQUIER (Alpes-de-Haute-Provence)

This old town is set on a hillside amid fine scenery. It has a few interesting old buildings including the one-time cathedral and the Porte des Cordeliers (Franciscan Gateway), all that remains of its fortifications. The clipped yew trees in the cemetery are unusual, as are the drystone cylindrical huts with pointed roofs which are descendants of the first free-standing architecture invented by man (see also *Gordes*). From the Terrasse de Notre-Dame de Provence there is a fine view of the surrounding mountains, where the air is so clear that an observatory has been built. This is about 13km (8 miles) away, at St-Michel-l'Observatoire. Another worthwhile trip is to Lure Beacon, but the last part of the climb has to be made on foot. A visit to the Ganagobie plateau (18km) gives a lofty view over the Durance Valley, and the partly ruined 12th-century priory can also be visited.

What to see One-time cathedral (12–14c); Cemetery (topiary); Couvent des Cordeliers (Franciscan Monastery – part 13c); Ganagobie plateau; Museum (local history); Porte des Cordeliers; Terrasse de Notre-Dame de Provence; Upper Provence Observatory.

FRÉJUS (Var)

This ancient town is built on a rocky plateau between the Maures and the Esterel. Its popularity as a tourist centre has encouraged development of self-catering accommodation on the outskirts. Fréjus was founded by Julius Caesar in 49 BC as Forum Julii and today it is famous for its varied Roman ruins. These include the oldest amphitheatre in Gaul, a theatre, an aqueduct and a gateway. The baptistry of the 10th-century cathedral dates from the 4th century and is one of the oldest buildings in France. The 13th-century cloister now houses an archaeological museum which contains a fine Roman mosaic. Orchards and vineyards flourish round about and there are a zoo and safari park about 5km (3 miles) away.
What to see Archaeological museum; Cathedral; Esterel Safari; Roman ruins; Zoological Park.

GAP (Hautes Alpes)

A busy town situated in a small valley on the Route Napoléon, Gap has an interesting museum dealing mainly with Alpine folklore, but its attraction lies mainly in its mountainous surroundings. There is ski-ing available at Ceüse nearby.
What to see Musée Départemental.

GORDES (Vaucluse)

An ancient village set on the slopes of the Plateau of Vaucluse. There are a number of quaint old buildings and the highest point of the town is crowned by a fine Renaissance-style château which also contains a museum devoted to the works of the artist Vasarely. A curious 'Black Village', a collection of prehistoric beehive-shaped huts, built of stone without mortar, lies a short distance to the south-west. These are thought to be in the earliest style of free-standing building invented by man. One even has an oven in it.
What to see Château (Renaissance); Village Noir (black village).

Artists in the Sun

The clear air, brilliant sunshine and entrancing views have long attracted artists to the South of France. Visitors have many opportunities to see where they worked and perhaps to enjoy some of their masterpieces.

Château Grimaldi at Antibes houses works by Picasso; Les Colettes, at Cagnes-sur-Mer, is preserved in memory of Renoir; and the Aix-en-Provence studio of his friend Paul Cézanne is also open to the public; while the countryside round Arles will ever recall the brilliant colours used by Van Gogh, who spent two productive and turbulent years there. Marc Chagall still lives in Vence, where the Rosary Chapel was designed and decorated by Henri Matisse, and outside Biot is the striking (if incongruous) Fernand Léger Museum. Nearby, at St-Paul, is the Maeght Fondation, its glass, steel and concrete gallery housing

a superb collection of 20th-century art. The dramatically-landscaped cliff-top gardens are a perfect setting for sculptures and water-powered mobiles.

83

GRASSE (Alpes-Maritimes)

The modern town with terraced houses and gardens stands on the hillside above the narrow alleys, linked by flights of steps, and the tall buildings which make up the old quarter. Grasse is famous for the manufacture of perfumes using locally grown flowers, an industry which has been flourishing here since the 16th century. Grasse has a cathedral and two museums, one dealing with the art and history of the region and the other devoted to the works of the artist Fragonard, born in the town in 1732. But the town's charm lies also in its gentle climate and the flowers which make a perfumed bower of the surrounding countryside. It is a good centre for touring the alpine foothills and the Loup Valley with its waterfalls, gorges and villages perched like eyries on the hillsides.

What to see Cathedral of Notre-Dame (12–17c); Perfumeries; Provençal Art and History Museum; Villa-Museum Fragonard.

HYÈRES (Var)

The oldest of the Riviera resorts, lying on a hillside in a sheltered position and noted for the production of early fruit and vegetables. The wide, tree-lined streets of the 'new town' contrast pleasantly with the ancient buildings and gateways of the old quarter which stands below the ruins of a feudal castle. The harbour is filled with pleasure craft and ferries serving the Hyères Islands, Porquerolles, Port-Cros (a National Park) and Levant, which lie a short distance from the shore and are known as the 'Golden Isles'.

What to see Cathedral of St-Paul (12–16c); Municipal Museum (natural history); Olbius-Riquier Gardens (rare plants); Port-Cros National Park.

LOURMARIN (Vaucluse)

A village on the slopes of the Luberon hills about 20km (13 miles) south of Apt (qv). It is overlooked by its medieval castle which, after restoration in 1925, was put at the disposal of the Aix-en-Provence Academy. The castle is still open to visitors and, apart from some fine internal decorations, has a tower from which extensive views may be obtained over the surrounding hills.

What to see Castle (15c).

The Fragrance of the South

Climbing inland from Cannes, the heady perfumes of Grasse waft to meet you, for the factories fill the air with the heavy, and sometimes sickly-sweet, scents of lavender, jasmine, rose, and other herbs and flowers.

Perfumes have been made at Grasse since the 16th century when the Medicis started the fashion of perfumed gloves. Of the many perfume factories, two – Molinard and Fragonard – conduct visitors over their establishments. The thoughtfully-arranged Fragonard Museum illustrates the history of perfume-making. Early copper boilers, primitive stills, scent bottles and labels, and old photographs are on display; while a tour of the workshops gives an insight into the essentials of distilling the precious essence – precious because a ton of fragrant flower petals makes only two pounds of perfume.

MANOSQUE (Alpes-de-Haute-Provence)

The tall narrow houses of Manosque are typical of old Provençal towns, but little is left of its fortifications. Boulevards now run where once walls encircled the town, but two 14th-century fortified gateways, the Porte Saunerie and the Porte Soubeyran, have been preserved. The modern town is the centre of the agricultural industry of the lower Durance Valley. Mont d'Or lies a mile to the north-east; a road leads to the summit, from where there is a fine panoramic view of the surrounding countryside.

What to see Fortified gateways; Mont d'Or.

MARSEILLE (Bouches-du-Rhône)

Marseille is one of the largest cities in France and it is certainly the oldest, having been founded by exploring Phoenicians in 600 BC. It has now evolved into a major Mediterranean port, known as the 'gateway to the East', and is a busy industrial centre. It still retains its old harbour, guarded by two forts, which has served the city since its earliest days. Remnants of the ancient Greek harbour fortifications can be seen near the Vieux Port, behind the Chamber of Commerce, and the harbour is linked to the modern town by the famous La Canebière, a thoroughfare crowded with shops, cafés and hotels. Marseille has some interesting churches including the Basilica Notre-Dame-de-la-Garde which towers above the city, providing excellent views from its terrace. There are many museums, covering most aspects of the town's history. One unusual feature is the local zoo which contains a wild-animal training school where displays are given; and a short boat ride from

Martigues, known as the Venice of Provence because of its canals, is linked to the sea by the Caronte Canal

the harbour is the legendary Château d'If which was the setting for Alexandre Dumas' novel 'The Count of Monte Cristo'. On the outskirts of the town, the suburb of Allauch nestles below the Étoile mountains. The terrace of the former château here affords good views.

What to see Basilica of Notre-Dame-de-la-Garde (19c); Borély Château (18c – containing Museum of Mediterranean Archaeology and Lapidary Museum); Cantini Museum (18c – modern art); Château d'If; Grobet-Labadié Museum (tapestries, works of art, etc); Longchamp Palace (19c – contains Fine Arts Museum and Natural History Museum); Maritime Museum; Museum of Old Marseilles; Roman Docks Museum; Zoo.

MARTIGUES (Bouches-du-Rhône)

An old fishing port and yachting centre on the Étang de Berre, linked to the sea by the Caronte Canal, and known to its admirers as Provençal Venice. It has developed enormously in recent years because of the nearby petrol refinery but has retained much of the charm which attracted painters such as Corot and Ziem. Martigues contains a number of quaint old buildings and the museum has a collection of paintings by Ziem. The best view of the quayside and the brightly coloured boats moored alongside is from the Pont St-Sébastien.

What to see Museum; Pont St-Sébastien.

MENDE (Lozère)

Mende, the capital of the Gévaudan, is some 70km (45 miles) north-west of Alès. The 12th-century Tour des Pénitents and the 14th-century Pont Notre-Dame are indications of the town's antiquity. The 14th-century cathedral contains fine choir stalls and an excellent set of Aubusson tapestries. Nearby are some narrow and picturesque streets.

What to see Cathedral (mainly 14c); Musée Ignon Fabre (various collections including jewellery, archaeology and ceramics); Pont Notre-Dame (14c bridge); Tour des Pénitents (12c).

MENTON (Alpes-Maritimes)

Menton enjoys the mildest climate on the Riviera coast and tropical plants flourish in parks and gardens. Lemons, which cannot stand the slightest frost, fruit all year round in its warm airs, which naturally attract many visitors too. The old quarter, with steep covered alleyways linking the harbour to the Baroque Church of St-Michel, contrasts startlingly with the artificial beach and the modern buildings (which include a casino) of the new sector of Menton.

Every year the town hosts a citrus fruit and tropical flower show (February); an International Festival of Chamber Music (August); and the summer carnivals (August–September).

Viewpoints such as the Parvis (or Place) St-Michel and the Quai Bonaparte give panoramic views of the town and coastline, especially striking at night when the lights of the town are reflected in the sea. There is a superb walk along the coast from Cap-Martin, about 4km (2½ miles) from Menton, to Monte-Carlo. Other memorable excursions are to Ste-Agnès (11km), Gorbio (8km) and Castellar (6½km), all old perched villages with interesting histories and lovely views.

What to see Musée Jean Cocteau (his works); Musée Municipal (local history and various paintings); Old quarter; Promenade George-V; Quai Bonaparte; Quai Napoleon III; Villa Val Rahmeh (botanical garden).

MONACO (Principality of)

The Principality of Monaco, situated on the Riviera and covering only eight square miles, attracts a cosmopolitan population both because it has a salubrious climate and because direct taxation does not exist in this sovereign territory. The small number of natives, known as Monégasques, are also free from military service. By arrangement with France and Italy, whose nationals make up a large proportion of the population, citizenship is given only in exceptional circumstances.

The capital is the old town of Monaco which stands on a rocky promontory 60m (200ft) above the sea. It has intriguing narrow lanes, ruins of former fortifications, and the Royal Palace where the daily changing of the Guard draws onlookers. Other attractions include the zoo, and the Oceanographic Museum which has one of Europe's best aquariums.

Across the bay is Monte-Carlo, noted for its casinos, villas, hotels and shops. Its most famous building is the Casino built in 1878 by Charles Garnier which, in addition to gambling rooms, has a theatre, restaurant, bars and a night club. Once the town's most elevated building, it is now backed by tower blocks of apartments. Garnier also built the villa where the National Museum, containing the Galea Collection which includes 18th- and 19th-century dolls in period costume, is housed. Most people know Monte-Carlo of course, from televised pictures of the Monaco Grand Prix in which cars are raced round the streets of the town.

Linking the town of Monaco with Monte-Carlo is the port of La Condamine which handles merchant shipping and pleasure boats. Between here and the mountains which embrace Monaco on the landward side lies the Jardin Exotique which contains magnificent cacti.

What to see Centre d'Acclimatation Zoologique; Grottes de l'Observatoire (limestone caves – in Jardin Exotique); Jardin Exotique; Jardins St-Martin; Monte-Carlo Casino; National Museum; Oceanographic Museum; Place du Palais; Port of La Condamine; Prehistorical Anthropology Museum (local prehistory collections); Prince's Palace (part 13c) and Napoleon Museum; zoo.

MONTMAJOUR (ABBAYE DE) (Bouches-du-Rhône)

The impressive ruins of this Benedictine abbey stand on a hill 7km (4 miles) from Arles. The abbey was founded in the 10th century and prospered until the French Revolution when parts of the building were dismantled and literally carried off by the highest bidder. The ruins include the 12th-century abbey church with fine intricately decorated cloisters and a formidable 14th-century keep. Do not miss the tiny and charming 12th-century Chapelle Ste-Croix, standing alone in a field below the abbey.

MONTPELLIER (Hérault)

A lively town, sometimes referred to as the 'Oxford of France', which has been the seat of a university since the 13th century and can boast the oldest medical school in Europe. Montpellier is the chief town of Bas Languedoc (the lower part of the region, bordering the Mediterranean), and is the prosperous centre of a fertile area. It is noted for numerous 17th-century mansions, many of them with elegant courtyards, its wide streets and beautiful gardens. From the terraced Promenade du Peyrou there is a fine view of the surrounding countryside. There are several museums, perhaps the best known being the Musée Fabre which contains 19th-century paintings covering most European schools; and there is a fine Botanical Garden which was one of the first to be established in France. Montpellier is a good centre for excursions both to the resorts and fishing villages around the Golfe du Lion and inland to the mountains.

What to see Musée Atger (Works of Art, etc); Musée Fabre; Jardin des Plantes (Botanical Gardens).

The town of Monaco – seen here from the Exotic Garden – is the oldest part of the Principality

THE SOUTH OF FRANCE

MOUSTIERS-STE-MARIE (Alpes-de-Haute-Provence)

A former monastic settlement, in an impressive setting against a background of rugged cliff scenery, about 30km (18 miles) west of Castellane. The gorge immediately behind the village is spanned by a chain from which a quaint gilded star dangles. This is said to be an offering of thanks from a Crusader following his release from captivity.

Moustiers has been famous for its pottery since the 17th century when the distinctive form of decoration known as 'grotesques' was perfected here. The museum, in the town hall, traces the development of the trade from its earliest period.

What to see Gorge; Musée des Faïences (Pottery Museum).

NARBONNE (Aude)

An important town in Roman times, Narbonne is today the chief town of the Department of Aude and has substantial interests in the wine trade. Very little of the old Roman settlement has been preserved but Narbonne can boast a magnificent medieval cathedral, one of the most impressive in the country, even though it was never properly completed. In the archbishop's palace are the Archaeology Museum, containing some of the last remaining traces of Roman Narbonne, and the Museum of Art and History. The drive along a ridge of hills to the waterside resort of Narbonne Plage is an enjoyable trip. In the lagoons along the coast here you may be lucky enough to see flamingoes, while inland are vineyards and several attractive villages. 14km (8½ miles) south-west is the 12th-century Abbey of Fontfroide, largely restored and a lovely example of Cistercian architecture.

What to see Cathedral of St-Just (13c); Lapidary Museum; Musée Archéologique; Musée d'Art et d'Histoire; Narbonne Plage (beach).

NICE (Alpes-Maritimes)

Nice, the capital of the Côte d'Azur, occupies a splendid position on the Baie des Anges and, sheltered by lofty hills, enjoys beautiful weather all year round. This, together with its spring fêtes and famous carnival, not to mention the conventions and trade fairs held at the new Palace of Exhibitions, has ensured Nice's continued reputation as the leading Riviera resort. Its tasteful blend of ancient and modern architecture does nothing to detract from the city's charm. From the world-famous 4-mile Promenade des Anglais, which encircles the bay, luxury hotels and mansions gradually give way to the steep, narrow alleys of old Nice lying below the hill which once supported an imposing fortress and now provides an unrivalled view over the city and the bay.

The National Museum is devoted to the works of the painter Marc Chagall; and another museum deals with the city's maritime history. Further inland, at Nice-Cimiez, the 3rd-century arena and Roman baths may be visited. Here, too, is a gallery devoted to the works of Matisse.

In addition to the attractions of its superb coastline, Nice is near enough to the mountains to make it possible to go ski-ing in the winter. It is also an excellent excursion centre to the dramatic valleys that fan out from the Nice amphitheatre, in particular to the perched villages of Peille, Peillon and Aspremont, and the Sanctuary of Laghet. The 3½hr journey by autorail to Digne, capital of the Department, is a scenic feast.

What to see Harbour; Matisse Museum; National Museum; Naval Museum; Palais Lascaris (17c); Pottery Museum (in Town Hall); Promenade des Anglais; Roman Arena and Baths (3c).

NÎMES (Gard)

A busy city with a thriving trade in locally produced wine and a glowing reputation as a tourist centre, Nîmes has some of the best-preserved Roman remains in the region, if not in the whole of France. The arena is one of the finest examples of 1st-century architecture, seating more than 20,000 spectators; and the Maison Carrée, dating from the same period when it was a temple, has been carefully restored to ensure its continued usage. It currently contains a fascinating Museum of Antiquities.

Other Roman edifices such as the baths and the Temple of Diana have been incorporated into an 18th-century landscaped garden, the Jardin de la Fontaine, which lies below Mount Cavalier, a noted viewpoint on the western side of the city. The spring around which this garden is made was the town's original water supply. As the town grew it proved inadequate and Agrippa had an aqueduct built to bring water from the Eure. At one point this is carried across a gorge on the Pont du Gard (qv).

What to see Archaeology Museum; Les Arènes (1c); Jardin de la Fontaine; Maison Carrée (1c); Tour Magne (1cBC); Musée des Beaux-Arts; Musée du Vieux Nîmes.

Set between sea and mountains, Nice jealously guards its reputation as the Riviera's most popular resort

Built in the first century BC, this great Roman aqueduct, the Pont du Gard, carries modern traffic on its lowest tier

ORANGE (Vaucluse)

Famous chiefly for its Roman buildings, Orange possesses a well-preserved theatre and the remains of a temple and gymnasium. The theatre contains one of the few statues of the Emperor Augustus in existence. Visitors entering from the north will be greeted by a most impressive 1st-century Triumphal Arch, rich in sculptured decoration. The whole Gallo-Roman area is best viewed from the Colline St-Eutrope, a hill in the southern part of Orange, surrounded by a pleasant park. An excursion to the J. H. Fabre museum at Sérignan (8km) will reward naturalists with the atmosphere of the home and garden of 'the insects' Homer'.
What to see Cathedral (Romanesque – restored); Gymnasium and Capitol (1c); Museum (Roman remains and local art, etc); Theatre (1c).

PERNES-LES-FONTAINES (Vaucluse)

A little town about 20km (13 miles) north of Cavaillon which has retained vestiges of its 13th-century defences. It owes its name to its fountains, most famous of which is the Fontaine du Cormoran (Fountain of the Cormorant) (18th century). The ruin of a feudal keep stands near the River Nesque; and the old bridge, guarded by a 16th-century gateway (Port Notre-Dame),

contains an unusual 16th-century chapel. The Tour Ferrande is another relic of the 13th century, with its lively murals painted in 1275; while the church, though restored, retains some 11th-century features. The town's main industry is preserving the cherries, strawberries, melons and grapes which grow in the surrounding countryside.
What to see Nesque Gorge; Old bridge; Tour Ferrande (13c).

PERPIGNAN (Pyrénées-Orientales)

Perpignan, the capital of the Roussillon region, is a busy university and market town on the River Têt. The older part of the town has a distinctly Spanish flavour which recalls Perpignan's glory in the Middle Ages when it was the seat of the Kingdom of Majorca. The royal palace (Palais des Rois-de-Majorque) still stands as an impressive monument to this period and is considered to be one of the best examples of medieval architecture in the country. Other places of interest include the impressive 14th-century cathedral with its Spanish-style interior decoration; the Loge-de-Mer, a 14th-century building in which all Perpignan's maritime affairs were handled (for the city was a thriving medieval port, despite being 8 miles from the sea today); and the Hyacinthe Rigaud Museum where the work of the 17th-century painter, born

in Perpignan in 1659, is on display. Another handsome building is the 14th-century Le Castillet which houses a museum of traditional Catalan arts, crafts and artisans' tools.

Nearby are vine-clad hills, and the sea on the one hand, and the mountains of the eastern Pyrénées on the other, are both within reach.
What to see Cathedral of St-Jean (14–16c); Loge-de-Mer (14c); Le Castillet (14c); Musée Hyacinthe Rigaud; Palais de la Députation (ancient Palais de Justice – 15c); Palais des Rois-de-Majorque (14c).

PÉZENAS (Hérault)

An unusual town surrounded by vineyards and containing many 16th- and 17th-century buildings, some of them in Renaissance style, with fine courtyards and staircases such as Hôtel de Lacoste. The Tribunal de Commerce, the Hôtel d'Alfonce and the Hôtel de Malibran are all notable for their intricate decoration.
What to see Musée Vulliod-St-Germain (works of art, etc); Place du 14-Juillet.

PONT DU GARD (Gard)

This Roman aqueduct, spanning the River Gardon, is one of the most impressive sights in France. It was erected in the latter half of the 1st century BC and has a structure of three tiers with arches. The third tier carried the water supply from Uzès to Nîmes; the first was adapted in the 18th century to carry the road across the river.

PUGET-THÉNIERS (Alpes-Maritimes)

Puget-Théniers is a quaint little town at the confluence of the Rivers Var and Roudoule. Many of the houses are old with overhanging roofs. The church, built by the Templars, dates from the 13th century and has some fine 15th-century sculptured groups in walnut wood. 10km (6 miles) away, the River Roudoule runs through a deep gorge which is crossed by a suspension bridge. Below can be seen the remains of the Roman Bridge with, on either side, sections of the ancient road leading to it. Near here is the picturesque old hilltop village of La Croix-sur-Roudoule.
What to see Church (13c); La Croix-sur-Roudoule; Roudoule Gorge and, further afield, the Daluis and Cians gorges.

RIEZ (Alpes-de-Haute-Provence)

A small resort which has a history stretching back to pre-Roman times, lying at the foot of Mount St-Maxime. Riez has retained two main relics from its past – a fine Merovingian baptistry, dating back to the 6th century, and four 1st-century Corinthian columns which stand on the western outskirts of the town – but its main attractions for visitors are its surroundings and the refreshing coolness of its air in summer. It is also a centre for lavender and truffles.
What to see Ancient Columns (1st century); Baptistry (6th–12th century).

THE SOUTH OF FRANCE

ROQUEBRUNE-CAP-MARTIN (Alpes-Maritimes)

A pretty seaside resort on a wooded peninsula below the ancient 'perched village' of Roquebrune where steep, covered streets lined with medieval buildings cluster around the keep of the oldest castle in the country. Founded by the Count of Ventimiglia towards the close of the 10th century as a defence against raiding Saracens, the keep's walls are up to 12 feet thick in places and there is a fine view from the upper storeys across the bay to Monte Carlo.

What to see Castle (10–12c).

ST GILLES (Gard)

An old town on the outskirts of the Camargue and 16km (10 miles) from Arles. It is well-known for the splendid abbey church which, despite extensive restoration, retains its 12th-century west façade, a masterpiece of medieval carving. The church also has a 12th-century crypt and a remarkable spiral staircase (Vis-de-St-Gilles), in the north belltower, which is so perfectly made that it used to be copied as a stonemasons' apprentice piece. Opposite the church stands the Maison Romane where Guy Foulque, later to become Pope Clément IV, was born during the 13th century.

What to see Church of St-Gilles (12–19c); Maison Romane.

ST GUILHEM-LE-DÉSERT (Hérault)

This is an outstandingly picturesque village surrounded by dramatic hills and gorges carved by the attractive River Hérault. It

The 'perched village' of Roquebrune overlooks Monte Carlo Bay

possesses an impressive abbey church built at various dates from the 11th century on. The remains of a protective wall lead up the spur of a hill to a ruined castle on the hilltop. A little to the south of the village are the Grottes de Clamouse, many of whose stalagmites are of a delicate and fantastical beauty.

ST-JEAN-CAP-FERRAT (Alpes-Maritimes)

A year-round resort in a marvellous situation on a sloping, irregular-shaped peninsula washed by the warm Mediterranean and sheltered on the landward side. The buildings of the old village of St-Jean cluster around the harbour, contrasting with the immaculate villas and lovely gardens of the wealthy who have made their homes among the

luxuriant trees of Cap Ferrat.

The Île-de-France Museum lies amid superb landscaped gardens overlooking the sea. It was turned into a museum when Baroness Rothschild bequeathed it to the Academy of Fine Arts in 1934. As well as art objects, porcelain and furniture, it has a room decorated with paintings of monkeys up to their tricks. This should amuse the younger members of the family, who will also like the zoo, which has a garden of exotic plants and a butterfly farm, and the Sun Beach swimming pool which is built among rocks near the lighthouse. There are some delightful walks in the area, including an attractive tourist path round St-Hospice Point to the east.

What to see Île-de-France Museum; Lighthouse (views); Old village; Zoo (Jardin animé).

ST-MAXIMIN-LA-STE-BAUME (Var)

Tradition says that Mary Magdalene was buried here after living for many years in a cave in the Ste-Baume mountain range. The town lies on the bed of a dried-up lake and was the Gallo-Roman town of Villa Lata. It took the name of St-Maximin in the 13th century when tombs thought to be those of St Mary Magdalene and St Maximinus were found.

The Abbey of St Maximin was started in 1295 and is considered to be the best example in Provence of Gothic architecture. During the revolution it was saved from destruction by Lucien Bonaparte, Napoleon's youngest brother who was then officer in charge of military equipment in St-Maximin, who used it as a store. He also saved the organ by instructing the organist to play the Marseillaise when revolutionary officials visited the Abbey. Among its treasures is a 22-panel painting of the Passion which includes the first painted view of the Papal Palace at Avignon, as well as the Coliseum in Rome.

The Ste-Baume range is popular with rock-climbers; and in the Ste-Baume forest, shaded by mountains, grow trees such as beeches and limes more normally seen further north. Another place nearby which makes an interesting excursion is Barjols, known for its waterfalls.

What to see Ste-Baume Forest; Ste-Baume Mountains; St-Maximin Basilica.

St Tropez attracts the fashionable elite, many of whom bring their luxury yachts to its exquisite sheltered harbour

Flavours of Provence

The essential ingredients of Provençal cooking are garlic (often nicknamed the truffle of Provence) and locally-pressed olive oil; both are used in *bouillabaisse*. The essentials of this dish are conger eel, gurnet and *rascasse*, to which can be added other seafoods – perch, turbot, sole, red mullet, crab, mussels, lobster – as available! The fish is cooked quickly in a stock containing tomatoes, onions, garlic, herbs and wine and the liquid is then thickened. It is served with toast and a garnish of hot peppers.

To eat bouillabaisse like a local, line your dish with toast, fill it with the sauce, season with peppers and add as much cooked fish as your appetite allows. Around Marseille they say it is best accompanied by the heady wine of Cassis (not to be confused with the black-currant liqueur of the same name).

Aïoli, a mayonnaise made from olive oil, crushed garlic and egg yolk, and served with vegetables or fish, is another local speciality.

ST-RAPHAËL (Var)

The Romans came to St-Raphaël to enjoy the sea air, but it had a less happy reputation later when it was plundered by pirates. From the 11th century it was owned by religious orders but was rediscovered as a resort in 1864 by Alphonse Karr, a journalist, who told his friends how beautiful it was. St-Raphaël, on the Bay of Fréjus, has a deep-water anchorage and a port which is used by cargo, fishing and pleasure boats, but it is also a very popular resort in both summer and winter.

By the simple Templars' church is a milestone from the Roman Aurelian Way – a name still used locally for the N7. Nearby are the narrow lanes of the old fishing hamlet and the remains of an aqueduct.

St-Raphaël offers a variety of entertainment facilities including a casino, a yacht club, open-air concerts and a golf course at nearby Valescure.

What to see Boulevards Réné-Coty and Général-de-Gaulle; Museum of Underwater Archaeology.

ST-RÉMY-DE-PROVENCE (Bouches-du-Rhône)

The area of St-Rémy-de-Provence, situated on the lower slopes of Les Alpilles, has numerous market gardens. The town, however, is most famous for the ruins (Les Antiques) of the ancient Gallo-Roman town of Glanum. A 1st-century AD mausoleum, erected in honour of the grandsons of Emperor Augustus, is the most impressive building and is claimed to be the only surviving monument of its type. Close by is a 1st-century Municipal Arch. Excavations have shown that there was a Gallo-Greek settlement dating from the 2nd century BC previously on the site.

It was at St-Rémy, in a hospital converted from the old St-Paul-de-Mausole Monastery, that Van Gogh was cared for after he cut off his ear. The town was also the birthplace of the 16th-century astrologer and prophet Nostradamus, whose predictions for the future of the world, which he called 'Centuries', are still studied.

What to see Glanum ruins; Hôtel de Sade (museum containing finds from Glanum); Musée des Alpilles Pierre de Brun (local folklore); Priory of St-Paul-de-Mausole.

ST-TROPEZ (Var)

One of the most fashionable resorts on the Riviera, St-Tropez owes its reputation to its superb position on a peninsula and to its sheltered harbour and yacht-marina which are a great attraction to sailors of all descriptions. It is lively and glamorous but is rather short of hotel accommodation, probably because it is a summer-only resort being exposed in winter to the *mistral* and to the wet easterly winds.

It was an important port and had its own fleet to protect it from raiders until 1830 when the French captured Algiers and were able to control piracy based on that part of the African coast. It then dwindled into a fishing village until the 1890s when it became a favourite gathering-place for artists and began its rise to international fame. A 16th-century citadel contains a Maritime Museum.

Near the town are some intriguing fortified hilltop villages such as Ramatuelle, a place of alleys and steps among oak woods, and Gassin.

What to see Annonciade Museum (early 20c paintings – one of the best collections in France); Citadel (16–17c); Harbour; Mole Jean Réveille (views); Place des Lices (where locals play *boules*).

STE-ENIMIE (Lozère)

An interesting old town standing on a sharp bend of the river in the Gorges du Tarn. Places of interest include the remains of the old monastery buildings, the Vieux Logis with its folklore museum, and the Fountain of Burle whose waters, according to legend, cured Ste-Enimie of leprosy. North of the town is the Grotte Ermitage where a chapel, dedicated to Ste-Enimie, is built into a cave. From this point there is a fine view of both the town and the rugged cliffs of the Gorges du Tarn.

What to see Fontaine de Burle; Grotte Ermitage; Le Vieux Logis (folklore museum).

STES-MARIES-DE-LA-MER (Bouches-du-Rhône)

An ancient fishing port, now surrounded by villas and the trappings of a holiday resort, in the dunes between the sea and the lagoons of the Camargue. It is famous for its annual 'gipsy' pilgrimages (in May and October) honouring the three Marys – St Mary Jacobé (sister – or perhaps sister-in-law – of the Virgin); St Mary Salomé (mother of James and John), and St Mary Magdalene – who, according to legend, landed here in AD 40. Sara, their black servant, is the particular attraction for the gipsies as she is regarded as their ancestress. In spring large numbers of them, in colourful costumes, converge on the church which contains her tomb. The church rises above the town looking more fortress than place of worship, having been a refuge during the too-frequent Saracen raids. It contains a reliquary of Sara (part of a Mithraic tomb) and her statue dressed in layers of shawls to which supplicants pin photographs of their loved ones.

What to see Baroncelli Museum (local history); The Camargue; Church (12c).

SALON-DE-PROVENCE (Bouches-du-Rhône)

A busy, attractive market town where an ancient gateway gives access to narrow, winding streets lined with plane trees. The Château de l'Empéri contains a military museum and the recently restored house of Nostradamus, who is buried in the church, can be visited.

What to see Château de l'Empéri (10–15c – contains military museum); Maison de Nostradamus.

SANARY-SUR-MER (Var)

A popular little seaside resort lying in the shelter of wooded hills. The small harbour is used by fishing boats and pleasure craft and there are good, safe beaches. There is a fine view from the approach to the Chapel of Notre-Dame-de-Pitié. Sanary is a good excursion centre with a tropical garden and zoo a few miles inland at Sanary-Bandol.

What to see Sanary-Bandol Garden and Zoo.

THE SOUTH OF FRANCE

SAULT (Vaucluse)

A little town in a charming situation on the edge of the Plateau of Vaucluse overlooking the Nesque Valley (whose gorges are well worth visiting), and noted for growing lavender and manufacturing honey and nougat. There is an interesting part-Romanesque church and a prehistoric museum is housed in the library.

What to see Church (12–14c); Museum.

SÉNANQUE (ABBAYE DE) (Vaucluse)

One of the best-preserved Cistercian abbeys in the country, Sénanque lies in a deep valley on the outskirts of the Plateau of Vaucluse about 6km (4½ miles) from Gordes. It was founded by St Bernard in the 12th century, and, despite a turbulent history, retains a fine Romanesque church and the dormitory and refectory. Since 1969 the abbey has been a lay research centre and work relating to the history of the Sahara Desert is on display.

SÈTE (Hérault)

Situated at the foot of Mount St-Clair and linked to the sea in the south and the Bassin de Thau in the north by a series of canals, Sète, built originally in the 17th century, is France's second-largest Mediterranean port.

It is the port through which much of the region's huge output of wine is exported. The city is well known for its 'Joutes Nautiques', aquatic jousting between combatants in specially constructed boats propelled by a crew of rowers, which have been staged there during August for over 300 years.

The 'new town' is intersected by waterways where ships moor among the buildings. The older section – 'Vieux Port' – is lively with fishing boats in the harbour and fisherfolk sorting the catch on the quays. The town is famed for its seafood.

Places of interest include the Paul Valéry Museum, containing work of this writer, who was born in Sète in 1871, and others, and including etchings by Cézanne, Manet and Renoir. Seven miles of sandy beach stretch south to Agde, and there is a walk round the corniche of Mount St-Clair, which rises to 175m (569ft) above sea level.

What to see Beach; Musée Paul Valéry; Old Port.

Lavender thrives on the dry chalky soil around Sénanque Abbey

SISTERON (Alpes-de-Haute-Provence)

Clinging to the side of a steep hill above the River Durance, Sisteron stands guard over the Provence/Dauphiné border, as it has for many hundreds of years. Tiers of closely-grouped old houses rise from the river towards the ancient citadel. Sisteron has managed to retain its essentially medieval appearance thanks partly to a tunnel through the hillside which keeps through-traffic away from the town, leaving the winding covered streets free from congestion. Fine views are obtained from the terrace of the citadel, which also contains an open-air theatre. There is superb mountainous and wooded country nearby and a trip up the valley of the Vançon to the east takes one through spectacular scenery.

What to see Citadel (13–16c); Upper Valley of the Vançon.

TARASCON (Bouches-du-Rhône)

Situated on the left bank of the Rhône at the spot where a suspension bridge crosses the river to Beaucaire (qv), Tarascon huddles beneath the massive walls of the Castle of Good King René. The castle, begun in the 12th century, was originally intended to guard the Provence border but was used as a prison for a number of years prior to 1926. It is now open to the public and is marvellously evocative of medieval chivalry and skulduggery. In the 18th century, during its time as a prison, British seamen scratched graffiti on the walls. Among details of ships and dates, is a rhyme which runs

Here be three Davids in one Mess
Prisoners we are in Distress
By the French we was caught
And to this prison we was brought.

Other places of interest include the local church, dedicated to St-Martha who, according to legend, delivered the region from la Tarasque, a grotesque creature who was pillaging the town. Tarascon has also acquired notoriety as the home of the hero of Alphonse Daudet's novel 'Tartarin de Tarascon', which depicts the local people as somewhat ridiculous and has earned the author no popularity in the town.

What to see Castle (12–15c); Church of St-Martha (12–14c).

THOR (LE) (Vaucluse)

A small town, beside the River Sorgue, which is a market for local grapes. Vestiges of the medieval defences can still be seen and the local church contains some unusual Gothic features. A limestone cave, the Grotte-de-Thouzon with a long passage full of weird and delicately-shaded stalactites and stalagmites, lies some two miles to the north.

What to see Church (13c); Grotte-de-Thouzon.

THORONET (ABBAYE DU) (Var)

This former Cistercian abbey is situated in an isolated valley surrounded by wooded hills 9km (6 miles) south-west of Lorgues. The Provençal/Romanesque church, its cloisters and conventual buildings, are all austere and date from the 12th century. Its chapter house contains the abbey's only decorative sculptures (on the capitals of its columns).

TOULON (Var)

Since the time of Richelieu and Louis XIV this town has been France's most important naval base, and it is now known also as a port for merchant shipping and pleasure boats. The town and colourful Old Port have been restored following World War II damage, the modern buildings harmonising well with their older surroundings. There is much to see in the old town with its colourful Rue d'Alger (main street), the Place Puget with a dolphin fountain, and the Vieille Darse (old harbour).

The atmosphere at the covered fish market is best savoured in the morning, when a wide variety of Mediterranean fish is offered for sale, and there is a busy vegetable and flower market on the Cours Lafayette. Other attractions include the Tour Royale (part of the former fortifications) and various museums. The Naval Arsenal cannot be visited by foreigners. A fine view of Toulon is obtained from Mount Faron Corniche and there are boat trips from the Stalingrad Quay.

What to see Alexandre I Garden; Art and Archaeological Museum; Harbour; Historical Museum of Old Toulon; Markets; The Mount Faron Corniche; Naval Museum; Rue d'Alger; Tour Royale (early 16c); Vieille Darse.

UZÈS (Gard)

The towers of Uzès' ducal castle (le Duché), with flags flying, and the tall Italianate campanile of its cathedral, rise against the sky and give this old city a romantic air. All that remains of the original cathedral is the light and graceful windowed 17th-century Tour Fenestrelle, quite unlike any other building in France. Around the castle, once the seat of the premier Duke of France, are mansions and a maze of arcaded streets.

Displayed at the Museon di Rodo (Museum of the Wheel) are vintage cars, velocipedes and model trains. All worth seeing, if only as a detour when visiting the Pont du Gard (qv), the Roman aqueduct which is only 16km (10 miles) from Uzès.

What to see Cathedral of St-Théodrit (12–17c); Crypt (2c); Duché; Museon di Rodo.

The Emperor's Isle

Lying only 182km (112 miles) from the southern coast of France is the beautiful scented island of Corse (Corsica). Named from the Phoenician word meaning 'covered', much of the island has a fragrant vegetation of rosemary, lavender, myrtle and juniper – a wonderful diversity of plants. Ski-ing lasts until May on Mount Cinto, at 2,700m (8,775ft) the island's highest mountain, but summer comes earlier to the coast and from early spring Corse is alive with visitors to its clifftop villages, sandy beaches and harbours.

The island was bought by the French in 1768 – just two years before Napoleon's birth. Maison Bonaparte in Bastia, the island's capital and Napoleon's birthplace, is now a museum; and every small village seems to have a street bearing his name.

But most visitors will remember Corse for its little towns, its wild hills, its golden beaches and its warm and fragrant air.

Villefranche was once the stronghold of kings. Now, with its beautiful bay, it is a popular holiday resort

VAISON-LA-ROMAINE (Vaucluse)

Lying amid wooded hills on the banks of the River Ouvèze, Vaison-la-Romaine is famous for its Roman city, where the foundations of mansions, gardens, paved streets and a small theatre give a good idea of the lay-out of a small Roman settlement. These remains have been little disturbed as the medieval town was built beside, and not above, the Roman city. There is a museum containing items found during the excavations. A 2,000-year-old bridge across the Ouvèze links the Roman area to the 'Haute Ville', the medieval town which has a 12th-century castle, an old cathedral, narrow alleys and attractive squares. This is a lovely place to visit in spring or early summer when flowering trees and shrubs add enchantment to the town and its surroundings.

What to see Castle ruin (views); Cathedral of Notre-Dame (11–13c); Medieval town; Roman bridge; Roman city and museum.

VILLEFRANCHE (Alpes-Maritimes)

The older part of this fishing port and holiday resort rises behind the harbour in a jumble of steep streets, steps, and covered alleys. It overlooks a most beautiful bay embraced by wooded hills, and from the waterfront one can look across to the hillside gardens of Cap Ferrat. The 14th-century Chapel of St-Pierre, once used by fishermen to store nets, was handed over in 1957 to Jean Cocteau who restored and decorated it. His paintings have an appealing simplicity.

What to see Citadel (16c); Chapel of St-Pierre; Rue Obscure.

VILLENEUVE-LÈS-AVIGNON (Gard)

Although almost a suburb of Avignon (qv), Villeneuve-lès-Avignon (lès with a grave accent means 'near') contains a number of interesting old buildings including the splendid Fort St-André which stands on a commanding hilltop, its twin towers flanking its only gate. When the Popes moved to Avignon, the Cardinals built their palaces across the river at Villeneuve and brought prosperity to what had until then been a small village. At the same time the Kings of France, wary of the Holy Roman Empire, fortified their side of the bridge. Reminders of this period, apart from the Fort, are the Tour de Philippe-le-Bel and the Val de Bénédiction Charterhouse.

What to see Abbaye St-André (founded in 10c); Church (14c); Fort St-André (14c); Municipal Museum (art collection); Tour de Philippe-le-Bel (13c); Val de Bénédiction Charterhouse (12–18c)

From the Alps to Alsace

The glittering peaks of Mont Blanc are seen from the lush, green hills of Hauteluce

Each province of France's eastern border has its own distinctive character. Alsace and Lorraine, divided by the magnificent Vosges mountains, have cultural ties with the German Rhineland. There are wide tracts of rolling forest and farmland, picturesque villages in the vine-growing Vosges foothills, old towns like Colmar and elegant cities such as Nancy.

South of Alsace the Jura range, gentler than the imposing Alps still further south, forms France's boundary with Switzerland – its rich greenery contrasting with its many jagged rock outcrops.

In Dauphiné and Savoie the Alps act as a climatic as well as a physical barrier. Olive trees grow in the southern foothills of Dauphiné where it merges into Provence while eternal snows and icefields cover the peaks of the northern Mont Blanc massif. This is a land of deep valleys, spa towns with their echoes of faded gentility, rivers, azure lakes and lively winter sports resorts.

FROM THE ALPS TO ALSACE

Alsace-Lorraine It has been Alsace-Lorraine's dilemma to have been one of those tracts of Europe over which nations have incessantly waged war. Even after the threat of English invasion had receded in the late 15th century there was the sustained menace of Prussian expansion as Napoleon III's power waned. Thus all of Alsace and much of the north of Lorraine displays a sort of split personality, its people speaking a Germanic dialect, living in typically Rhineland houses, clustered in towns with distinctly German names, and yet, like many peoples rescued from unwelcome occupation, fervently patriotic.

Today the least perceptive traveller will recognise that French France ends on Lorraine's plateau near Nancy while, to the north and the east, architecture, cuisine, language and industrial endeavour show Germanic influence.

Neither region is all industry. From Nancy north to the border is a region of outstanding natural beauty, part of it national park, with dense woodlands the haunt of boar and deer herds. South of Nancy are the spa towns and villages such as Vittel, Bains-les-Bains and Plombières, and the birthplace of St Joan of Arc at Domrémy. To the west the Pays des Étangs (land of small lakes) is an ornithologist's and angler's paradise of woodlands and pools.

Nancy, at the junction of the Meurthe and Moselle rivers, owes many of its architectural attractions to Duke Stanislas, an exiled King of Poland. Influenced by Louis XV (his son-in-law), he modelled the town in the mode favoured by the Court – elaborately embellished façades, imaginative use of gardens and fountains, and vanities like the Arc de Triomphe off the Place Stanislas. Nearby Lunéville received similar attentions although the miniature château, a celebration of the greater house of Versailles, predates Stanislas.

The Vosges crests formed part of the battle front in World War I and military requirements dictated the building of the road now known as the Route des Crêtes, which link these natural ramparts. Approached from the west the route can be reached on the N59 from St-Die to Sainte-Marie-aux-Mines and it runs south to Cernay and Mulhouse, taking in the major peaks of Hohneck and Grand Ballon. The mountain tops are a vigorous mile or two's walk from the road.

You can descend from the Vosges tops via several routes right into the Alsace vineyards and the fairy-tale wine villages and towns which fringe the broad Rhine Valley. From Mulhouse to Colmar and north almost to Strasbourg the vineyards follow the contours of the foothills and are dogged by another well-signposted tourist track, the Route des Vins. Look in on the most picturesque towns – Obernai, Riquewihr and Ribeauvillé – and don't miss the medieval and Renaissance buildings of Colmar's old heart.

Strasbourg, capital of Alsace, is a teeming city with a wide industrial girdle and an exquisite medieval centre. Many of the houses are decorated in the carved-wood style of the Rhineland, there is a canal quarter where the merchants traded goods brought from all over Europe by water, and a towering Gothic cathedral built of an almost rose-hued sandstone. The cathedral's clock is a famed landmark – at noon ingenious mechanisms present a religious tableau while the figure of Death tolls the hour. The quickest way of seeing the town is by the tourist train which can be picked up near the cathedral for a circle of the city's major sights. At the Rhine port – Strasbourg is still a major barge-loading centre – there are both brief and all-day river cruises to choose from.

A dazzling sun shines over Aiguille Vert and the other mountains in this dramatic range, viewed from Aiguille de Midi

French or Swiss? Thoirette, in the Jura district, cannot make up its mind

The Jura Franche-Comté is the name used for the departments of Jura, Ain and Doubs on France's border where it faces Switzerland across Lac Léman (Lake Geneva) and Lac Neuchâtel. This area was annexed in 1676 but has never lost its Swiss character. The Jura does not have quite the same reliance on dairy herds in postage-stamp fields, and there is a gentler aspect to the hills. Nevertheless the clear gushing rivers tumbling through tree-fringed meadows have echoes of verdant Swiss valleys, and the self-reliant people have a tradition of small souvenir industries like horn-carving, jewellery and pipe-making. Besançon, the Jura's main town, is a major centre of watch-making and several large works turn out some of the best of France's timepieces. Here the River Doubs, which encircles much of the Jura, loops round the ancient rock-top citadel below which the old town lies. Building styles in this hilly town, a Roman regional capital, reflect the many influences of occupying nations including brief sojourns by Spaniards, Hungarians and Prussians. There is an unusual museum of the work and instruments of apothecaries, as well as a museum devoted to the struggle of the French Resistance – the 'Maquis', as the guerillas were known. There is also a fine art collection. Frenchmen revere the city as the home of the national drink, Pernod.

The Jura has a place in scientific history, too. It was in the vineyards of Arbois, one of the three main wine centres of the region, that Louis Pasteur first studied the development of yeasts, work that led directly to his discovery of bacteria.

The wine area is unusual in that it runs across a band of country in which *cirques* abound. A cirque is a ring or horseshoe of rock peaks forming a natural bowl of considerable beauty. Major cirques in the Jura are within a few miles of Arbois – the Cirque de Baume, the Reculée des Planches and the Cirque de Ladoye. This is beautiful walking country, the many rivers tumbling to join the Doubs and the Ain (Rhône tributaries) teem with fish and the sparkling white Jura heights attract a growing band of skiers.

Savoie and Dauphiné Lying between the Rhône Valley and the Alpine borders with Switzerland and Italy are the old provinces of Savoie and Dauphiné. This is an area of enormous granite outcrops deeply riven by spectacular glacier-hewn and river-etched valleys. It has become one of the world's leading winter-sports playgrounds and a summer relaxation delight. From Chambéry north to the shores of Lac Léman (Lake Geneva) are many towns and villages that have, since Roman times, attracted visitors to take the waters. Aix-les-Bains, Évian and Annecy were three major lakeside spa resorts of the Victorians; while Chamonix, under Mont Blanc, and Grenoble, capital of Dauphiné, attracted the more active (often British) 19th-century travellers who pioneered modern ski-ing and alpinism. Much of Dauphiné and Savoie is designated as Regional Parks and Nature Reserves, the main areas being Le Vercors (south-west of Grenoble), Les Écrins (south-east of Grenoble), Le Queyras (south of Briançon, main town of the High Alps) and the Vanoise. These take in the modern ski resorts of Tignes, Val d'Isère and Courchevel.

For car tourists almost every road across this remarkable region affords glimpses of high peaks from the depths of spectacular gorges or the heights of convoluted mountain passes – try the Col du Granier over the Chartreuse massif from Chambery to Grenoble, the Col de l'Iseran through Val d'Isère on the edge of the Vanoise and the Col des Aravis between Flumet and Bonneville. A more unusual way to see some vertical scenery is to take the train. The Grenoble-Aspres line south over the Col de la Croix Haute is an amazing day's return trip; there is a tourist steam train from Pontcharra through the Bréda gorge in summer; and (again in summer and at weekends only) a private volunteer-run line above the Drac Valley from La Mure to St-Georges-de-Commiers.

Grenoble, a bustling town with academic eminence in high technology and industry to match, has a good art museum and a 12th-century cathedral. You can view the entire town and the surrounding peaks from the Parc Guy Pape, reached by cable car. To the north is the region of Chartreuse famous for its monastery, where the famous liqueur was produced. The genuine item is now made commercially in Spain but there are many small distilleries in the area selling a semblance of the herbal *digestif*. Chambéry, surrounded by raspberry and strawberry farms and a centre for the dairy industry, is a more intimate city, once the home of the Dukes of Savoie. Their château dominates the old town heart.

Places of Interest

AIME (Savoie)
The little town of Aime, north-east of Moutiers, was founded by the Romans on a site which had long been a human settlement. There is a twisting but reasonably wide road to La Plagne, a winter sports 'satellite' 18km (11½ miles) away, from where one can take a cable car to the summit of La Grande Rochette. From the top one can see Mont Blanc and pick out most of the major peaks in the French and Italian alps.
What to see La Grande Rochette (mountain – 2,505m (8,212ft)); Musée St-Sigismond (local archaeology).

AIX-LES-BAINS (Savoie)
A Roman settlement, on the shore of Lac du Bourget, which is today a celebrated health resort specialising in the treatment of rheumatism. It has retained several features from the Roman era including the remains of the ancient baths which can still be seen within the spa buidings, and a Gallo-Roman museum which is located in the former Temple of Diana. Aix has all the facilities associated with a leading resort, including a casino and an open-air theatre, and is a good centre for boat trips on the lake, for visits to the spectacular Gorges du Sierroz or further afield to Les Bauges and the Combe de Savoie.
What to see Lac du Bourget; Musée d'Archéologie et de Préhistoire; Musée du Dr-Faure (works of art); Thermes Nationaux (Spa buildings).

ANNECY (Haute-Savoie)
This ancient town is a popular tourist resort on the shores of Lac d'Annecy amid picturesque mountain surroundings. It also has a number of industries including the bell foundry which cast the 19-ton bell, for the Sacré-Coeur in Paris.

Le Vieil Annecy (the old town) is charming with its canals and narrow streets. The rue Ste-Claire, the main street, is lined with arcades and 16th- to 17th-century houses. One of the principal attractions is the 12th-century Palais de l'Isle. This is an island fortress, in the River Thiou, which was once a prison. From here there is a good view of the old town.

There is a public garden by the lake and at the eastern end of the fine Avenue d'Albigny is the Parc de l'Impérial, with an aviary and facilities for water sports. There are regular boat services to other places on the lake and a lake tour which includes the ascent of Mont Veyrier by cable car.
What to see Avenue d'Albigny; Cathédrale St-Pierre (16c); Château (part Renaissance); Jardin public; Lake Annecy; Old town; Palais de l'Isle (12c); Parc de l'Impérial.

ARBOIS (Jura)
Arbois is a small picturesque town, surrounded by vineyards, on the River Cuisance. It has retained fragments of its ramparts and has a number of 18th-century houses with wrought-iron balconies. Louis Pasteur spent his early years here and today his parents' house is a tourist attraction. Some of the vineyards, including the Vigne de Pasteur where the scientist did his early research on yeasts, may be visited. There is a wine harvest festival, the Fête du Biou, during the first week in September.
What to see Church of St-Just (part 12c); Maison paternelle de Pasteur (Pasteur's parents' house); Musée Sarret de Grozon (includes art collections); Musée de la Vigne et du Vin (wine); Pont des Capucins (bridge); Place de la Liberté (18c).

BAR-LE-DUC (Meuse)
The older part of Bar-le-Duc, with its steep streets and picturesque old houses, exists beside a modern industrial town which is the commercial centre of the region. It has fine shops and holds numerous fairs and markets.

From Bar the Voie Sacrée (Sacred Way) runs to Verdun across one of the battlefields of World War I.
What to see Church of St-Étienne (15c); Musée Barrois (local history and science).

A lively holiday centre, Annecy incorporates a pretty 'old town' where picturesque houses, bedecked with flowers, are crammed between canals and narrow streets

Taking the Cure

The principles of hydro-therapy, based on the curative properties of spa waters, are enshrined in French medical practice. It is even possible to get a grant towards spa treatments on the country's social security system.

At Aix-les-Bains you don't just drink the water. There are cures involving total immersion, pummelling with high-pressure jets, wading through deep troughs, mud packs and scalp irrigation, to mention but a few ingenuities administered by a dedicated band of scantily clad attendants and mas-seuses called *curistes*.

Cynics say that it is the clear mountain air of the spa re-sorts, the undoubted laxative and diuretic properties of the waters, exercise, the fore-swearing of drink and tobacco, and relaxing in beautiful sur-roundings that so often work curative miracles.

Even if you do not 'take the cure', many spa towns offer a wide range of entertainment, from boat trips to casinos.

BAUME-LES-MESSIEURS (Jura)

The village lies in a beautiful situation at the junction of three wooded valleys which form the splendid Cirque de Baume. Above is the Belvédère des Roches de Baume, a viewpoint in the rocky heights from which there are magnificent views of the Cirque and of the village with the steeple of its old abbey church rising above the trees. There is an interesting museum relating to crafts and trades, including a replica of a blacksmith's forge.

Baume is on the D471 north of Lons-le-Saunier.

What to see Abbey (13c); Belvedere; Grottes de Baume (caves); Musée de l'Artisanat.

BEAUJOLAIS (LE) (Rhône)

North of Lyon and south of Mâcon are the Beaujolais hills, home of the much-loved youthful Beaujolais wines. Little roads meander past the celebrated vineyards such as Moulin-à-Vent, Fleurie, Juliénas and Chénas that belong to the Coteaux du Beaujolais. At their centre is the village of Vaux-en-Beaujolais, the original *Clochemerle* of Gabriel Chevalier's hilarious novel.

Beaujolais and Beaujolais Supérieur come from vineyards south-west of Villefranche-sur-Saône.

The higher hills are dotted with woods, villages and pleasant views which provide a leisurely circular tour.

BELFORT (Territoire-de-Belfort)

Belfort has stood guard for centuries over the Belfort Gap, a pass between the Jura and Vosges mountain ranges, which provided a natural route for invaders.

The old quarter, which was turned into a star-shaped fortified town by Vauban during the 17th century but has now lost most of its fortifications, huddles on the left bank of the river while the new city spreads itself over the right. Both are overlooked by the medieval citadel which was strengthened by Vauban. Also imposing is the 72ft Lion of Belfort, a sandstone sculpture by Bartholdi (the creator of the Statue of Liberty in New York harbour) which commemorates the town's heroic resistance when besieged by the Germans in 1870.

What to see Citadel (13–17c); The Lion; Musée d'Art et d' Histoire.

BESANÇON (Doubs)

An ancient town lying in a loop of the River Doubs and almost hemmed in by hills, Besançon's outstanding feature is the citadel. This now contains three museums, one of them dealing with the French Resistance, and a well-stocked zoo. Other places of interest include a fine medieval cathedral and the impressive Renaissance-style Palais Granvelle. The town is known for its clock and watch making and a section of the Fine Arts Museum is devoted to horology. The 19th-century Astronomical Clock has around 30,000 working parts. The inventors of cinematography, Auguste and Louis Lumière, were born in the town. This is a good touring centre, with forested hills, old forts and pretty villages.

What to see Botanical Gardens; Cathedral of St-Jean (12–18c); Citadel (17c – Museum, Zoo); Fine Arts Museum (clocks and watches section as well as paintings etc); Astronomical Clock; Lapidary Museum; Palais Granvelle (works of art etc); Promenade Micaud (viewpoint); Square A-Castan (Roman remains in a pretty garden).

BOURG-EN-BRESSE (Ain)

The strategic position of the town, situated between the Jura Mountains and the Massif Central, has contributed to its prominence over the years. It is now the market for the area's farm produce and is especially noted for its poultry. There has been extensive industrial development but two old crafts, furniture-making using the wood of fruit trees and the modelling of figurines in glazed pottery, survive. Bourg has a number of fine old buildings including the part-Renaissance Church of Notre-Dame. The local museum is located in the buildings of the 16th-century monastery in the suburb of Brou. It contains displays relating to the folklore and history of the Department of Ain.

What to see Church of Notre-Dame (16–17c); Craft shops; Market; Museum of Ain (Brou).

Besançon enjoys a dramatic setting in a loop of the lovely River Doubs

FROM THE ALPS TO ALSACE

CHAMBÉRY (Savoie)

Chambéry, situated on the River Leysse, was the capital of the Duchy of Savoie until the 16th century. It is a delightful town whose old quarter is composed of narrow streets winding below the ducal château. This building was damaged by fire in the 18th century and only parts of it were reconstructed. It is now occupied by the Préfecture but organised tours take visitors to the more interesting parts, including the massive medieval tower and the chapel. The Fontaine des Éléphants, which has four huge elephants spouting water from their trunks, is one of the sights of Chambéry, and another attraction is the rue de Boigne, lined by arcades under which are little shops and cafés. Les Charmettes, where Rousseau once lived, is situated on the outskirts of the town in delightful countryside and is open to the public.

What to see Les Charmettes; Château (part medieval); Fontaine des Éléphants; Musée des Beaux-Arts (fine arts); Musée Savoisien (local history).

CHAMONIX-MONT-BLANC (Haute-Savoie)

This modern resort lies in a charming alpine valley at the foot of Mont Blanc, at 4807m (15,771ft) the highest peak in the Alps. Its location has made Chamonix-Mont-Blanc a celebrated winter-sports centre, a popular health resort and a climbing-base of international fame. A mountain railway (to the Mer de Glace), cable-cars and ski lifts take visitors to the ski slopes, and Chamonix has an all-year-round artificial ice rink and other sports facilities. The Saussure Monument, commemorating the first scientific ascent of Mont Blanc by Saussure and Balmat in 1787, is on the banks of the River Arve. The route to the Mont Blanc tunnel starts from Chamonix, making an excursion to Italy possible, and other favourite trips are by mountain railway to La Mer de Glace, where there are superb views, an ice cave and zoo, and, in summer, walks through the meadows of the lower slopes.

What to see Casino; La Mer de Glace; Saussure Monument.

Winter Wonderland

Europe's highest mountain, Mont Blanc, dominates the French Alps and is the focus of an area increasingly popular for winter holidays. The foreslopes of Mont Blanc are laced with ski-lifts and mountain railways. The premier resort is Chamonix, at the centre of a complex of pistes and smaller ski villages. Les Houches, Les Bossons, Le Tour, Les Praz and Argentière come alive during the long snow season, with weekenders and package skiers using the many lifts to the top of such famous runs as Grands Montets, Col de Balme and Bellevue. Newcomers to the sport will find that equipment can be hired, and there are top-class ski schools at most resorts. Many also have ice rinks and other indoor sports facilities.

Spectacular scenery, good food, and plenty of evening entertainment make a visit to the French Alps memorable in summer or winter, even if you do not ski.

Those wishing to find the way to the summit of Mont Blanc need only follow the pointing finger of the Saussure monument

CHAMPLITTE (Haute-Saône)

An attractive town with many old buildings built on a hillside overlooking the green valley of the River Salon. Champlitte's principal building is the castle, which today contains the town hall, and the Albert Demard Museum, devoted to the folklore and history of the region.
What to see Château (16–17c); Musée Albert Demard.

CHARLIEU (Loire)

Charlieu has been a market town since Roman times and now has many small industries and craft workshops. It lies north-east of Roanne beside the River Sornin, a tributary of the Loire, and the mountains of La Madeleine and Beaujolais can be seen in the distance. There are a number of medieval-style houses around the Place St-Philibert but the town is chiefly noted for the remains of its Benedictine abbey, including the ruins of a 9th-century church and a well preserved 15th-century cloister.
What to see Abbey (11–12c); Church of St-Philibert (13c); Couvent-des-Cordeliers (14–15c).

CLERMONT-EN-ARGONNE (Meuse)

A small town in a picturesque setting among wooded hills above the Aire Valley west of Verdun. The castle which once commanded the area has more or less vanished, and Clermont's main attraction is its proximity to the Argonne, an area of considerable charm.
What to see Argonne Forest; Chapelle of Ste-Anne (16c).

COLMAR (Haut-Rhin)

Colmar, the capital of Alsace, lies at the edge of the Vosges foothills on the banks of the River Lauch. The city is renowned for its medieval appearance, having an abundance of half-timbered, gabled homes, many of them, such as the Maison Pfister with its carved wooden galleries, dating from the 16th century. The old tanners' quarter (Quartier des Tanneurs) has recently been tastefully restored to provide the inhabitants with modern facilities whilst leaving the exterior of the buildings virtually untouched by time. The early 17th-century Maison des Têtes, decorated with sculptured heads, is now a restaurant.

Colmar is also famous for its art treasures and the Unterlinden

The 16th-century church of Notre Dame, with its distinctive elegant spire, presides over Dole, birthplace of Louis Pasteur

Museum contains many examples of the work of Mathias Grünewald and Martin Schongauer, both natives of Colmar. There is another interesting museum devoted to the works of Bartholdi, the sculptor of the Statue of Liberty in New York and the Lion of Belfort (see page 97), who was also born in Colmar and gave it numerous attractive fountains. 6km (4 miles) to the north there is a large natural park 'in the English style' but designed by a Scottish architect (1850) and called the Parc Naturel de Schoppenwihr! It is a beautiful, restful place.
What to see Ancienne Douane (Customs House – 15c); Bartholdi Museum; Maison Pfister (16c); Parc Naturel de Schoppenwihr; Unterlinden Museum.

DIE (Drôme)

A small town in the beautiful Drôme Valley with Gallo-Roman remains which include a finely decorated gateway, the Porte St-Marcel, and numerous items which have been recently excavated there and are displayed in the local museum. It is perhaps even better known for its sweet white sparkling wine 'Clairette de Die'.
What to see Cathedral (12c – restored); Municipal Museum.

DOLE (Jura)

Dole, situated on the banks of the River Doubs and the Rhône-Rhin canal, was the ancient capital of the Franche-Comté. Today it is an industrial and commercial centre and holds regular markets.

Despite contemporary developments, the old part of the town (Le Vieux Dole), clustered around the church of Notre Dame (easily recognisable by its tall spire), has retained much of its original character. Towers, statuettes in niches, arcades, stairways, and wrought-iron handrails and window grilles all combine to make the ancient houses full of interest. Dole is associated with Louis Pasteur, born here in 1822. His house, in the rue Pasteur, has been converted into a museum which contains a number of mementoes of his life and work.

To the south the Doubs Valley is very picturesque, and interesting places near at hand include Mont Roland, from where one has a fine panoramic view of the attractive Doubs plain.
What to see Church of Notre-Dame (16c); Maison natale de Pasteur (his birthplace); Mont Roland; Musée de Dole (includes local history and paintings); Le Vieux Dole.

DOMRÉMY-LA-PUCELLE (Vosges)

Joan of Arc was born in this small village beside the River Meuse in 1412. Her birthplace (Maison natale de Jeanne d'Arc) has been preserved and adjacent to it is a small museum containing some mementoes of her life. One mile to the south of Domrémy-la-Pucelle is the Basilique du Bois-Chenu. This marks the spot where Joan of Arc first heard the voices summoning her to fight for France.
What to see Basilique du Bois-Chenu (19c); Church (medieval); Maison natale de Jeanne d'Arc (medieval); Museum.

ÉPINAL (Vosges)

A picturesque town with many parks and gardens, Épinal lies on the banks of the River Moselle. It is the capital of the Vosges region and there is an industrial area to the north of the town. During the 18th century Épinal became famous for its coloured prints (images d'Épinal) and examples of this work can be seen in the Imagerie Pellerin which carries on the craft and has a shop where prints may be purchased. There are a number of old, arcaded houses, particularly around the Place des Vosges and the town takes on a colourful aspect each year in the week before Easter when a folklore festival is staged.
What to see Imagerie Pellerin; Musée des Vosges et de l'Imagerie (local history, prints etc); Place des Vosges.

EVIAN-LES-BAINS (Haute-Savoie)

A town on the southern shore of Lake Léman (Lake Geneva) which has developed into a popular health spa and holiday resort. The waters of Evian are much sought after and the town is well endowed with sporting and entertainment facilities. Pleasant gardens run down to the lakeside where a variety of boat trips run to neighbouring resorts.

GRAY (Haute-Saône)

An attractive agricultural and tourist centre built in a natural amphitheatre among hills beside the River Saône. There are a number of interesting old buildings including a fine Renaissance town hall; and the Baron-Martin Museum, located in the 18th-century chateau, is devoted to works of art.
What to see Hôtel-de-Ville (16c town hall); Musée Baron-Martin.

FROM THE ALPS TO ALSACE

GRENOBLE (Isère)

The former capital of Dauphiné, Grenoble is now the administrative centre of the Department of Isère and the principal city in the French Alps. It stands beside the River Isère backed by the Grande-Chartreuse Mountains, a setting which has earned it the reputation of being one of the most beautifully located cities in the country. It is a popular holiday resort and has all the facilities expected of a large winter-sports centre, including a 'Palais des Sports' with an ice rink.

The best view of Grenoble, and of the surrounding area, can be obtained by taking the cable car to the Fort-de-la-Bastille from which both the modern development (including the Olympic complex built for the 1968 Winter Olympics) and the old quarter, can be seen. Grenoble has a number of parks and gardens and a host of places of interest such as the Palais-de-Justice, where the ancient Dauphiné parliament sat, and several museums including the Dauphinois Museum, a local history museum located in the old convent of Ste-Marie-d'en-Haut, and a museum devoted to the writer Stendhal who was born in Grenoble in 1783.

What to see Fort-de-la-Bastille (17c); Palais-de-Justice (15–16c); Cathedral of Notre-Dame (11–13c – restored); Musée des Beaux-Arts (works of art etc); Musée Dauphinois; Museum of Natural History; Museum of the French Resistance; Stendhal Museum.

HAGUENAU (Bas-Rhin)

An old fortified town on the southern extremity of the Forest of Haguenau which was one of the favourite residences of the Emperor Frederick Barbarossa. A visit to the potteries at Soufflenheim, which can be seen during working hours, makes an interesting day out.

What to see Musée Alsacien; Musée Historique.

HAUTECOMBE (ABBAYE ROYALE DE) (Savoie)

This Benedictine abbey, founded in medieval times, underwent extensive alterations during the 19th century, It stands right on the edge of Lac du Bourget opposite Aix-les-Bains (see page 96). The abbey church, which was completely restored in the 19th century in Gothic style, contains the tombs of 41 Princes of Savoie.

KAYSERSBERG (Haut-Rhin)

Kaysersberg, once the home of kings, is now a small wine-growing centre in Alsace. It lies below the hill-top ruins of its medieval castle and has retained much of its original character. This is highlighted in the Hôtel-de-Ville and other half-timbered buildings (16th to 17th century) adjacent to the picturesque fortified bridge.

Kaysersberg is famous for its associations with Dr Albert Schweitzer who was born here in 1875. His house still stands and today contains a museum dedicated to him. The town lies north-west of Colmar.

What to see Fortified bridge (15–16c); Hôtel-de-Ville (Renaissance style); Musée Communal (local history); Museum of Dr Albert Schweitzer; Old houses.

LONS-LE-SAUNIER (Jura)

An important commercial centre and spa town situated among the vineyards of the Jura foothills. There are a number of 16th- to 17th-century buildings, particularly in the arcaded rue du Commerce which also contains the house where Rouget de Lisle, composer of the 'Marseillaise', was born in 1760. A statue of de Lisle, by Bartholdi, stands in the Promenade de la Chevalerie. The museum contains many

prehistoric items recovered from nearby Lake Chalain.

The Cirque de Baume, 19km (12 miles) to the east and the Croix Rochette are both fine viewpoints. There are also a number of châteaux within reach, including the 13th-century Château de Pin.

What to see Church of St-Désiré (11–15c); Hôpital (18c); Museum.

LUNÉVILLE (Marne-et-Moselle)

A spacious town in forested surroundings with a fine 18th-century château which earned Lunéville the title of 'Little Versailles'. The château stands in the landscaped Parc des Bosquets, where *son et lumière* performances are held during the summer. It contains a museum mainly concerned with the pottery for which Lunéville is famed.

What to see Château (18c); Château Museum; Musée de la Moto et du Vélo (motor museum).

LUXEUIL-LES-BAINS (Haute-Saône)

An ancient spa town, lying among forests and small lakes in the Vosges foothills, which retains some fine 15th-century buildings such as the former home of Cardinal Jouffroy, a favourite of Louis XI, and the Hôtel des Échevins which now contains a local history museum. Luxeuil is a

popular excursion centre and has good entertainment facilities including a casino.

What to see Hôtel-des-Échevins (15c – museum); Hôtel du Cardinal Jouffroy (15c).

LYON (Rhône)

Lyon, at the confluence of the Rivers Rhône and Saône, is France's third largest city, after Paris and Marseille. It is an important centre of the textile industry and is renowned for the manufacture of silk. The Lyon Trade Fair occurs every spring during which products are exhibited from the city's varied industries.

The history of Lyon dates back to the Romans, who settled here in 42BC. Remains from this settlement (known as Lugdunum), including baths, aqueducts and a theatre, can be seen on Fourvière hill to the west of the River Saône in the city centre. During the French Revolution many people were guillotined in the square now known as the Place des Terreaux. In addition much of the city was damaged but an area to the east of the Saône, known as Le Vieux Lyon, has been preserved. This consists of narrow streets and passageways, such as the rue St-Jean and the rue Juiverie, lined with beautiful old houses.

Today the life of Lyon is centred

The streets of Kayserberg are lined with half-timbered houses between 300 and 400 years old

around the Place Bellecour, a famous square with a fine statue of Louis XIV. The city has numerous parks; particularly fine is the Parc de la Tête d'Or (Golden Head), which has a lovely Rose Garden. There is a magnificent view of Lyon from the tower of the Basilique de Notre-Dame-de-Fourvière.
What to see Basilique de Notre-Dame-de-Fourvière (viewpoint); Museums (various); Parc de la Tête d'Or; Place Bellecour; Place des Terreaux; Quais du Rhône; Roman ruins (Fourvière hill); Les Traboules (area containing old passageways); Le Vieux Lyon (old Lyon).

MEGÈVE (Haute-Savoie)
This alpine village, at the foot of Mount Blanc, has become one of the most fashionable winter-sports and summer resorts in France and is noted for its fine hotels. It is composed of narrow streets and has picturesque surroundings of hills and fir-tree forests. Megève has excellent skiing facilities and offers a wide range of sports in its modern Palais des Sports. The resort's entertainment is varied and includes a casino, shows and night clubs.

MENTHON-ST-BERNARD (Haute-Savoie)
A small town in a lovely setting on the shores of Lake Annecy. The town has a fine château which stands on the site of an earlier building where St-Bernard of Menthon, founder of the St Bernard hospice which provided an early 'mountain rescue service' and known world-wide for the large dogs named after him, was born in 923. The room in which the saint is said to have been born has been converted into an oratory.
What to see Château (15–16c); Roc de Chère (Viewoint).

METZ (Moselle)
This ancient town, founded in the Gallo-Roman era, lies in the fertile Moselle Valley and is today the administrative centre of the Department of Moselle. Fortified during medieval times because of its strategic position at the junction of several major routes, Metz has retained fragments of its 13th-century strongpoints including the formidable Porte des Allemands, a double gateway protected by two round towers and two gun bastions. There is an attractive 'old quarter' centred

Wide streets, tree-lined quays and elegant restaurants can be found at Lyon, France's third-largest city

round the Place d'Armes where the 13th-century Cathedral of St-Étienne stands high above the surrounding narrow streets and old houses. Metz can boast the remains of what is probably the oldest church in France, the church of St-Pierre-aux-Nonnains which was once attached to a Benedictine abbey and possibly dates from around the 7th century.
Metz has a very comprehensive museum, occupying several floors in one of the buildings belonging to an old convent – it covers Gallo-Roman remains, art and natural history, and has a section dealing with military equipment since the Napoleonic era. An esplanade, laid out on the southern bank of the river and passing through a pleasant wooded park, provides fine views along the Moselle.
What to see Cathedral of St-Étienne (13c); Church of St-Pierre-aux-Nonnains (7c); Museum; Porte des Allemands (13c).

MIOLANS (CHÂTEAU DE) (Isère)
The castle, built on a rocky platform above the Isère Valley, is one of the finest and best-preserved examples of medieval military architecture in the Savoie area. The keep and the Tour St-Pierre are open to visitors and from the terrace there is a magnificent view of the surrounding mountains. It is situated about 3km (2 miles) off the N7 south-west of Albertville.

MONTBÉLIARD (Doubs)
An ancient town which, despite some industrialisation including the establishment of a Peugeot car factory at nearby Sochaux, has retained a number of interesting old buildings. Pride of place must go to the fine fortified château which dates from the 15th century. It contains a museum with exhibits relating to the work of Georges Cuvier, the 18th-

century naturalist, and Étienne Oehmichen who invented the helicopter in 1924, both of whom were born in Montbéliard.
What to see Château (15–19c); Château Museum; Peugeot Works at Sochaux (guided tours available by arrangement).

MONTBENOÎT (Doubs)
An interesting town with its own dialect, style of architecture and traditions because many of its citizens are descended from natives of Switzerland brought here from Valais centuries ago. It lies beside the River Doubs north east of Pontarlier. Montbenoît is famous for its splendid 12th-century abbey which contains some later innovations such as the intricate 16th-century decorations on the choir stalls.
What to see Abbey (12–16c).

MOREZ (Jura)
Morez is a small town situated along the deep, wooded valley of the River Bienne, which once provided energy for its industries. These now range from numerous sawmills to watchmaking and the making of spectacles, a craft which has been carried on here since the end of the 18th century. It is appropriate, therefore, that the National Centre for Optical Research is in Morez.
The town and the valley, crossed by several railway viaducts, are best appreciated from La Roche au Dade or the Belvédère de la Garde to the west of the river.
What to see National Centre for Optical Research; La Roche au Dade (viewpoint); Belvédère de la Garde (viewpoint).

MOUTHIER-HAUTE-PIERRE (Doubs)
A lovely village beautifully situated in the valley of the Loue. The lower part (Mouthier-Bas) is on the river bank, while the upper village (Mouthier-Haut) crowns a small hill. Behind is a curve of wooded hills forming the natural amphitheatre in which the village is set. It is particularly beautiful in spring when the trees are in bloom.
La Roche de Hautepierre 5km (3 miles) away has a viewpoint from which one can see all the valley of the Loue, the main peaks of the Jura and, in clear weather, the outline of Mount Blanc can just be distinguished.
What to see Cluniac priory (7c); La Roche de Hautepierre.

MOÛTIERS (Savoie)

An ancient town full of picturesque narrow streets lying in a narrow valley at the confluence of the Rivers Isère and Dorons. Moûtiers is a popular excursion centre and has a medieval cathedral containing some fine woodcarving. The local museum deals with the archaeology and history of the region.

What to see Cathedral of St-Pierre (15c); Musée de l'Académie de la Val-d'Isère.

MULHOUSE (Haut-Rhin)

Despite industrialisation Mulhouse retains traces of the fortified town which stood here during the Middle Ages. These include the Tour de Bollwerk, which is dwarfed by a tall modern building, the European Tower. The town hall (Hôtel-de-Ville) is a fine example of Renaissance architecture with an interesting painted façade. There are several museums including the Museum of Printed Fabrics (Musée de l'Impression sur Étoffes), with examples of this craft from all over the world, and the French National Railway Museum (Musée Français du Chemin de Fer).

To the south-east of the town is a good zoo with a viewpoint nearby from which one can see not only Mulhouse but the Black Forest, the mountains of the Jura and, in clear weather, the distant Bernese Alps.

What to see Hôtel-de-Ville (16c); Musée des Beaux Arts; Musée Français du Chemin de Fer; Musée de l'Impression sur Étoffes; Zoo and Botanical Gardens.

Framed in the wrought-iron archway of Place Stanislaus at Nancy, the Church of Sainte Epure

NANCY (Meurthe-et-Moselle)

A fine and spacious city with many elegant buildings, Nancy was once the capital of the Duchy of Lorraine. Louis XV gave the Duchy to his father-in-law, the disinherited King of Poland, and the hand of this monarch can be seen in the wealth of Baroque architecture. A statue of the former king stands, amidst some magnificent 18th-century buildings including the town hall (Hôtel-de-Ville) and a triumphal arch, in the Place Stanislas which was named after him. Other places of interest include the old Ducal Palace, where the history museum (Musée Historique Lorrain) is located, and the church of Notre-Dame-de-Bon-Secours where Stanislas and his wife, Catherine Opalinska, are buried. There are several museums including the Museum of Zoology which has a fine aquarium. The Pépinière Park contains a zoo and pleasant gardens.

9km (5½ miles) to the south is the Château de Fléville, which was built in the 16th century on ancient foundations and 'improved' at the time of Stanislas. It is open to the public at weekends during the summer.

What to see Cathedral (18c); Church of Notre-Dame-de-Bon-Secours (18c); Ducal Palace (13–17c); Hôtel-de-Ville (18c); Musée des Beaux-Arts; Musée de l'École de Nancy (work by regional artists); Musée Historique Lorrain; Musée de Zoologie; La Pépinière Park.

NOZEROY (Jura)

This old village, built on top of a solitary hill to the east of Champagnole, has commanding views of the surrounding pasture-land and was once fortified. The 12th-century château is now just a ruin but the Porte de l'Horloge (Clock Gate) survives and there is a walk-on part of the ancient ramparts. Some picturesque old houses line the Grande Rue.

What to see Château (12c – ruin); Grande Rue; Porte de l'Horloge; Promenade des Fossés de Trébief (walk-on ramparts).

NYONS (Drôme)

Nyons is a summer and winter tourist centre much appreciated by French families. With one foot in Dauphiné and the other in Provence, Nyons is Mediterranean in character and climate (and sometimes calls itself Nyons-la-Nicoise). It is surrounded by the warm, yellow, tip-tilted Baronnies hills with their olives, lavender fields and truffle-oaks. The old town (Quartier des Forts) has little

The Storks of Alsace

If you keep your eyes open you may see one of the really curious sights of Alsace. High over the sharp-pitched roofs, crowning steeples and perching on chimney stacks, are the enormous higgledy-piggledy nests of the white stork (*cigogne blanc*). And atop the nests may be seen the tall, gangling occupants.

Courting storks dance with much flapping of wings and clattering of bills. Two ungainly chicks are the norm, the parents taking it in turn to flap lazily away from their eyrie for a supply of food to be regurgitated into the youngsters'

thrusting beaks. Banks, churches and many homes have rooftop plinths on which storks can build but sadly their numbers have declined in recent years.

French ornithologists are trying to breed storks in captivity and hope they will mate with wild storks. The offspring are expected to home in on Alsace when they return from a winter's sojourn in Africa.

Oddly, Alsace has no stork baby mythology – these idiosyncratic birds are cherished as an unusual aerial addition to the region's architecture.

stepped and vaulted streets and small arcaded squares. The River Aygues is crossed by a single-arched, 14th-century pack-bridge.

The major excursion from Nyons is to Mont Ventoux and the villages around its huge base: Malaucène, Buis-les-Baronnies, Sault.

Due west, the great engineering works of the Donzère-Mondragon canal, locks, dam and hydro-electric system can be viewed from close by, or else from the delightful heights of Clansayes or Barry. They offer the advantage of seeing the old village of La Garde-Adhémar, the nearby romantic ruins of the Chapel of Val des Nymphes, the cathedral of St-Paul-Trois-Châteaux, and the colourful perched village of St-Restitut, whose decorated Romanesque church and funerary tower should not be missed.

OBERNAI (Bas-Rhin)

Obernai, situated at the foot of Mont Ste-Odile, is one of the most picturesque towns in Alsace. It is best seen unhurriedly and on foot, walking round the surviving ramparts, narrow lanes and lovely old buildings. The latter include the Hôtel de Ville (town hall), the Ancienne Halle aux Blés (Corn Exchange) and houses dating from the Gothic and Renaissance periods. The Place de l'Étoile is especially attractive, with its half-timbered houses.
What to see Ancienne Halle aux Blés (16c); Hôtel de Ville; Place de l'Étoile; Place du Marché (market square); Puits aux Six-Seaux (six-bucket well); Tour de la Chapelle (13c and 16c).

ORNANS (Doubs)

This is an attractive village situated on the banks of the River Loue. It has a number of industries including saw-mills, machine-knitting and the making of kitchen furniture. The houses are old and full of character, particularly those on the river bank which are floodlit during the tourist season. These are best appreciated from the Grand Pont (bridge).

Ornans is associated with the mathematician Pierre Vernier (17th century) and the painter of 'social realism' Gustave Courbet (19th century) who were born here. Courbet's house, one of the many that practically rise out of the river, contains a museum dedicated to him.
What to see Grand Pont; Hôtel de Grospain (15c); Musée Courbet.

OSSELLE (GROTTES D') (Doubs)

The Grottes d'Osselle were discovered in the 13th century and have been visited since 1504. They are a fine collection of chambers and galleries with examples of stalagmites and stalactites. The caves are 9km (5½ miles) north-west of Quingey which is on the N83 south of Besançon.

PESMES (Haute-Saône)

This old town is beautifully situated on the River Ognon about 20km (13 miles) south of Gray. Its many narrow lanes are lined with houses dating from the Renaissance period. A good view of Pesmes can be obtained from the river bridge.
What to see Bridge over river, south of Pesmes (viewpoint); Houses by the River Ognon and on the island of the Sauvageonne.

PLOMBIÈRES-LES-BAINS (Vosges)

Plombières-les-Bains is an attractive spa and holiday resort in the lovely Augronne Valley, famous since Roman times for the health-giving properties of its waters.

There are a number of arcaded houses, dating from the 18th century, and the Thermal Buildings contain the remains of a Roman bath. There is also a gallery devoted to the works of painter Louis Français, a native of the town, and his contemporaries such as Corot and Diaz. Plombières is a very pleasant place to stay and there are many places to visit nearby. These include the awesome Valley of the Rocks, waterfalls, and the wooded valley of the Semouse.
What to see Musée Louis-Français; National Park (rare trees); Thermal Buildings.

Old houses on the rock face at Pont-en-Royans

POLIGNY (Jura)

The countryside around the little town of Poligny is fertile and productive and the town is known for the manufacture of a gruyère-type cheese and for its wine. The town itself is situated at the mouth of a blind valley, the Culée de Vaux, and is overlooked by the rocky heights of Grimont and Croix du Dan, where there is a viewpoint. There are some 17th-century houses with carved wooden doors in the Grande-Rue; and in the Hôtel-Dieu, which also dates from the 17th-century, there is a well-preserved pharmacy. Poligny is situated in a beautiful touring area, with deep narrow valleys such as those at Cirque de Baume and Cirque du Fer à Cheval, and vineyards on the hillsides of the Seille Valley.
What to see Croix du Dan (viewpoint); Hôtel-Dieu (17c – pharmacy).

PONT-À-MOUSSON (Meurthe-et-Moselle)

An industrial town on the banks of the River Moselle. A number of picturesque old arcaded buildings may be seen around the Place Duroc and in the nearby rue Clemenceau. Pont-a-Mousson has a relatively modern abbey and a fine town hall (Hotel-de-Ville), both dating from the 18th century.
What to see Abbaye des Prémontrés (18c); Church of St-Laurent (15–19c); Church of St-Martin (14–18c); Hôtel-de-Ville (18c).

PONTARLIER (Doubs)

An old town concerned with the manufacture of cheese, Pernod and chocolate and situated on the River Doubs at the entrance to one of the most attractive valleys in the region. There are several interesting old buildings including an 18th-century triumphal arch built in honour of Louis XV.

PONT-EN-ROYANS (Isère)

A picturesque village above the River Bourne at the entrance to the gorge; old houses lean perilously over the river bank. A fine view of the impressive scenery may be obtained by ascending to the Panorama des Trois Châteaux via a stairway from the Place de la Porte-de-France. The town lies on the dramatic road which runs south-west from Grenoble through the Gorges of the Bourne.
What to see Panorama des Trois Châteaux (viewpoint).

PRALOGNAN (Savoie)

An attractive Alpine resort surrounded by pine forests and a favourite centre for exploring the Vanoise National Park, a superb area of mountains, deep valleys and small lakes. From Pralognan a mountain railway runs to La Chollière where fields round about are filled with narcissi, gentian and other flowers in season.

What to see La Chollière (viewpoint); Mont Bochor (viewpoint – cable-car available).

REMIREMONT (Vosges)

This old town, set on the banks of the river Moselle, was associated with the convent which existed until the Revolution. Some parts of the abbey have survived, the best example being the Ancien Palais Abbatial (abbess's lodging). One of the most picturesque parts of Remiremont is the rue Charles-de-Gaulle with its lovely arcaded shops. The Promenade du Calvaire commands a splendid view of Remiremont and its surroundings.

What to see Ancien Palais Abbatial (medieval – now the Palais de Justice); Musée Charles-Friry (mementoes of the nuns of the abbey); Musée Municipal (local history); Promenade du Calvaire (viewpoint); rue Charles-de-Gaulle.

RIBEAUVILLÉ (Haut-Rhin)

The old town of Ribeauvillé lies at the foot of the Vosges and is overlooked by three châteaux, the ruined Château du Haut-Ribeaupierre, Château de St-Ulrich which dates from the 12th to 14th centuries and is worth exploring, and the Château de Girsberg which was abandoned in the 16th century. Ribeauvillé is famous both for the production of wine and as a holiday resort.

Much of the original walls and towers from the town's fortifications have remained intact including the infamous Tour des Bouchers (Butchers' Tower) and the Nids de Cigognes, two old towers at the south and east entrances to the town which are favourite spots for storks to build their nests. Ribeauvillé also contains many 16th- to 17th-century houses which line streets like the Grand Rue and the rue des Juifs.

During the summer the town is the venue for two popular events – the July wine market and Le Pfifferday (Strolling Musicians' Day) on the first Sunday in September. The latter is light-hearted with a procession, folk celebrations and free wine-tasting.

What to see Fountain; Nids de Cigognes; Old Houses (16–17c); Pfifferhus (Musician's house); Tour des Bouchers (part 13c).

RIQUEWIHR (Haut-Rhin)

An attractive little wine-producing town in the centre of the sinuous Route du Vin from Marlenheim to Thann, which links many delightful wine villages. Riquewihr has retained much of its medieval character and vestiges of the ancient defences, such as the 13th-century Dolder Gate, have survived. There are also a number of ornate 16th- and 17th-century mansions, many of them with fine courtyards, around the rue Général-de-Gaulle. The castle, with its postal museum, is also located in this area and there is a museum of archaeology in the Dolder Tower.

What to see Castle (16c); Dolder (13c); Rue and Cours des Juifs; Musée d'Histoire des PTT d'Alsace (Postal); Maison Preiss-Zimmer (17c).

ROANNE (Loire)

Founded in Roman times, Roanne is now a busy port located on the Roanne to Digoin Canal. The remnants of its feudal castle can still be seen in the centre of the town and there is an interesting museum containing Gallo-Roman remains and medieval pottery etc. Roanne makes a centre from which to visit the Gorges de la Loire, to the south, and Ambierle's church and museum of the peasant past, to the west.

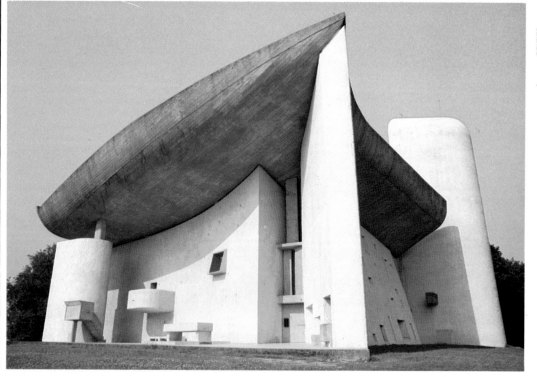

Le Corbusier's unusual chapel, shaped like a nun's headdress, is Ronchamp's most famous building

Eaux de Vie

The Eaux-de-Vie (Waters of Life) of Alsace bring a spasm to the throat and tears to the eyes. These spirits, distilled from cultivated and hedgerow fruits, have a minimum alcoholic strength of 90° proof and are produced at the wine villages in the Vosges foothills of the Rhine Valley.

Jean-Paul Mette of Ribeauvillé is a dedicated distiller who made his first brew at the age of 15 and has stayed single and single-minded in his quest for spirits which truly capture the natural flavours of the fruits from which they are made. Doing everything himself, his year progresses from strawberries to the autumn crop of wild fruits such as rowan berries. Each fruit is fermented naturally and is then distilled twice.

Eaux-de-Vie, which should be mellowed for at least three years, are drunk at room temperature and taken as *digestifs*.

Many distillers like Mette are proud to show visitors their stills – but beware the potency of the samples proffered!

RONCHAMP (CHAPELLE) (Haute Saône)

A small industrial town in a charming valley, Ronchamp is famous for the Chapel of Notre-Dame-du-Haut which stands on a hilltop above the town. Built in 1955, to a most unusual design by the architect Le Corbusier, the chapel combines a stark white façade with an extraordinary wing-shaped roof. It is a most impressive site when first viewed against its backdrop of rolling green hills.

What to see Chapel of Notre-Dame-du-Haut (20c).

ROUFFACH (Haut-Rhin)

An ancient town in a well-known wine-producing area. In the Place de la République is the medieval Sorcerers' Tower (Tour des Sorcières) which is sometimes chosen by nesting storks, and there are some interesting old houses both here and in the rue Poincaré.

ST-CLAUDE (Jura)

An industrious town in a most attractive situation at the confluence of the Rivers Bienne and Tacon which attracts visitors to its craft workshops. St-Claude is famous for the manufacture of briar pipes, a trade which has flourished here since the 19th century. Examples, some of them richly decorated and shaped into human heads, are on display in a local museum and the craft of fashioning briars may be seen at local workshops. Another museum deals with diamond-cutting which is also one of St-Claude's industries.
What to see Cathedral of St-Pierre (14–18c); Exposition de diamants et pierres fines (precious stones); Exposition de Pipes.

ST-DIÉ (Vosges)

A cathedral town standing on the River Meurthe amid attractive wooded scenery. St-Dié's main claim to fame is that the 'Cosmographia Universalis', the first document to refer to 'America' by that name, was printed on a local press in 1507. A copy of this publication is on display in the local library (Bibliothèque Municipale).
What to see Cathedral of St-Dié (14–18c).

ST-ÉTIENNE (Loire)

Although St-Étienne is a heavily industrialised town, with a thriving steel industry centred on one of the largest coalfields in the country, it is also a popular tourist centre due mainly to its location in the midst of beautiful hill country. Places of interest in the city include the Museums of Art and Industry, Mining and Arms. Just on the outskirts there are woods to walk in, rocky heights and charming villages. A favourite excursion is to Mont Pilat, particularly to see the alpine flowers on its slopes.
What to see Cathedral of St-Étienne (15–16c); Col du Grand Bois (woodlands); Musée d'Armes; Musée d'Art et d'Industrie; Musée de la Mine.

An elegant 18th-century town hall graces Salins-les-Bains which has stood by the river for centuries

ST-GERVAIS-LES-BAINS (Haute-Savoie)

A year-round holiday resort right in the heart of the Alps at the entrance to the Montjoie Valley which has all the facilities of a major winter sports centre. St-Gervais is both spa and climatic health centre and is a traditional starting-point for the ascent of Mont Blanc. There is a cable-railway service to the well-known viewpoint Le Nid d'Aigle (the Eagles' Nest).
What to see Le Nid d'Aigle (viewpoint).

ST-JEAN-DE-MAURIENNE (Savoie)

Once the capital of Maurienne, the little market town of St-Jean stands in a deep valley at the confluence of the Rivers Arc and Arvan. The town has retained many of its old buildings including the cathedral, which contains some fine examples of early sculptures and woodcarvings.
What to see Cathedral of St-Jean-Baptiste (11–15c).

ST-NIZIER-DU-MOUCHEROTTE (Isère)

A lovely little summer and winter resort in a magnificent location below the Moucherotte Mountain south-west of Grenoble. Fine views of the surrounding alpine scenery may be obtained from the Belvédère in the town or from the summit of Mt Moucherotte, which can be reached by cable-railway.
What to see Belvédère (viewpoint) Church (18c); La Moucherotte (viewpoint – via cable-railway).

SALINS-LES-BAINS (Jura)

Its setting in the beautiful Furieuse Valley is the chief attraction of Salins-les-Bains. It is a minor health resort but the treatments offered at the Thermal Establishment do not make much use of the local salt water springs from which the town's name is derived. The salt mines, which have been worked here since Roman times, are open to the public during the summer months and a visit to the underground galleries to see the salt-extraction process makes an interesting outing. Salins is an old-established town and traces of its feudal defences can still be seen. There is an interesting Gothic church and a 17th-century hospital (Hôtel-Dieu) which has a pharmacy with a fine collection of earthenware pots and dishes once used in preparing medicines.

A marvellous panorama from Burgundy to the Alps can be seen from Mont Ponpet, to the north.
What to see Hôtel-Dieu (17c); Les Salines (salt mines).

SAMOËNS (Haute-Savoie)

This alpine village is a small summer and winter-sports resort in a striking position at the foot of limestone cliffs and surrounded by pine forests. There are ski-lifts and cable cars to take you to the fine snow slopes above the town. The alpine garden 'Jaÿsinia', on a sloping site, covers three hectares with zig-zag paths and waterfalls, as well as fine displays of plants. Samoëns is an ideal base for those who wish to venture into the upper Valley of the Giffre, and there are several pleasant local walks for those preferring less strenuous exercise.
What to see 'Jaÿsinia' alpine garden.

SAVERNE (Bas-Rhin)

An ancient town, noted for the cultivation of roses, lying at the foot of the Vosges Mountains in pleasant wooded surroundings. A number of fine old buildings may be seen around the Grand Rue area but pride of place must go to the Rohan Château, the former residence of the Bishops of Strasbourg, which dates predominantly from the 18th century and has a superb north façade. It contains a fascinating museum of regional archaeology and history.
What to see Old Château (16c); Rohan Château (17–18c).

STRASBOURG (Bas-Rhin)

Situated on the River Rhine and honeycombed by its tributary the Ill, Strasbourg has been strategically important since pre-Roman times. The city emerged from the Middle Ages as a thriving industrial port and university centre and, in more recent times, has become the seat of the Council of Europe. Strasbourg retains more than a flavour of its past, especially in the riverside area known as Petite France, where old covered bridges and half-timbered houses line the waterfront; and around the Place de la Cathédrale where several museums and the château, which contains an extensive museum, are to be found. The Cathedral of Notre-Dame is noted chiefly for its astronomical clock, dating from 1838. Strasbourg's museums include one devoted to religious art (Musée de l'Oeuvre Notre-Dame) and the Musée Historique which has a section dealing with military uniforms and weapons.

Strasbourg is a noted tourist and conference centre and has good sporting and entertainment facilities, including trips by boat around the old port area.

What to see Cathedral of Notre-Dame (10–11c); Château des Rohan (18c); Musée Alsacien (local folklore etc); Musée d'Art Moderne.

THANN (Haut-Rhin)

Thann, a small town situated on the River Thur at the southern end of the Route du Vin, contains picturesque half-timbered buildings and remnants of its former fortifications. It has a very fine collegiate church which dates from the Gothic period and is particularly noted for its western doorway and beautifully carved interior woodwork.

What to see Collégiale St-Thiébaut (Gothic); Oeil de la Sorcière (part of the ruined Engelbourg château); Tour des Sorcières (Witches' Tower).

THONON-LES-BAINS (Haute-Savoie)

An interesting little resort and thermal spa perched on the mountainside overlooking Lac Léman (Lake Geneva). Thonon has a modern harbour and sports and entertainment facilities, and there is a group of picturesque fishermen's houses. Places of interest include the Musée du Chablais dealing with regional folklore, and the Church of St-Hippolyte noted for its fine internal stonework and its 12th-century crypt. There are lovely views of the lake from the terraces of the Place du Château, and from the gardens which overlook the old fishing quarter of Rives. Trips out include expeditions by boat to the pretty villages, such as Yvoire, on the lakeside.

What to see Church of St-Hippolyte (12–17c); Jardin Anthoinoz and Jardin Anglais (gardens); Musée du Chablais; Place du Château.

TOURNON (Ardèche)

Busy Tournon on the right bank of the Rhône faces Tain-Hermitage and its celebrated vineyards on the left bank. Impressive granite cliffs form the town's backdrop, pierced by roads which lead into the varied hill-country of the Vivarais. Steam-train excursions by the Chemins de fer du Vivarais between Tournon and Lamastre (and return) pass through the Gorges du Doux. 21km west of Lamastre, at St-Agrève, is another railway enthusiasts' steam-train run by Chemins de fer de Haut-Vivarais for a slow and enjoyable trip as far as Dunières and back.

By car, the round-trip between Tournon and St-Peray by the Corniche du Rhône is rewarding.

What to see Church of St-Julien; Château (with historical museum and views of Rhône).

VAL D'ISÈRE (Savoie)

Once a remote alpine village, Val d'Isère has developed into a popular summer and winter resort with excellent skiing and entertainment facilities. During the summer months the town is widely used as an excursion centre for exploring the Vanoise National Park and there is a good cable-car network serving the surrounding mountains.

VALENCE (Drôme)

An ancient town beside the River Rhône, founded in Roman times and famous, until the late 18th century, for its university which numbered the satirist Rabelais among its students. Napoleon, aged 16, attended the School of Artillery in 1785. The old quarter with its network of narrow lanes is dominated by the imposing Cathedral of St-Apollinaire which contains a monument to Pope Pius VI who died here in exile in 1799. Adjoining the cathedral is the 18th-century former Bishop's Palace which is now a museum devoted mainly to 18th-century works of art.

What to see Cathedral of St-Apollinaire (17–19c); Church of Notre-Dame-de-Soyons (17c); Maison-des-Têtes (Renaissance mansion); Museum.

VALLON-PONT D'ARC (Ardèche)

This is a lively little summer resort on the River Ardèche. It is the base from which to visit the handsome Gorges de l'Ardèche, either by car along D290 which follows the twists and turns of the river along its left bank, or else by boat between Pont d'Arc and St Martin-d'Ardèche. Gorges, rocky pinnacles, caves and belvederes follow in spectacular succession; at Pont d'Arc the river is arched over by an immense natural rock-formation.

Just off the Ruoms road, 3km from Vallon-Pont d'Arc, at the hamlet of Les Mazes, is one of the last remaining silkworm factories; it can be visited between May and September.

19km south of Vallon-Pont d'Arc, by a winding lane, is the Aven d'Orgnac. Immense caves contain fantastic concretions of rock which are among the most remarkable of any caves in France.

A huge terrace to the south, the Champ de Mars, commands splendid views across the Rhône to Mont Crussol and a ruined castle.

Much of Strasbourg's charm lies in its many waterways

Parc du Vercors

To the south-west of Grenoble lies the Parc du Vercors, a huge national park which is rarely visited by the French, let alone tourist hordes. It is an area of peaks, dramatic gorges and green plateaux, the home of large deer herds as well as genets and stone martens.

The park's footpaths give a wide choice between gentle rambles and stiff climbs. Car tourers should not miss the gorge of the Bourne River and the Col de Rousset on the main route through the park, Grenoble to Die.

Vercors became the grave of over 700 villagers and resistance fighters in an assault by German troops in 1944. La Chapelle, the central village of the region, was razed and 186 villagers were executed. Now rebuilt, La Chapelle houses a Museum of the Resistance.

Hang-glider pilots are able to enjoy the spectacular scenery around Val d'Isère in the Alps

VIENNE (Isère)

An ancient town in the lower Rhône Valley noted for its Roman remains which include a theatre, dating probably from the 1st century, and the Temple of Augustus and Livia, an even earlier building which was converted into a church during the 12th century. There is also a well-preserved Gallo-Roman city with paved streets, villas and shops. Vienne is also well endowed with medieval monuments in the shape of the Gothic-style cathedral and the Church of St-Pierre, dating partly from the 6th century, which is now a lapidary museum.
What to see Temple d'Auguste et de Livie (25BC); Theatre (1c); Cathedral of St-Maurice (12–15c); Church of St-André-le-Bas (9–13c); Church of St-Pierre (6–12c); Musée des Beaux-Arts et d'Archéologie.

VIZILLE (Isère)

Vizille is situated in the Romanche Valley and is famous for the 17th-century Château du Connétable de Lesdiguières. Many believe the French Revolution began here in July 1788 when the Estates of the Dauphiné met in the Salle du Jeu-de-Paume (tennis court) and proposed personal freedom for all Frenchmen. Today the Château is a residence of the President of France.

VOIRON (Isère)

Voiron, a commercial and business town, is famous for its Caves de la Grande-Chartreuse. This is a Chartreuse liqueur distillery where the Carthusian monks use a formula claimed to be over 300 years old. The distillery is open to the public and is worth visiting.

WISSEMBOURG (Bas-Rhin)

This is a picturesque Alsatian town situated on the River Lauter. It was formerly fortified and contains many lovely old houses particularly in the Quartier du Bruch. There are good views from the river bridge and from the Promenade des Remparts, a walk laid out on the old ramparts.
The large church of St-Pierre-et-St-Paul has many interesting features including a Romanesque west tower and medieval stained-glass windows.
What to see Church of St-Pierre-et-St-Paul (part 13c); Musée Westercamp (local prehistory and early history); Promenade des Remparts; Quartier du Bruch.

VANS (LES) (Ardèche)

This popular summer resort lies in the southern Cevennes hills where the Mediterranean climate and flora begin to exert an influence. Les Vans makes an excellent centre from which to explore the Ardèche hills, in part by following the Corniche du Vivarais Cévenol. Villages such as Chambonas, Payzac, St-Jean-de-Pourcharesse, Thines and Bannes should be visited. Some 11km east of Les Vans is the Bois de Païolive, an area of strikingly shaped eroded rocks best seen on foot; the walk along the path known as Corniche du Chassezac takes about three-quarters of an hour.

VAUCOULEURS (Meuse)

A small town amid wooded scenery in the Meuse Valley. Vaucouleurs is chiefly known as the place where Joan of Arc stopped to request an escort on her way to the royal court in 1428. The castle in which she visited the town's governor, Robert de Baudricourt, is now in ruins but the gate through which she is said to have eventually set out on her mission, the Porte-de-France, has been preserved. The house in which Joan stayed and the church where she often worshipped can also be seen.
What to see Castle Ruins (13c); Musée Municipal (local archaeology and history).

VERCORS (LE) (Isère)

An area of dense forests and deep gorges situated between Grenoble and Valence, the Vercors was a French Resistance centre during World War II. It is chiefly remembered for the savagery of the German forces who 'invaded' the area in 1944, destroying a number of towns and killing many resistance fighters.
Attractions include the Gorges-de-la-Bourne, where the caves of Bourmillion and Choranche may be visited, and the Grand Goulets Gorge on the River Vernaison where the main road ascends steeply in a series of winding tunnels.

VERDUN (Meuse)

Strategically situated on the River Meuse, Verdun has been in existence since Roman times. The town was heavily fortified by Vauban in the 17th century, which enabled it to withstand a concerted assault by German forces for more than five months in 1916. Some of the most savage fighting of World War I took place to the north of Verdun and the town is a centre for touring the battlefields and hill forts such as Fort de Vaux and Fort de Douaumont. There is also a large military cemetery at Douaumont.
The town itself retains several features from the more distant past including the Citadel, reconstructed by Vauban on the site of a 10th-century abbey, with its famous underground passages and galleries. Double 14th-century towers guard the Porte Chaussée; the Cathedral of Notre-Dame is noted particularly for its fine 14th-century cloister; and the Municipal Museum, located in a 16th-century mansion, is devoted to local history.
What to see Citadel (12–17c); Hôtel-de-Ville (17c town hall); Bishops' Palace (18c); Cathedral of Notre-Dame (12–18c); Musée Municipal (in Hôtel de la Princerie).

Burgundy and Champagne

Known for vineyards, historic buildings and sun, the region is seen at its best at Château Berze near Mâcon

Many people think of Burgundy and Champagne as liquids, not as places; but these provinces have many attractions other than the wines for which they are justly famous.

From dry chalk uplands to lush valleys and warm hillsides, from wild areas of rocks and rushing streams to deep forests, from populous towns to areas where the skies are wide and the few people live in scattered hamlets, Burgundy and Champagne have great variety and much to enjoy.

And at the end of each day there is the hospitality, the good food, and the wine which 'maketh glad the heart of man'.

BURGUNDY AND CHAMPAGNE

Burgundy

Throughout the province architecture, art and artifacts are eloquent of the glorious and sometimes bloody history which lies behind the tranquil face of this part of France. Burgundy was for centuries an independent country but in the 15th century Charles the Rash rebelled ineffectually against Louis XI of France and the Burgundian empire came to an end.

The granite core of the province is the Morvan, around which there is low-lying land, rising again to limestone hills. Politically the centre is Dijon, ancient capital, cultural centre, and important commercial city; and the lovely little town of Beaune, capital of the Côte d'Or – the 'golden slopes' where the best of wine is produced – is the centre of the wine trade. There are pockets of industry but the province is, despite its great cathedrals and châteaux, a land of hamlets and country roads.

The Vineyards Although vineyards occupy only 1.5% of the land, its wines are Burgundy's pride. It is thought that Greek and Roman settlers introduced vines into Gaul, but their cultivation and the making of wine was revived in medieval times by Cistercian monks. As Burgundy was a centre of trade and many pilgrims passed that way, the fame of its wines soon spread.

Vines are grown in areas where the composition of the soil and the aspect of the hillsides together produce favourable conditions. The most northerly area is that around Chablis, a delightful little town on the banks of the River Serein. The Côte d'Or, between Dijon and Chagny, is divided into the Côte de Nuits and the Côte de Beaune. This gives way, around Chalon-sur-Saône, to the less known Mercurey region which produces mainly red wines. Mâcon is the most southerly of Burgundy's vine-growing regions. The time to see these seductive hillsides is in early summer when the vines are in bloom, or later when bunches of grapes hang in the sun, ripe and ready for harvesting.

The Wines Generally speaking, wines are named after the village or town nearest to the vineyard: Chablis, a dry white wine superb with seafood; Corton-Charlemagne from the Côte de Beaune; golden-sweet Meursault; Vosne-Romanée 'velvet and satin in a bottle' and very expensive; delicately perfumed Volnay; full-bodied Pommard; and fine Gevrey-Chambertin: these are some of the best wines and best-known names. With important exceptions, a hyphenated name indicates that the wine comes from a village which has associated itself with the 'known' name of the locality. Generalised names such as 'Bourgogne Ordinaire' are given to undistinguished wines. Altogether there are about 115 appellations contrôlées (registered names) which guarantee the origin of wines.

Much depends on the year, the age (most wines need to be kept for five to ten years) and the grower, as well as the region from which the grapes come. Burgundy is a good place to find out about wines and a number of firms arrange 'wine tours'.

The Countryside In the south, beyond the wild forests and lakes of the Morvan, the white Charollais cattle are bred; and in the hilly region to the east they produce, it is said, the tastiest chickens. Elsewhere farmers grow rape, grain and sunflowers in small hedgeless fields, creating a charming patchwork landscape with brilliant contrasts of green and gold; and there are warm, moist valleys where dairy cattle thrive, producing the creamy milk which has so influenced Burgundy's cuisine.

Architecture Many of the farms and churches are fortified and the villages sometimes present a curiously shut-in appearance as the farms, built round courtyards, mostly have the windowless stone walls of their barns facing the street.

Great houses and châteaux often have roofs of colourful ceramic tiles arranged in complex geometrical patterns of green, red, gold and black. This distinctive style had its origin in Constantinople and reached Burgundy via Flanders in the wake of the Crusades. Flemish influence can also be seen in the architecture of many of the castles, with their steeply-pitched roofs and pinnacles; but the glories of Burgundian architecture are the Romanesque churches of Auxerre, Vézelay and Autun, and the great monasteries of Cluny, Tournus and Fontenay.

Medieval towers and Renaissance mansion blend in La Rochepot's colourful château

Breakfast-time in the vineyard. The grapes are collected into huge tubs

Champagne

Champagne is essentially a place of rural peace, though there is some heavy industry in the north. Reims and Épernay are centres for the wine trade and lie close to the vineyards of the Côte des Blancs.

The Vineyards The fabulous Champagne vineyards are the most northerly in France. The vines flourish in the sheltered, sunny hills of La Montagne and the Marne valley. Here the grapes are grown from which a light, dry wine is made, but it is the special processing which turns this into 'le champagne' (see page 117).

In exceptionally good years a 'vintage' is declared. Vintage champagne is dated and should be made wholly from grapes of that year. It is not the names of the vineyards that have become famous but those of the shippers, such as Moët & Chandon and Veuve Clicquot, who are responsible for the blending of the champagne.

The Countryside Areas of dense woodland are still to be found in the Ardennes and in parts of the south. Wild boar are hunted, but visitors are unlikely to see any except in the controlled environment of nature reserves. Deer, on the other hand, are quite common, and so are the smaller mammals such as squirrels and martens. The Forêt et Lac d'Orient, east of Troyes, and the Regional Park of the Montagne south of Reims are large expanses of woodland which may be visited. In the south west of the province is 'la Champagne sèche' – dry chalk hills where cereals, lucerne and beet are grown; and to the south east is 'la Champagne humide' where dairy cattle browse. Here the landscape is charming, made up of undulating hills and broad, well-wooded valleys. In spring, the woodlands are full of flowers, cowslips and orchises being among the most common, and in summer the field paths are bright with scabious,

cornflowers, blue succory and many types of vetch.

Architecture The traditional houses of the province are either stone-built or, more typically in the regions where wood is plentiful, half timbered with wattle and daub infill. Farms, built around courtyards, often have a first-floor gallery covered by a projecting roof to protect the walls from the worst of the weather. At the back the roof will slope steeply to within three or four feet of the ground, making the interior dark and poky but producing an undeniably picturesque appearance. In spite of the ravages of war, Champagne is rich in Gothic architecture and decoration. The great cathedrals at Reims and Troyes are good examples.

Both Burgundy and Champagne have, like their wines, to be seen, savoured and tasted to be appreciated.

111

Places of Interest

AIMÉ (MONT) (Marne)

This 'mountain', situated about 15km (9miles) north east of Sézanne, rises to a height of 237 metres (770ft). It was fortified successively by the Gauls, Romans and Counts of Champagne who built a castle the ruins of which can still be seen. Today it has an orientation table and offers fine views north over the Côte des Blancs and east to the vineyards around Châlons.

ANCY-LE-FRANC (CHÂTEAU D') (Yonne)

This château, 18km (11 miles) south east of Tonnerre, was designed by Serlio, an Italian employed at the Court of Francis I, during the 16th century (restored 19th century). It has an austere façade which contrasts with the sumptuous interior decoration. One of the most outstanding rooms is the Salle des Gardes with its splendid fireplace and chimneypiece. The château is privately owned but there are guided tours of the house daily except during December, January and February.

ARCY-SUR-CURE (GROTTES D') (Yonne)

These caves, on the left bank of the River Cure near the village of Arcy, consist of a series of

Reflections in the River Yonne make Auxerre's cathedral and old houses doubly beautiful

limestone caves the largest of which, La Grande Grotte, has a small lake and fine examples of well-illuminated stalactites and stalagmites. From La Grande Grotte a shady path leads to a score more caves, and further along the path is the Fountain of St-Moré. The nearby village clings to a hillside above the river.

AUTUN (Saône-et-Loire)

A fascinating town and a good holiday centre, Autun is filled with narrow streets and tall buildings. It is backed by wooded hills from which comes timber for its main industry, furniture-making.

It was one of the most important cities in Roman Gaul and has retained the remains of its theatre, a temple and traces of its Roman fortifications including two gate-ways, the Porte d'Arroux and the Port St-André.

During the Middle Ages the town became famous for the relics of St-Lazare (Lazarus) which were preserved in the cathedral, but today the cathedral is better known for its fine sculpture of the 'Last Judgement', the work of the 12th-century artist Gislebertus which, unusually for that period, bears his signature. The Rolin Museum, in the former 15th-century Bishop's Palace, is

devoted to local history, with the emphasis on Roman remains and medieval art.

There are many other places of interest in the area, including the Cascade de Brisecou, a waterfall in a beautiful setting of rocks and trees, only 2km (1¼ miles) from the town.

What to see Cascade de Brisecou; Cathedral of St-Lazare (12–15c); Lapidary Museum; Medieval Ramparts; Rolin Museum; Temple de Janus (Roman remains); Theatre (Roman remains).

AUXERRE (Yonne)

A peaceful medieval town on the banks of the River Yonne, with many 15th-century and Renaissance-style houses, which has recently been declared a preservation area. There is an impressive view of Auxerre from the right bank of the river, with the spires and towers of the town's principal churches starkly silhouetted against the skyline. The most imposing of these buildings is the cathedral of St-Étienne. The abbey church of St-Germain is also worth a visit and the Leblanc-Duvernoy Museum contains some magnificent 18th-century tapestries. Auxerre is surrounded by vineyards and orchards, particularly beautiful when the cherries are in bloom, and makes a good touring centre.

What to see Abbey of St-Germain (13c); Cathedral of St-Étienne (13–16c); Church of St-Eusèbe (12–16c); Lapidary Museum; Leblanc-Duvernoy Museum; St-Bris-le-Vineux, a pretty village about 10km (6miles) SE; Vaux, 6km (4 miles) S on the Yonne.

AUXONNE (Côte-d'Or)

A former frontier town which has retained traces of its ancient fortifications and is noted for its beautiful shaded gardens overlooking the River Saône. Napoleon was stationed here during the early part of his military career and there is a section dealing with this period of his life in the local museum.

What to see Bonaparte Museum; Church of Notre-Dame (12–16c).

AVALLON (Yonne)

This small picturesque town is situated on a spur overlooking the Cousin Valley. Its ramparts, reconstructed by Vauban (17th century) and containing the Tour Beurdelaine, have survived from Avallon's former fortifications. There are a number of old

buildings including houses, the Church of St-Lazare and the Tour de l'Horloge (Clock Tower). Magnificent views can be obtained from the ramparts, the Promenade de la Petite-Porte and the Parc des Chaumes. It is excellent centre for visiting places along the Cousin Valley and for the Morvan mountains.

What to see Church of St-Lazare (11-12c); Old houses (15,16,18c); Museum (includes archaeology and works by Lautrec and Rouault); Parc des Chaumes; Promenade de la Petite-Port; Ramparts; Tour Beurdelaine (15c); Tour de l'Horloge (15c).

AZÉ (GROTTES D') (Saône-et-Loire)

This vast series of caves with a subterranean river is situated on the northern outskirts of Azé, 15km (9 miles) north of Mâcon. There is a museum in the village exhibiting prehistoric and Gallo-Roman items which were found in the caves.

BAR-SUR-AUBE (Aube)

Bar-sur-Aube, now a small market town, was the venue for one of the famous Champagne fairs held during the Middle Ages. The town's two churches date from this period. Bar-sur-Aube is girdled by boulevards built on the site of its ancient ramparts.

What to see Chapelle St-Germaine (4km (2½ miles) SW – viewpoint); Church of St-Maclou (medieval); Church of St-Pierre (medieval).

BEAUNE (Côte d'Or)

A beautiful old city in the heart of the Burgundy vineyards. Beaune was the seat of the Dukes of Burgundy during the Middle Ages and has many ancient houses and well-preserved medieval ramparts, parts of which have now been converted into wine cellars. One of the most outstanding buildings in the town is the Hôtel-Dieu, founded as a hospital for the poor during the 15th century. Its Gothic architecture has remained virtually intact and the arcaded courtyard is surrounded by well-preserved wards and kitchens, which have altered hardly at all since their construction; a museum contains works of art etc. Other places of interest include the Church of Notre-Dame, noted for its frescoes and tapestries, and the Wine Museum.

What to see Church of Notre-Dame (12–14c); Church of St-Nicholas (13c); Hôtel-Dieu (15c); Montagne

Joys of the Table

Did you know that snails (*escargots*) found in the hedgerows have to be 'parked' and fed on lettuce, thyme and water for several days before they are cooked? Burgundy is famous for snails fed on vine-leaves but they are now bred in 'batteries', for the use of chemicals has made vineyards no-go areas for snails. The local way to serve escargots is to stuff them with garlic butter and serve them sizzling hot.

Dijon specialises in mustards, delicious ginger-bread, a blackcurrant liqueur called-

crème de cassis' which with dry white wine makes a thirst-quenching drink known as Kir, and delicious ham, *le jambon persillé*, from the Morvan.

Internationally famous are *boeuf bourguignon* and *coq au vin*, which are cooked with red wine and bacon.

Champagne has excellent sausages and *charcuterie* (pork delicacies) and, in the north especially, game including wild boar. In the Aube region *patissiers* specialize in a mouthwatering savoury cheese pastry called *gougère*.

de Beaune (viewpoint); Musée des Beaux-Arts (Fine Arts); Musée du Vin de Bourgogne; Old houses and ramparts.

BEUVRAY (MONT) (Nièvre)

Here, about 30km (18 miles) west of Autun at an altitude of 820 metres, is the site of the ancient Gallic citadel of Bibracte, one of the most powerful and impregnable in the whole of the country. Fine views may be obtained from the summit including, in good visibility, the Jura Mountains and Mont Blanc.

BLANOT (Saône-et-Loire)

A small village 10km (6 miles) north east of Cluny, at the foot of Mount St-Romain, noted for its lava-stone houses and its Romanesque church. An extensive cave system riddles the mountain-side to the north and may be visited during the summer.

What to see Caves; Church (12c).

BOURBON-LANCY (Saône-et-Loire)

A thermal spa and holiday centre on a hill overlooking the Loire Valley. The spa buildings,

standing in a lovely wooded park, have been completely modernised and are mainly used by those suffering from rheumatism or circulatory disorders. Bourbon-Lancy contains some fine old houses such as the Maison de Bois, a richly-decorated 16th-century wooden building; and exhibits relating to local history and art are on display in the museum, located in the former Church of St-Nazaire, dating from the 11th century.

What to see Maison de Bois (16c); Museum.

The old clock-tower seen between colourful half-timbered houses in picturesque old Bourbon-Lancy

BURGUNDY AND CHAMPAGNE

BOURBONNE-LES-BAINS (Haute-Marne)

A holiday resort and spa set on a hill-top in thickly wooded surroundings. The waters of Bourbonne have been recognised for their healing qualities since Roman times and are particularly beneficial to those suffering from rheumatism or the after-effects of recently broken bones. Places of interest include the Municipal Museum with a section devoted to Gallo-Roman remains, and excursions can be made to beauty spots around the Plateau de Langres, an area of forests, limestone caves and springs.
What to see Church (12–13c); Municipal Museum.

BRANCION (Saône-et-Loire)

Once a strategically important fortified town, Brancion, which is 15km (9 miles) south west of Tournus, has retained sections of its old defences including its château which stands high above the town's narrow streets. The town is picturesquely sited on a ridge between deep ravines, and many of the houses, bordered by lanes, have been tastefully restored. Well worth a visit.
What to see Château (14c); Church of St-Pierre (12c).

BRIENNE-LE-CHÂTEAU (Aube)

Brienne-le-Château is famous for its associations with Napoleon, who studied at the local Military School from 1779-1784. This has since disappeared and today the town's attractions include a château, church and the Halles (market place).
What to see Château (18c); Church (part 14c); Halles (13c).

CHABLIS (Yonne)

This small town, situated on the River Serein, is known as the 'Porte d'Or' (Golden Gate) of Burgundy. For many years Chablis has been an important wine-producing centre and has given its name to the famous white wine. The town is also the venue for an annual wine festival on the last Sunday in November. A permanent wine exhibition can be visited in the Caveau Chablisien. There is a pretty view of the town and river from the Promenade du Pâtis, a shady walk by the Serein.
What to see Caveau Chablisien; Church of St-Martin (part 12c); Church of St-Pierre (part Romanesque); Promenade du Pâtis.

This elegant mansion in Châlons-sur-Marne is the unexpected home of the town's Savings Bank

CHALON-SUR-SAÔNE (Saône-et-Loire)

Once the principal Roman settlement in Gaul, this town is now a busy inland port and commercial and industrial centre at the junction of the River Saône and the Central Canal. Chalon contains a number of fine old houses, and the former hospital, dating from the 16th century, stands on an island in the Saône beside the 15th-century Tour de Doyenné, from which there are fine views. There are two museums, one concerned with art and archaeology (Musée Denon) and the other devoted to the life of Joseph Nicéphore Niepce, the 'father' of photography.
What to see Hôpital (16c hospital); Musée Denon; Musée Nicéphore Niepce; Tour de Doyenné (15c).

CHÂLONS-SUR-MARNE (Marne)

A pre-Roman settlement which rose to prosperity during the Middle Ages, Châlons is now the centre of the local wine trade. The cathedral of St-Étienne, dating from the 13th century, is particularly noted for its medieval stained glass, and the Gothic Church of Notre-Dame-en-Vaux is considered to be one of the most beautiful in the area. The cloisters of this church contain a museum of sculpture. Other places of interest include the Hôtel de l'Intendance de Champagne which now serves as the Préfecture. The 17th-century Hôtel des Gouverneurs de Châlons contains a library with a fine collection of old books and manuscripts (an unusual item is Marie-Antoinette's prayer book) and the Garinet Museum has a section devoted to Goethe and Schiller. Several old bridges, 17th- and 18th-century mansions, half-timbered houses and beautiful trees along the banks of the Marne give the town considerable charm.
What to see Bibliothèque (18c library); Cathedral of St-Étienne (13–17c); Hôtel des Gouverneurs de Châlons; Le Jard (gardens overlooking Marne canal); Musée du Cloître-de-Notre-Dame-en-Vaux; Musée Garinet; Musée Municipal (archaeology and art); Préfecture (18c).

Treasure!

Frieze on 500BC bronze bowl

A young princess of Gaul was buried near the Seine, where the river becomes navigable, some time around 500BC. In 1953 the undisturbed tumulus was discovered and her grave was opened.

She had taken with her on her last journey a solid gold diadem, bracelets, two little winged horses and other personal items of gold, silver and bronze. A complete wine service was found; so the princess too enjoyed wine, though it may not have been produced in Burgundy at that period. Most spectacular of all is an enormous bronze bowl, 1.6m (almost 5½ft) high and weighing 208kg (468lb) which would hold about 1375 litres (275 gallons). It has Gorgons' heads for handles and is decorated with a frieze of charioteers, which indicates that it probably came from a Greek colony in Southern Italy.

The site of this find is at Vix between Mont Lassois, an isolated hill, and the Seine. The Treasure of Vix can be seen at the museum in the Maison Philandrier, Châtillon-sur-Seine (qv).

CHARITÉ-SUR-LOIRE (LA) (Nièvre)

A busy market town famous during the Middle Ages for its Benedictine priory. The priory's church of Notre-Dame, modelled on that of Cluny, stands today as a magnificent example of Burgundian Romanesque architecture. It was one of the largest churches in the country until a fire destroyed the west end in 1599 and is still very impressive with a bell tower which soars above the town. A stairway links the church to the other surviving priory buildings dating mainly from the 16th century. Other places of interest include a museum dealing with local art and folklore. The river is spanned by a picturesque bridge with many arches and cutwaters, a reminder of the days when the Loire was navigated and Charité was a busy port.
What to see Church of Notre-Dame (11–18c); Museum.

CHARLEVILLE-MÉZIÈRES (Ardennes)

Charleville and Mézières were two distinct towns lying on either side of the river Meuse until their amalgamation in 1966, and each retains its individuality.

Charleville is a good example of 17th-century chequerboard town planning but is, today, a commercial area. Its life is centred around the arcaded Place Ducale (Duke's Square) which is very similar in style to the Place des Vosges in Paris. Charleville is also noted for its associations with the poet Arthur Rimbaud who was born here at 14 rue Thiers in 1854. The Vieux Moulin (Old Mill) houses a museum containing some of his possessions.

In comparison, Mézières is an old settlement which has retained its 16th-century ramparts. It is now the administrative centre and its buildings include the Préfecture. The marriage of Charles IX and Elizabeth of Austria took place in the Church of Notre-Dame d'Espérance. in 1570.
What to see
Charleville Musée de l'Ardenne et Musée Rimbaud (local folklore and Rimbaud's mementoes; situated in the Vieux Moulin); Place Ducale (16–17c); Rimbaud's house; Vieux Moulin.
Mézières
Church of Note-Dame d'Espérance (part Gothic); Préfecture (17–18c); Ramparts (16c).

CHÂTEAU-CHINON (Nièvre)

This small town, known as the capital of the Morvan, lies at the foot of a steep hill. From Roman times this hill was a defensive settlement, and in the Middle ages had a feudal château which gave its name to the town. Today there is a Calvary and an orientation table on the hill, which affords splendid views of the surroundings. Château-Chinon also has a museum whose displays include an interesting collection of regional costumes. It is an excellent centre for touring the picturesque Morvan region.
What to see Musée du Folklore et du Costume; Panorama du Calvaire; Promenade du Château.

CHÂTILLON-SUR-SEINE (Côte-d'Or)

An ancient town on the banks of the River Seine which has been extensively rebuilt following damage during World War II. A pleasant walk has been laid out around the rocky source of the River Douix, on the eastern outskirts.

Near Vix, 7km (4¼ miles) away from Châtillon, Mont Lassois, with a little 12th-century church on top, is worth a visit. It was between this hill and the Seine that the Vix Treasure (see facing page) was found. It is now in the Maison Philandrier at Châtillon and tends to overshadow the many other fine archaeological finds on display there.
What to see Forest of Châtillon; Mont Lassois; Museum (Treasure of Vix).

CHAUMONT (Haute-Marne)

An old town situated on an escarpment between the valleys of the Rivers Suize and Marne. Chaumont has a number of elegant houses dating from the 17th and 18th centuries and some medieval style streets with houses which retain corner staircase turrets. But it is chiefly known for its magnificent 50-arched viaduct which spans the Suize valley and for its fine twin-spired church which contains a number of 18th-century sculptures.
What to see Basilica of St-Jean-Baptiste (13–16c); Viaduct.

CHAUMONT (CHÂTEAU DE) (Saône-et-Loire)

A part Renaissance, part 19th-century-Gothic château noted particularly for its 17th-century stables, built on behalf of Henrietta de la Guiche, wife of Louis de Valois, to accommodate 99 horses (only the king was allowed 100!). Examples of old horse-drawn vehicles are occasionally on view to the public. The château itself still has the look of a medieval fortress. It was built at the Crown's expense for the Chaumont-Amboise family after their previous château had been razed on the orders of Louis XI, and no doubt defence was a factor taken into account when the house was built. It was this château which Catherine de Medici foisted on to Henry II's mistress in place of Chenonceaux (qv). This château is not in the town of the same name, but near Charolles in the south of Burgundy.

CLAMECY (Nièvre)

An ancient town, full of old houses and narrow winding streets, standing at the confluence of the Rivers Beuvron and Yonne. Clamecy was once famous for its 'Flotteurs' who were engaged in the transport of locally cut logs. These were made into rafts and floated down river to Paris, but the trade died out early this century. A statue of a 'Flotteur' stands on the Pont de Bethléem and the local museum contains a section devoted to this ancient industry.
What to see Church of St-Martin (13–15c); Museum; Statue of 'Flotteur' (on bridge).

Chaumont's 50-arch viaduct is one of Europe's most spectacular examples of railway architecture

BURGUNDY AND CHAMPAGNE

CLUNY (Saône-et-Loire)
A peaceful little town which developed around the 10th-century Benedictine Abbey. Cluny became a fountain of learning and philosophy during the Middle Ages and members of the original order travelled to all parts of Europe founding sister houses. Cluny was also well-known for its distinctive style of architecture and its Abbey Church, some 613 feet long, was the largest in the Christian world until St-Peters, Rome, was built. Unhappily, the greater part of the church was destroyed in the early 19th century, but the sections that remain give a clear indication of its former grandeur. The best view of the town and abbey is from the Tour des Fromages (11th century) – if you can climb 118 steps!

The town contains a number of old houses and from the Promenade du Fouettin one has a fine view. A stud farm (Haras National), built from stones of the Abbey Church, is open to the public.
What to see Abbey remains (11–18c); Church of Notre-Dame (part 13c); Haras National; Hôtel-de-Ville (15–16c town hall).

COLOMBEY-LES-DEUX-ÉGLISES (Haute-Marne)
Colombey-les-Deux-Églises is a small village situated about 25km (15 miles) north east of Chaumont, on the northern outskirts of a large forest. It was the home of Géneral Charles de Gaulle from 1933 until his death in 1970, and has since become a popular tourist attraction. His house, La Boisserie, is open to the public and his grave may be seen in the village churchyard. There is also a hill-top memorial (pink granite cross of Lorraine) which was erected in honour of this great man, who led the Free French during World War II and was later President of the Republic.
What to see La Boisserie; Grave of Géneral de Gaulle; Memorial (1972) to de Gaulle.

CORMATIN (Saône-et-Loire)
Cormatin, situated in the valley of the river Grosne 13km (8 miles) north of Cluny, is renowned for its Renaissance château. This has an appealing interior with rich decoration, fabulous ceilings and various works of art by 17th- to 18th-century artists like Nattier, Claude Lorrain and Mignard.

DIJON (Côte-d'Or)
Dijon, associated by many with Dukes, mustard and gingerbread, is one of the most interesting and historical towns in France. From 1364-1477 it was the capital of the Dukes of Burgundy and has since become the chief town of the Côte-d'Or. It is an important industrial, commercial, university, wine and gastronomic centre – the latter highlighted by the fact that Dijon is the venue for the International Food Fair every November and has good hotels and restaurants.

Once one has penetrated the outer shell of industry, the old town has much to offer with its Place de la Libération and the former Palais de Ducs et des États de Bourgogne (Ducal Palace and Palace of the States of Burgundy). One of its wings now houses the Musée des Beaux-Arts (Fine Arts) which ranks among the best museums in France and includes the immense ducal kitchens. Another interesting feature is the Gothic church of Notre-Dame. One of its towers contains the famous Jacquemart bell and there is an unusual chiming clock struck by models of a blacksmith and his family. In addition the interior has an 11th-century Black Virgin which is claimed to be one of the oldest pieces of French wood sculpture.

Dijon contains many other churches, museums and gardens and it is worth ascending the Tour Philippe-le-Bon which affords good views of the town. It is a centre for excursions, too, and makes a fine holiday base.
What to see Cathédrale St-Bénigne (part Gothic); Church of Notre-Dame (Gothic); Jardin de l'Arquebuse which includes the Natural History Museum; Musée archéologique; Musée des Beaux Arts; Musée de l'Hôpital (art and sculpture); Musée Magnin (16–19c paintings); Musée de la Vie Bourguignonne (exhibits relating to regional life); Palais de Ducs et des États de Bourgogne (part medieval); Palace de Justice; Parc de la Colombière; Place de la Liberation (17c); Rue des Forges (old street); Square Darcy (gardens); Tour Philippe-le-Bon.

DORMANS (Marne)
A little town on the banks of the River Marne, mainly noted for its Chapelle de la Reconnaissance, built to commemorate the two battles of the Marne (1914 and 1918). There is a fine view from the terrace outside the chapel.
What to see Chapelle de la Reconnaissance; Church.

ÉPERNAY (Marne)
A charming town in the Marne Valley surrounded by vine-clad wooded hills. Together with Reims (see page 120), Épernay is the centre of the local champagne industry and the town's vast underground cellars may be visited during the spring, summer and early autumn.

Much of Épernay's ancient past has been destroyed over the centuries – the town has been burned to the ground at least 25 times since its foundation and suffered a good deal of damage during each World War. Places of interest include a museum which is located, together with the library, in the 19th-century Château Perrier, which has sections devoted to the champagne trade and to local archaeology.

Épernay is a good centre for trips to places in the Marne Valley and the hilly country to the west of the town.
What to see Les Caves de Champagne (Wine Cellars); Musée de Champagne et de Préhistoire.

The huge granite Cross of Lorraine at Colombey-les-Deux-Églises commemorates Géneral de Gaulle

Putting the sparkle in 'Bubbly'

Although wine has been made in Champagne for centuries, It was comparatively recently that it became possible to control the fermentation which takes place in the bottle. Often the bottles exploded, and the fermentation produced a yeasty deposit which it was impossible to clear without losing the sparkle. In the Abbey of Hautvillers at the end of the 17th century a monk, Dom Pérignon, found that the secondary fermentation could be controlled by adding small amounts of sugar syrup to the wine. And Veuve Clicquot, the young widow of a wine shipper, discovered that by standing the bottles upside-down the sediment could be collected on the corks, which could be later replaced. Madame Clicquot got a shipload of her champagne through to Russia in 1814, only two years after Napoleon's retreat from Moscow and before peace was secure.

Grapes growing near Épernay, home of 'Dom Pérignon' vintage champagne (label inset)

ÉPINE (L') (Marne)
A small town on the N3, 6.5km (4 miles) from Châlons-sur-Marne, famous for its Flamboyant/Gothic Basilica of Notre-Dame, built between the 15th and 16th centuries on the same lines as Reims Cathedral but on a much reduced scale. The church became a place of medieval pilgrimage following the discovery by local shepherds of a statue of the Virgin in a burning thorn bush. Its interior is remarkable for the great amount of ornamentation it contains, including gargoyles which are particularly grotesque.

FLAVIGNY-SUR-OZERAIN (Côte-d'Or)
A good example of a medieval fortified town, with traces of its ramparts and some gateways and old buildings, in a picturesque setting near Flavigny Forest south east of Montbard. Not surprisingly, the place captivated the artist, Augustus John.
What to see Abbey remains (8–18c); Church of St Genest (13–15c); ancient houses.

FONTENAY (ABBAYE DE) (Côte d'Or)
Said to be the oldest Cistercian abbey in France, Fontenay lies in a narrow valley 6km (3½ miles) north-east of Montbard. The abbey was founded by St-Bernard in 1118 and achieved ecclesiastical importance during the Middle Ages, only to be converted into a paper mill after the French Revolution. It was restored to its former purpose in the early part of the present century and its buildings, including the fine 12th-century abbey church, are in a good state of repair.
At the approach to the gate is a trout pool, once private to the Kings of France and the Dukes of Burgundy. To the north are lovely beech and pine woods where one may walk.

GIVET (Ardennes)
An old-established town on the banks of the River Meuse near the Belgian border, dominated by the 15th-century Charlemont Fort. The Fort was established by Charles V and has later additions by Vauban who also built Givet Church. Four kilometres to the east lie the Caves of Nichet which are well worth a visit.
What to see Church (17c); Fort-de-Charlemont (16–17c); Grotte de Nichet (Cave).

HAUTVILLERS (Marne)
An attractive village 6km (3½ miles) north of Épernay, surrounded by vineyards and overlooking the Marne Valley. It was in the Benedictine Abbey at Hautvillers that a monk, Dom Pérignon, began the research which resulted in the manufacture of 'champagne' (see above). The creator of the wine died in 1715 and is buried in the local church. A favourite walk is to Damery, 5km (3 miles) to the west.
What to see Abbey Church (part 17–18c).

JOIGNY (Yonne)
A charming town, lying on both banks of the River Yonne, which seems to have changed very little since medieval times. Joigny is a maze of narrow, twisting streets, sloping towards the water's edge, broken up by courtyards and covered passageways – definitely a place to explore on foot. Two old churches stand in the centre of the town, surrounded by gabled, half-timbered houses, many of which date from the 13th century, and the remains of a feudal château can be seen in the shape of the Porte du Bois, a fortified gateway dating from the 12th century. There is a lovely view from the bridge over the river.
What to see Côte St-Jacques (1.5km (1mile) away – viewpoint); Old quays by river; Port du Bois.

JOINVILLE (Haute-Marne)
A small town beside the River Marne. Joinville is historically famous as the home of Jean-de-Joinville, the 13th-century chronicler. The principal building is the Château-du-Grand-Jardin, in a park stocked with exotic plants, which was once the seat of the Dukes of Guise.
What to see Château-du-Grand-Jardin (16c); Church of Notre-Dame (13–16c).

BURGUNDY AND CHAMPAGNE

LANGRES (Haute-Marne)

Langres is an old fortified town situated on a high plateau above the Marne Valley. It is picturesque with many cobbled streets, a medieval cathedral and old houses. These include two from the Renaissance period situated in the rue du Cardinal-Morlot and the rue St-Didier. Langres is still enclosed by its ancient wall, containing seven towers and six gateways, which commands a good view of the surroundings. It is also famous as the birthplace of the philosopher Diderot (1713). Langres makes a good stopping place when touring and is close to the source of the Marne.

What to see Cathédrale St-Mammès (12–13c); Church of St-Martin (part 13c); Maisons Renaissance; Musée du Breuil de St-Germain (art and Diderot); Musée St-Didier (Gallo-Roman remains, medieval and Renaissance sculpture, paintings by local artists); Promenade des Remparts; Tour St-Fergeux (1471).

MÂCON (Saône et Loire)

This town, situated on the banks of the river Saône, is known for its wine and is a commercial centre. During the Revolution many of its buildings were destroyed, including the old Cathédrale St-Vincent, apart from its porch and twin towers. Mâcon is known to the French as the birthplace of the poet Lamartine (1790) and, apart from a museum dedicated to him, a 'Lamartine Circuit' takes visitors to the places which inspired his verse. It is also worth crossing the pont St-Laurent (bridge) which commands fine views of the town and its picturesque quays.

What to see Hôtel-Dieu (18c – contains a fine apothecary's shop in the style of Louis XV); Mâconnais hills and vineyards; Maison de Bois (fine Renaissance house at 22 rue Dombey); Musée Lamartine; Musée Municipal des Ursulines (includes African musical instruments); Pont St-Laurent (14c, restored 19c); Vieux St-Vincent (old cathedral).

MONTBARD (Côte-d'Or)

Montbard, situated on the river Brenne, owes much to the naturalist Georges-Louis Leclerc, Comte de Buffon who was born here in 1707. During the 18th century he established an ironworks where the gates for the Tuilerie Gardens in Paris were made. Today Montbard is an industrial centre particularly

noted for its metallurgical industry. Buffon also created a park incorporating a small pavilion where he edited his famous 'Histoire Naturelle' (Natural History). This parkland surrounds the old château and contains two towers – the Tour St-Louis housing mementoes of Buffon's work, and the Tour de l'Aubespin. This is 52 metres high and provides splendid views of Montbard. Fontenay Abbey (qv) can be visited from here.

What to see Cabinet de travail de Buffon (pavilion); Chapelle de Buffon; Parc Buffon; Tour de l'Aubespin (local history collections); Tour St-Louis (mementoes of Buffon's work).

MONTHERMÉ (Ardennes)

A popular resort and excursion centre about 16¼km (10 miles) north of Charleville-Mézières in the Meuse Valley. It is noted for the unusual towering rock formations which ring the town, most of which are within a few kilometres of the town centre and provide magnificent views over the surrounding forests. Monthermé has a number of old houses, mainly to be found around the fortified church of St-Léger which is noted for its 16th-century frescoes.

It is a good centre for excursions in the valleys of the Meuse and the Semoy.

What to see Church of St-Léger (12–15c); Rock formations and viewpoints: Longue Roche; Roche-de-Roma; Roche-à-Sept-Heures; Roche-aux-Sept-Villages; Roc-de-la-Tour.

MONTIER-EN-DER (Haute-Marne)

The town has been rebuilt following partial destruction in 1940, and most of the 7th-century Benedictine abbey, for which it was famous during the Middle Ages, has now vanished though the abbey church, much restored, remains. The main abbey buildings were incorporated in 1811 into a stud farm where Ardennes racehorses and showjumpers are bred; visits can be arranged at most times of the year. Close by is the village of Ceffonds, the birthplace of Joan of Arc's father, where the Church of St-Remi, with a Norman tower and splendid 16th-century stained glass, is worth visiting.

What to see Church of Notre-Dame (10–12c); Haras (stud farm).

MONTMIRAIL (Marne)

An old-established town overlooking the Petit Morin Valley. It is noted mainly for its 17th-century château, completed by the architect Louvois and surrounded by gardens laid out by Le Nôtre.

An interesting excursion from here is along the D43 to the Vallée du Petit Morin on the edge of the St-Gond marsh south of Baye. Here, among poplar groves, are tiny villages, each with a few houses grouped around a church.

MONTRÉAL (Yonne)

A town of medieval appearance set on a hillock overlooking the Serein Valley 12km (7 miles) north east of Avallon. Ancient ramparts encircle numerous picturesque old houses, but pride of place must go to the splendid early Gothic church, tastefully restored in the 19th century. The church contains box pews, unusual for that period, decorated with some remarkable 16th-century carvings. There is a magnificent view right across the valley to the Monts du Morvan from the terrace in the churchyard; towards Thizy one can see a large fortified farm.

What to see Church (12–19c).

MUSSY-SUR-SEINE (Aube)

A charming little town nestling in a loop of the River Seine, which is crossed by numerous little bridges. Mussy is best-known for its church which contains so many medieval works of art it could almost be mistaken for a museum. These items include a 14th-century statue of St-John the Baptist and a 15th-century representation of St-Michael despatching a dragon. Other places of interest include the former château, now the town hall; and a museum, devoted to the French Resistance, in one of the old houses which make Mussy so attractive.

What to see Church (13–16c); Hôtel-de-Ville (15–18c); Musée de la Résistance.

Monthermé lies in a 'dead-end' valley where the Meuse turns back on itself in a tight loop

NEVERS (Nièvre)

An interesting old town situated on the River Loire, near its confluence with the Allier, which was once a stopping place for pilgrims on their way to Santiago de Compostela. Viewed from a distance the town presents a somewhat medieval aspect with gabled buildings, turrets and church spires rising from narrow streets. Nevers is famous for the manufacture of pottery and glassware, trades which have flourished there since the 16th century, and the local museum traces the history of Nevers pottery, or 'faience'. The town's principal buildings include the impressive cathedral, a mixture of Romanesque and Gothic architecture; the 15th-century Ducal Palace; and the Porte du Croux, a 14th-century tower which formed part of the medieval defences and now contains a museum of archaeology. The Convent of St Gildard contains the embalmed body of St-Bernadette of Lourdes (qv) who died there in 1879. A modern church, dedicated to the saint, contrasts sharply with its ancient surroundings. The countryside to the south, between the Rivers Loire and Allier, is a quiet haven for those who seek peace.

What to see Cathedral of St-Cyr-et-Ste-Julitte (10–16c); Church of Ste-Bernadette-du-Banlay (20c); Ducal Palace (15–16c); Municipal Museum (pottery collection); Port du Croux (archaeology museum).

Formal gardens set off Nevers' tidy houses, fine cathedral and 15th-century Ducal Palace

ORBAIS (Marne)

This little town, about 10km (6 miles) north west of Montmort, makes a good starting point for excursions in the Surmelin Valley and Vassy Forest. It was famous in the Middle Ages for its Benedictine abbey, founded in the 7th century, but only a few of the old buildings remain.

PARAY-LE-MONIAL (Saône-et-Loire)

This town, situated north of the Brionnais on the Canal du Centre, which links the Saône to the Loire, has been a place of pilgrimage since the 17th century. Its attractions include the Basilique du Sacré-Coeur (a smaller duplicate of Cluny Abbey Church) and the Chambre des Reliques containing souvenirs of Ste-Marguerite-Marie (17th-century).

What to see Basilique du Sacré-Coeur (12c); Chambre des Reliques; Hôtel de Ville (Renaissance town hall); Musée du Hiéron (religious exhibits); Tour St-Nicolas (16c).

POMPELLE (FORT DE) (Marne)

The subterranean remains of a 19th-century fort, 9km (5½ miles) south east of Reims, which played an important part in the Marne battles during World War I. A museum here contains medals, arms, uniforms and a collection of German helmets.

PONTIGNY (Yonne)

A village 18km (11 miles) north east of Auxerre on the River Serein. It is famous for its 12th-century Cistercian abbey, the main feature of which is the church, one of the best examples of Cistercian architecture in the region. During the Middle Ages the abbey gained a reputation as a haven for clerical refugees from England. Thomas à Becket (1164-6), Stephen Langton (1208-13) and Edmund Rich (1240-2) all sought sanctuary there and Rich, later canonised as St-Edmund, is buried in the church.

QUARRÉ-LES-TOMBES (Yonne)

This village, situated on a plateau in the picturesque Morvan region, is an ideal excursion centre. Two places quite near to Quarré which are worth visiting are Les Isles Ménéfrier, 5km (3 miles) to the south, where the River Cure tumbles spectacularly over the rocks; and la Roche des Fées, a granite outcrop in the Forêt au Duc, which can be reached by walking through the forest along a pretty footpath.

Fromage~that means cheese

In local markets all over the region little goats'-milk cheeses can be bought from farm-produce stalls. They come in three sorts – 'fresh' (*frais*), 'mellow' (*moelleux*) and 'very ripe' or 'dry' (*sec*).

The most famous cows'-milk cheeses are as follows. In Burgundy: Époisses, a soft cheese flavoured with cloves, fennel and brandy, which the celebrated gastronome, Brillat-Savarin, considered was 'the king of cheeses'; and St-Florentin (called locally Soumaintrin), a soft, salty yellow cheese encased in an orange rind. In Champagne: Brie (made in an area which it shares with the Ile de France), is by far the most famous; but there is also Chaource, a soft creamy-white cheese from the Aube district, which has a very agreeable flavour.

BURGUNDY AND CHAMPAGNE

REIMS (Marne)

The historic city of Reims acquired its name from the Remi, a Celtic tribe which settled here. It was then occupied by the Romans – illustrated by the surviving triumphal arch, Porte Mars, and remains of the forum. During the 5th century Clovis, King of Franks, was baptised by Bishop St-Remi. This led to the emergence of Reims as the coronation place of early French kings. Today this site is occupied by the Gothic Cathedral of Notre-Dame.

Despite extensive damage during World War I, and to a lesser extent World War II, this Cathedral still dominates the city and remains one of the most inspired masterpieces of Gothic art. Its western façade is particularly delightful with three fine doorways and a splendid rose window.

Reims also has a number of museums worth visiting, such as the Palais du Tau with its cathedral treasures, and the Musée St-Denis containing an outstanding collection of pictures and tapestries. Another place of interest is the Salle de Guerre (War Room – 12 rue Franklin-Roosevelt); this was General Eisenhower's headquarters, where the capitulation of the German army was signed in 1945. Reims is now a prominent champagne-producing city and a visit is not complete without a tour of one of the cellars.

What to see Basilique St-Remi (11–12c); Cathédrale Notre-Dame (13c); Caves de Champagne (champagne cellars); Hôtel de la

The superb west front of Reims Cathedral, still a gem of Gothic architecture despite the ravages of two world wars

Salle (Renaissance – birthplace of St Jean-Baptiste-de-la-Salle in 1651); Hôtel-de-Ville (part 17c); Musée-hôtel le Vergeur (local art – historic); Musée St-Denis (paintings and tapestries); Palais du Tau (cathedral treasures); Parc Pommery (park with children's playground and sports facilities); Place Royale (city square – 18c); Porte Mars (3c); Salle de Guerre.

RETHEL (Ardennes)

This ancient town is situated on the river Aisne and the Ardennes canal. It suffered considerable damage during World War II and now looks like a new town, though some old buildings, such as the Church of St-Nicholas, have been restored. There is an orientation table near the ruins of the château, from which fine

views of Rethel and its surroundings are obtained.

What to see Ancien château (ruin – medieval); Church of St-Nicolas (part medieval); Musée du Rethelois et du Porcien (folklore, archaeology, religious art).

RÉVEILLON (Marne)

Réveillon has a large moated château built in the style of Louis XIII. Its central building is flanked by two pavilions around a courtyard – very nearly a carbon-copy of the original château at Versailles. It lies near the N34, west of Sézanne.

RICEYS (LES) (Aube)

Les Riceys lies in a beautiful setting on the D17 south east of Troyes and is noted for its rosé wines. It has had a hectic past, being claimed in turn by Burgundy and Champagne, but retains some ancient houses and three Renaissance churches. Its attractions for holiday-makers are its recreational facilities, particularly tennis and fishing.

ROCHEPOT (LA) (Côte'd'Or)

La Rochepot, situated 15km (9 miles) south west of Beaune, possesses a picture-book château which stands on a steep hillside. Six pepper-pot towers catch the eye. This dates from the 15th century and has been restored several times since. The château is famous for its associations with the Burgundian knight Philippe Pot who was born here in 1428. Nearby is Nolay; its centre of interest is the 14th-century *Halles* (covered market).

On the Wine Trail

Beneath the streets of Reims and Épernay there are mile upon mile of limestone caverns where the casks and bottles of champagne are stored. Any of the famous shippers will arrange tours, on which all the processes of turning grape juice into the world's most famous sparkling wine are demonstrated. There are three official *routes du champagne* which wind their way through the vineyards. Following one of these is a good way to see the countryside and a map can be obtained from the local *syndicat d'initiative* (tourist office).

In Burgundy you can visit the cellars in Beaune, where, for a small fee, the visitor may taste many famous wines, and there is a *route des grands vins* taking in all the famous-name villages along the Côte d'Or. If you want to buy wine, stop where there is a 'Visitez nos Caves' sign and you will usually be invited to taste the produce before buying. The Mâcon and Mercurey areas are cheapest.

A visit to Beaune during 'Les Trois Glorieuses', the three days in November when wines are auctioned for charity and there are lots of festivities, is a memorable experience.

ROCROI (Ardennes)

Rocroi is a splendid example of a star-shaped bastion town which was fortified by Vauban during the 17th century. It bacame famous after the French victory over the Spaniards in 1643 (Thirty Years' War). Twelve miles to the south east is the Lac de Vieilles Forges, a good place for fishing, bathing, boating and picnics.

RUMILLY-LÈS-VAUDES (Aube)

This small town lies on the northern edge of the Forêt de Rumilly. Its attractions include a church, with a splendid reredos depicting the Passion, and an old manor house which is now the Hôtel-de-Ville (town hall).
What to see Church (16c); Hôtel-de-Ville (16c).

ST-DIZIER (Haute-Marne)

St-Dizier's main attraction for the tourist is the fine Motor Museum, 6km (3¼ miles) north west of the town. Situated on the river Marne, St-Dizier is largely concerned with metallurgy. There are only a few surviving old buildings, which include the interesting medieval church of St-Martin.
What to see Church of St-Martin (13–15c); Motor Museum.

ST-FARGEAU (Yonne)

St-Fargeau is famous for its 17th-century château built for Louis XIV's cousin Anne-Marie-Louise d'Orléans, known as 'La Grande Mademoiselle'. It is a splendid but rather forbidding construction of rose-coloured bricks with six towers; in the surrounding park there is a lake fed by a stream, the Bourdon. The Tour de l'Horloge (clock tower) was originally part of the 15th-century fortifications. Le parc naturel St-Hubert, a country park with deer, wild boar, and European bison, lies 9km (5½ miles) to the south east.
What to see Château (17c); Lac de Bourdon; Parc naturel St-Hubert; Tour de l'Horloge.

ST-FLORENTIN (Yonne)

A busy little town situated on a hill above the River Armance. There are a number of old buildings including a graceful medieval church, embellished by Renaissance stained glass and statuary. The Promenade du Prieuré (Priory Walk) provides splendid views over the Armance Valley. It is the centre of an area noted for cheeses, and is a favourite resort for anglers. Also in the area are the forests of Othe and de Pontigny, so it has plenty to offer the holiday-maker.
What to see Canal de Bourgogne; Church (14–17c); Forests; Rivers.

ST-PÈRE-SOUS-VÉZELAY (Yonne)

A little town on the banks of the River Cure. There is an impressive Gothic church and an archaeology museum containing many articles from excavations at the ancient Gallic site of Fontaines-Salées which lies 2km (1¼ miles) to the south-east.
What to see Church of Notre-Dame (13–16c); Fouilles des Fontaines-Salées (Gallo-Roman remains); Musée Archéologique Régional.

STE-MENEHOULD (Marne)

Situated in the Aisne Valley, Ste-Menehould has become a popular tourist centre due to its proximity to the Argonne Forest. The town was virtually rebuilt following a fire in 1719 but there are a few ancient houses in the old 'Le Château' quarter which also contains the church of Notre-Dame, dating from the 13th century and known as the Church of the Château. Dom Pérignon, the 'inventor' of Champagne (see Hautvillers, page 117) was born here in 1638.
What to see Argonne Forest; Church of Notre-Dame (13–18c); Hôtel-de-Ville (18th century town hall); old houses.

Semur-en-Auxois, with its houses and old ramparts terraced above a peaceful stream, seems still to linger in the past

SAULIEU (Côte-d'Or)

An hospitable town, known for its comfort and good food since the 17th century when it was a favourite stopping place for travellers between Paris and Lyon. Saulieu has a fine 12th-century church, noted for the intricate carving on the pillars of the nave. A museum contains much of the work of François Pompon, the animal sculptor, who was born in the town (1855-1933). One of Pompon's best-known works 'le taureau' ('the bull') can be seen in a square near the point where the N6 enters the town. The nearby forests, hills, lakes and streams of the Morvan Regional Nature Park are fine places for picnics, games, walking, horse-riding, canoeing and water sports.
What to see Basilica of St-Andoche (12–18c); Church of St-Saturnin (15c); Forest; Morvan Regional Nature Park. Museum.

SEDAN (Ardennes)

An industrialised town on the River Meuse, dominated by its extensive Château-Fort, the largest of its kind in Europe. The fortress was originally established in the 15th century but was greatly strengthened during the 16th century. The famous Marshal Turenne was born there in 1611 and the château became the seat of the Princes of Sedan about the same time. There is a museum of local archaeology and history in the château and Sedan also has fine botanical gardens noted for their roses.
What to see Château-Fort (13–18c); Jardin Botanique (Botanical Gardens); Museum.

SEMUR-EN-AUXOIS (Côte-d'Or)

This small town, situated in the Armançon Valley, is one of the most picturesque in Burgundy. It was once fortified, and some portions of its ramparts and the towers of its château can still be seen. Many of the buildings are medieval and full of character. A fine view of Semur-en-Auxois may be obtained from the Joly bridge. Nearby is the Lac de Pont, a big lake in pretty surroundings, with facilities for water-sports.
What to see Church of Notre-Dame (Gothic); Lac de Pont; Musée et bibliothèque (including geology and 13–18c works of art); Pont Joly; Ramparts; Tour de l'Orle d'Or et Musée (tower containing folklore and archaeological museum).

121

SEMUR-EN-BRIONNAIS (Saône-et-Loire)

A delightful village situated on a fruit-growing promontory. Its attractions include a well-proportioned church and two remaining towers from its feudal château.

What to see Château St-Hugues (part 9c); Church (late 12c).

SÈNE (MONT DE) (Saône-et-Loire)

The Mont de Sène, 10km (6 miles) west of Chagny, is also known as the 'Montagne de Troix-Crois' because it has three crosses on its summit. It commands magnificent views of the surroundings.

SENS (Yonne)

An ancient town retaining a number of interesting old houses and encircled by pleasant boulevards which have been laid out on the site of the old ramparts. The most prominent building is the cathedral of St-Étienne, one of the earliest of the large Gothic cathedrals to be built in France. It is chiefly famous for its magnificent treasury which contains one of the richest collections of vestments and religious objects in the country. The adjoining Palais Synodal has an exhibition of Gallo-Roman and medieval works of art and the Municipal Museum deals with local archaeology, although it also contains souvenirs of the Napoleonic era.

Sens is an excursion centre for touring the Forest of Othe and the valley of the Yonne.

What to see Cathedral of St-Étienne (12c); Church of St-Jean (13c); Palais Synodal (13c).

SÉZANNE (Marne)

A small industrial town and market centre. An attractive promenade, the Mail des Cordeliers, occupies the site of the town's former fortifications. Sézanne is noted for its fine Flamboyant/Gothic church and also for paintings by the early French-Canadian artist, Brother Luc, depicting the life of St-Francis, displayed in the former chapel of Recollets. Don't miss visiting the pretty village of Bricot-la-Ville, about 10km (6 miles) to the south west in the Forêt de la Traconne.

What to see Chapel of the Recollets; Forêt de la Traconne.

SOLUTRÉ (Saône-et-Loire)

A prehistoric site about 10km (6 miles) west of Mâcon, at the foot of the towering crag known as the Solutré Rock. The site may date back as far as 17,000 BC when it is believed to have been occupied by a hunting tribe. 1,000,000 animal skeletons (some 10,000 of them wild horses), found at the foot of the rock, are evidence of the tribe's hunting activities. There is a museum of prehistory on the site and a splendid view over the neighbouring Pouilly-Fuissé vineyards may be obtained from the summit of the rock.

SUIN (BUTTE DE) (Saône-et-Loire)

This hill, 18km (9½ miles) east of Charolles, rises to a height of 593 metres. The path to the summit passes a church and a statue of the Virgin, and terminates at an orientation table. From here there are spectacular views of the surrounding hills and valleys.

SULLY (CHÂTEAU DE) (Saône-et-Loire)

The Château de Sully is a magnificent example of Renaissance architecture, the 'Fontainebleau of Burgundy'. The public are not admitted but can see the exterior, which is beautifully decorated with square towers and an arched bridge over the surrounding moat. Marshal MacMahon (1808-1893), who became President of France, was born here. It lies 25km (15 miles) south of Arnay-le-Duc.

TAIZÉ (Saône-et-Loire)

8km north of Cluny is the now world famous Ecumenical Community, founded in 1940. Its concrete church of the Reconciliation was built in 1962; the adjoining booth sells high-quality pottery. Primarily a place of pilgrimage, especially for the young, the church and the Romanesque parish church may be visited.

TANLAY (CHÂTEAU DE) (Yonne)

This moated château, surrounded by a fine park, lies about 9km (5½ miles) east of Tonnerre and is one of the most magnificent Renaissance houses in France. It is a fanciful building with pepper-pot towers and has particularly outstanding interior decoration.

Stone Age men must have been drawn by the strange Solutré rock – a million animal skeletons found nearby show their skill as hunters

TONNERRE (Yonne)

A small town, surrounded by fields and vineyards, overlooking the Armançon Valley, A fire during the 16th century destroyed a number of old buildings but the splendid old hospital, founded by Marguerite de Bourgogne in the 13th century, has survived with the help of some 18th-century restoration. The building is notable for its enormous main hall and has some interesting old documents on display. The Fosse Dionne, on the south-eastern outskirts of the town, contains a spring of bluish-green water which has served Tonnerre since Roman times.

What to see Church of St-Pierre (14–16c); Hôpital (13c).

TOURNUS (Saône-et-Loire)

A town in an exceptionally lovely location beside the River Saône, famous for its abbey buildings which date originally from the 10th century. The abbey church of St-Philibert is one ot the most impressive Romanesque buildings in France and has a particularly fine nave and a 10th-century crypt. The refectory and the cellars, both dating from the 12th century, have also been preserved. Other places of interest include the Perrin-de-Puycousin Museum, devoted to Burgundian folklore, and the Greuze Museum, named after the artist who was born in Tournus in 1725, which contains examples of Greuze's work and sections on prehistoric and medieval art.

What to see Abbey Buildings (12–15c); Abbey Church of St-Philibert (10–12c); Hôtel-Dieu (18c hospital); Musée Greuze; Musée Perrin-de-Puycousin.

TROYES (Aube)

The ancient capital of Champagne and the chief town of the Department of Aube, Troyes achieved great prosperity during the Middle Ages due to the markets and fairs which were held there, and has been the foremost producer of hosiery in France since the 16th century.

The town has retained a wealth of artistic history and its timber-framed, turreted Renaissance houses and public buildings, particularly those in and around the rue des Chats, are a constant reminder of Troyes' glorious past. There are an astonishing number of old churches, many of which contain outstanding works of sculpture and stained glass and a

Vézelay has the feel of a medieval town though the ramparts have given way to pleasant walks

collection of Limoges enamels. Foremost among these is the Cathedral of St-Pierre and St-Paul, an impressive building with a fine medieval treasury. Outstanding secular buildings include the Louis XIII style town hall, the 13th-century hospital and the Hôtel de Vauluisant, a Renaissance mansion which contains the Troyes and Champagne Historical Museum and the Musée de la Bonneterie.

This is a good holiday centre, a round trip to the Lac et Forêt d'Orient (Lake and Forest of the East) a regional park with a bird sanctuary, being particularly worthwhile.

What to see Cathedral of St-Pierre-et-St-Paul (13–17c); Hôtel-Dieu (18c hospital and pharmacy); Maison de l'Outil et de la Pensée Ouvrière (16c); Musée des Beaux-Arts (Fine Arts); Musée de la Bonneterie (Hosiery etc); Musée Historique de Troyes et de Champagne (local history etc).

VERTUS (Marne)

A charming little town with irregular streets and little courtyards, Vertus – once an important market town – lies at the foot of the Côte des Blancs, in an area famous for its black grapes, some 18km (11 miles) south of Épernay.

What to see Church of St-Martin (12c – restored); Well of St-Martin.

VÉZELAY (Yonne)

One of the high spots of any tour of Burgundy, Vézelay is a leafy town with winding streets of picturesque old houses, some with carved doors, mullioned windows and staircase turrets.

There is a walk – the Promenade des Fossés – on the site of the ramparts which once encircled the town.

In the Middle Ages pilgrims from all over Europe visited the town to venerate relics of St Mary Magdalen, and it was here that St-Bernard exhorted Christians to embark on the Second Crusade in 1146. It was also the gathering point for the armies before the Third Crusade. This period is recalled by the Basilica of Ste-Madeleine, from the tower of which a fine view is obtained.

What to see Ancient houses; Basilica of Ste-Madeleine (12c); Port Neuve (14–16c gateway); Porte Ste-Croix (12c gateway) Promenade des Fossés.

VILLENEUVE-SUR-YONNE (Yonne)

An attractive town on the River Yonne which has retained its medieval ramparts and fortified gates, the Port de Sens and the Porte de Joigny, dating from around the 13th century.

What to see Church of Notre-Dame (12–15c); Maison-des-Sept-Têtes (18c); Tour Louis-le-Gros (12c).

VITRY-LE-FRANÇOIS (Marne)

Important during the Middle Ages on account of its strategic location beside the River Marne, Vitry-le-François was almost entirely destroyed during the Second World War. A few 17th-century buildings have survived, including the church of Notre-Dame. The remainder of the town has been reconstructed to its original 16th-century plan. It lies in an area of farms with pockets of woodland here and there, and excursions could include one to Vitry-en-Perthois, a village which was rebuilt after it had been burned down by troops in 1544.

What to see Church of Notre-Dame (17–18c); Hôtel-de-Ville (17c town hall).

WASSY (Haute-Marne)

A quiet little town, in spite of the foundries which are its main industry, on the D2 south of St-Dizier. It is chiefly remembered for the notorious 'Massacre of Wassy' when soldiers of the Duke of Guise murdered a large number of Protestants assembled in a local barn on 1st March 1562. There is a reservoir, in rural surroundings just south of the town, which is used for swimming and boating.

What to see Hôtel-de-Ville (18c town hall with interesting astronomical clock); Lac réservoir des Leschères.

The Eiffel Tower – unmistakable symbol of the city that is often hailed as the most elegant and romantic in Europe. Designed by Gustave Eiffel as one of the marvels of the World Fair in 1889, the tower then stood 300m (984ft) high, and was the tallest building on Earth. A television mast added in 1957 increased its height by 20m (67ft). Although many skyscrapers in other cities now surpass the tower's once record dimensions, it has surely won a permanent place among the world's most familiar landmarks

Paris and the North

The French like to tell people that while London was built for the English, Paris was built for the world. Both cities have their virtues but Paris, with its feeling of spaciousness and light, its good food, its reputation for 'naughty' night life, its superb art collections and the vitality of its people, has an immediate appeal to most visitors, whatever their age or nationality.

The Champs Élysées, probably Europe's most famous street, breathes luxury from its hotels, airline offices, expensive shops and smart cafés. It is truly cosmopolitan, and yet, like the rest of Paris, retains an essential 'Frenchness'. However, the wise traveller not only visits the elegant, perfumed shops and famous restaurants of the Right Bank, seductive though these are. He also explores the city of intriguing alleys and steps, tree-shaded squares and boulevards, of little cafés, vegetable markets and old buildings – all the sights and sounds of the real Paris.

The area around Paris and north to the Belgian border is perhaps unfairly neglected, for its farmlands, open landscapes and beautiful forests have much charm; and, although the region has been ravaged by two world wars, many of its cities and towns are attractive places where the old buildings and quaint corners are cherished.

Paris is an easy city to understand, but one that takes a long time to know. It is a city of contrasts, and therein lies part of its charm.

Basically a group of villages, linked and encircled by boulevards, Paris has an ancient core centred on the Île de la Cité. Administratively it is divided into 20 *arrondissements* numbered clockwise in three rings, numbers 1 to 7 forming the inner ring. To the west is the fashionable Right Bank (8th arrond). Some of the famous 'villages' – Montmartre (the 'Bohemian' quarter of the 19th century), Montparnasse (still favoured by artists) and Beaubourg (where the Georges Pompidou Centre is located) – are still known by their old names.

Accommodation The closest thing to English 'Bed and Breakfast' are the *pensions*, small family-run hotels that tend to be clustered around older neighbourhoods like the Latin Quarter (5th arrond). Slightly more expensive but still within range for most travellers on a budget are the hotels in

Above: Paris's sumptuous 19th-century opera house – the biggest theatre in the world

Right: The dome of the Sacré-Coeur seen from Montmartre's colourful Place du Tertre

St-Germain-des-Prés (6th arrond) and Montparnasse (14th arrond). Hotels on the Right Bank, especially along the Champs Elysées, are expensive. Not quite so expensive are hotels in the adjoining 16th and 17th arrondissements and in the Opéra/Palais Royal neighbourhoods of the 1st, 2nd and 9th arrondissements.

Food This is one of the very special treats of Paris and the variety of restaurants is unmatched in the rest of the country. Paris does not have a cuisine all its own so it borrows something from the rest of the

The Making of a City

Paris started as a settlement of the Parisii tribe on an island (now the Île de la Cité) in the River Seine and spread during the Roman occupation to the southern bank of the river, when it was known as Lutetia. From the early sixth century, when Clovis, first Christian King of the Franks, made Paris his capital city, it grew quickly, eventually absorbing the marshlands on the north bank (le Marais) and many villages which were originally outside the city wall.

During the Middle Ages the beautiful Cathedral of Notre Dame, several royal palaces, public buildings and churches were built. So Paris was already a great city when, in the 17th century, Louis XIV (self-styled 'Sun King') desired that his capital should reflect his own magnificence. During his reign the Tuileries Gardens in front of the Louvre – which Louis first extended and then abandoned – and a number of great squares (designed as backgrounds for statues of the king) were constructed. Louis also built the vast and elaborate Palace of Versail-

les outside the city, as his main residence and administrative centre.

Napoleon's vision, 150 years later, was of an Imperial city to rival Rome. Under his direction existing monuments were given surroundings which enabled them to be seen properly, the Louvre was completed, and three additional Seine bridges, squares and wide roads were built, bringing a new spaciousness to a city which already had its full quota of great buildings.

There were still many areas of narrow streets which we would now think picturesque but which undoubtedly bred disease. In the mid-19th century Napoleon III apointed Baron Haussmann as 'Préfect de la Seine'. He carried out a controversial plan for 'slum clearance', replacing miles of narrow alleys by boulevards, including tree-lined avenues on the site of the old city walls. Paris lost much of its medieval heritage but it is partly this 19th-century modernisation which makes many people acclaim Paris as the finest city in the world.

Paris as it appeared during the 17th century

country; with very little trouble you can taste all the local dishes of France. Paris also has a wide choice of foreign restaurants, such as Vietnamese and North African. Many Paris restaurants close for a month or so in summer, and on Sundays.

Entertainment To find out what is happening in the city during your visit, a weekly 'what's on' is essential. Guides (sold at news kiosks everywhere) will tell you everything you want to know about music, theatre, sporting events and films (including some in English). Even if you do not speak French, a production of Molière at the Comédie Française is memorable – the best inexpensive seats are in the 2nd and 3rd *loges*. For opera or ballet, go to the Paris Opéra where some seats are very low priced. You will find light opera at the Opéra Comique, and excellent plays and concerts are performed in the Théâtre National Populaire at the Palais de Chaillot. If you do speak some French, it is well worth seeing one of those 'Pièces de Boulevard' – farces where the husband thinks he has been cuckolded and the wife has lovers hidden behind every door. If you do not

speak the language, the Comédie Wagram sometimes has English translations.

'Paris By Night' can be an expensive affair, but if you do not mind spending 50f on the obligatory bottle of champagne you can see the most lavish nude productions ever staged. The best of them is the Crazy Horse Saloon. Less expensive because it is in a theatre and not a bar, and even more traditional – can-can and all – is the Folies Bergère, which is so much geared to tourism that the show is in several languages and very respectable.

One of the best shows in town is free and takes place on summer evenings at the Hôtel des Invalides and twice weekly at the Château de Vincennes on the east side of Paris. This is *Son et Lumière*, each performance an extravaganza of sound and light filled with the history of France. Then too, for the price of a cup of coffee or a draught of beer you can sit in a café and watch the crowds stroll by.

Shopping Paris is not quite the mecca it used to be for shopping. Prices are high, including Parisian exports, although souvenir items are an exception. You can buy

high-quality French goods in England for no more than they cost in Paris.

Dress shows at the *haute-couture* salons are free of charge but admittance is by invitation only. If you wish to go you must register with the salon and show your passport. The salon will want to be assured that you will be in Paris for at least three weeks; naturally their aim is to sell their clothes, and fittings are spread over three weeks. Chanel, Dior, Lanvin and Nina Ricci offer the readiest invitations. The afternoon showings begin around 3 pm and both men and women are welcome.

Sightseeing Paris is an easy city to explore on your own with the help of a good guidebook. Each museum and *palais* also offers a printed brochure and some have guided tours in English. Paris is a city of wide avenues, squares and parks, bridges across the Seine and cafés on every corner; it is a pleasant city to explore on foot.

A more leisurely way to see Paris is to take a *Bateau-mouche*. These are glass-topped barges that ply the Seine, leaving regularly every day (half-hourly in summer) from a pier near the Pont d'Alma, on the Right Bank. They are inexpensive and provide commentaries in several languages. Some offer lunch or supper trips. Coach tours of the city are also available.

The North

Picardy is a region too frequently hurried through by tourists on their way south. Amiens has a beautiful cathedral and the Picardy Museum there has one of the finest collections in the country of paintings, sculpture and objects of local archaeological interest. In Compiègne there is a magnificent castle now containing the best collection of First Empire furniture in France. There is also the National Museum of the Automobile and Tourism which presents carriages and cars dating back as far as the 18th century.

In Melun the River Seine flows through the town on its way to Paris, while in Beauvais stands the highest cathedral in Europe – the roof is 42½m (140ft) from the ground. Lille is one of the great industrial towns of France but the old city is interesting architecturally as it was built by the Spanish who ruled this part of Europe in the 16th century and interpreted the Flemish style of building. The cathedral's crypt is a museum of religious art and artifacts, while the Palais des Beaux-Arts contains a substantial collection, including important works by Rubens, Goya, Van Dyck and the French Impressionists, plus sketches by Raphael and Michelangelo.

Further south you will find splendid chocolates, excellent beers and wonderful local cheeses, and the region is also well respected for its pottery.

Places of Interest PARIS

Top: The great Arc de Triomphe, at the top of the Champs-Élysées

Bottom: the ultra-modern Georges Pompidou Centre

ARC DE TRIOMPHE
The Arc de Triomphe originally stood in the centre of the Place d'Étoile, now renamed the Place Charles-de-Gaulle. Probably the largest arch in Europe, it was designed by the architect Chalgrin in the early 19th century to commemorate Napoleon's victories and many of the sculptures on its sides depict scenes from the Emperor's battles. Beneath the arch lies the tomb of the Unknown Soldier where an 'eternal flame' burns over the remains of an anonymous Frenchman who fell at Verdun during World War I. The tomb was established here on 11th November 1920 and the flame was ignited exactly three years later. A platform on the top of the arch provides fine views over the twelve streets which join the square at this point and there is also a museum of events with which the Arc de Triomphe has been identified.

BEAUBOURG ART AND CULTURE CENTRE

This extremely modern building, also known as the Georges Pompidou Centre after the former President of France, stands on the site of Beaubourg, a medieval village which was once outside the city's defensive wall. This soaring structure of steel and glass was designed by a British and an Italian architect (Richard Rogers and Renzo Piano) between 1972 and 1977. The Centre contains a Public Information Library, an Industrial Design Centre, the Institute for Acoustic and Musical Research and the National Museum of Modern Art, which is one of the most comprehensive of its kind in the world and covers all schools of contemporary art and sculpture. It is also a venue for temporary exhibitions and cultural activities. A feature of the building's design is the external escalators which climb the walls and provide unusual views over the Paris rooftops.

The Place Beaubourg buzzes with vitality. It is a favourite place for buskers, and all sorts of bizarre acts – mime, dance, puppetry, illusion – entertain passers-by.

BIBLIOTHÈQUE NATIONALE
Here, in a restored 17th-century mansion, is a vast collection of books and manuscripts believed to be the largest in the world under a single roof. The library is based on the collections of the medieval kings of France and took on its present form during the 16th century when a copyright act decreed that a copy of every published volume should be held in a national centre.

BOIS DE BOULOGNE
An enormous area of woodland covering more than 2,000 acres on the site of an ancient forest where the kings of France hunted boar and deer. The park was laid out in its present form during the 19th century by the architect Haussmann and contains lakes, gardens and facilities for most sporting activities. It includes Paris's major racecourses, Longchamp and Auteuil. Other features are the Bagatelle area with its 18th-century mansion set among landscaped gardens, and the Jardin d'Acclimatation, a children's amusement park comprising, in addition to the usual fairground attractions, a theatre, a miniature railway, a giant dolls' house and a small art and craft museum (Musée en Herbe). Standing near the amusement area is the National Museum of Popular Arts and Traditions (Musée National des Arts et Traditions Populaires).

BOTANICAL GARDEN (JARDIN DES PLANTES)
Established during the 17th century as a Royal Medicinal Herb Garden, the Botanical Gardens have grown into a vast area containing not only some 10,000 species of plants and trees but also a maze, a well-stocked menagerie and several museum-type galleries. The menagerie, which also incorporates an aquarium, started life as the royal menagerie from Versailles and includes many species of mammal and reptile. The galleries deal with mineralogy, fossils, prehistoric animals etc.

CHAILLOT PALACE
There has been a palace on this site, overlooking the River Seine and the Eiffel Tower, since the 16th century when Catherine dei Medici built herself a country retreat there, but the present Palace dates from 1937; it is a low

building of white stone set amid pleasant gardens. The Palace contains a vast theatre (Théâtre National Populaire) and four museums – the Maritime Museum, the Museum of French Monuments, dealing with the evolution of architectural styles and art forms, the Museum of Man (Musée de l'Homme) and the Henri Langlois Cinema Museum.

CHAMP-DE-MARS
A collection of formal gardens running between the Chaillot Palace and the École Militaire (Military Academy) which have been laid out on the former parade ground of the École and contain the famous Eiffel Tower. From the late 19th century the site was used for national exhibitions.

CHAMPS-ÉLYSÉES
One of the most famous thoroughfares in the world, covering a distance of some four miles between the Place Charles-de-Gaulle and the Tuileries Gardens (see page 134). The Champs-Élysées was established in its present form in the early 19th century and presents the visitor with a vista of cheerful bustle, its tree-lined pathways shielding rows of luxury shops, airline offices, motor showrooms, pavement cafés and cinemas from the stream of traffic which fills the roadway at most times of the day.

The Museum of Scientific Discoveries, including the Planetarium, is in the avenue Franklin D Roosevelt, off the Rond-Point.

CLUNY MUSEUM
Hôtel de Cluny is a very fine example of medieval French domestic architecture dating from the 15th century. It contains an outstanding museum of the arts and crafts of the Middle Ages, a veritable panorama of the life of those times through costumes, textiles, embroideries, furniture, sculpture, jewellery, stained glass and ironwork.

Adjoining the mansion are remains of Roman baths.

CONSERVATOIRE NATIONAL DE MUSIQUE
This museum, in the rue de Madrid, has a large collection of wind, stringed and percussion instruments. Famous items include Marie-Antoinette's harp, Beethoven's clavichord and the piano on which Rouget de Lisle played his 'Marseillaise'.

Between the Chaillot Palace and the École Militaire is the Champ de Mars – Napoleon's parade ground

ÉCOLE MILITAIRE
The École Militaire, or French Military Academy, is situated at the end of the Champ-de-Mars. It is a splendid 18th-century building which was designed by Jacques-Ange Gabriel. Former pupils of the Academy include Napoleon Bonaparte, who was admitted at the age of fifteen (1784). Today the École Militaire serves as a military teaching centre for French and Allied Officers.

EIFFEL TOWER
This structure, the most famous in Paris, was built as a commercial enterprise by Gustave Eiffel and completed in 1889. At that time it was the highest construction in the world (984 feet) and was the centre of much controversy. In 1957 the Tower was heightened to 1,051 feet by the addition of a television mast. It weighs 7,000 tons and consists of three platforms crowned by a searchlight. Magnificent views of Paris and its surroundings are commanded from this great tower, particularly one hour before sunset when the light is at its best.

The tower stands in the Champ-de-Mars, whose formal gardens stretch from the Seine as far as the École Militaire. They were landscaped by C J Formigé between 1908 and 1928.

FAUBOURG ST-GERMAIN
Formerly a suburb of Paris which grew up around the Abbey of St-Germain-des-Prés (see page 134), the Faubourg St-Germain quarter is noted for its 18th-century houses. A number of government buildings and foreign embassies are to be found here and the Hôtel Matignon, the 18th-century Paris home of the Prime Minister, can be seen in the rue de Varenne. The Palais-Bourbon, an imposing building dating from 1722, overlooks the Seine near the Pont de la Concorde and is now the seat of the National Assembly. Nearby, on the Quai Anatole France, is the Palace of the Legion of Honour (Palais de la Légion d'Honneur). The palace was built in 1786 and restored after fire damage during the late 19th century. It contains a museum relating to the Legion, created by Napoleon in 1802. Other places of interest include the Hôtel Biron, now the Rodin Museum where many of the sculptor's famous works can be seen. Among these are 'The Thinker' and the 'Burghers of Calais', displayed in the garden.

FAUBOURG ST-HONORÉ
This quarter is well-known for its exclusive shops and 18th- to 19th-century mansions. Its most important building is the Palais de l'Élysée, the Paris residence of the President of France, which stands on the rue du Faubourg St-Honoré quite near the British Embassy. The Chapelle Expiatoire, on the boulevard Haussmann, dates from the 18th century and contains the tombs of the Swiss Guards slaughtered by Revolutionaries who stormed the Tuileries Palace in 1792, and those of many who died on the guillotine. There are two museums in the area – the Conservatoire National de Musique (qv), and the Jacquemart-André Museum, dealing with 18th-century European and Italian Renaissance works of art, located on the boulevard Haussmann.

GEORGES POMPIDOU CENTRE
See *Beaubourg*, page 128.

GOBELINS' TAPESTRY FACTORY
Located at 42 avenue des Gobelins, this factory uses 17th-century methods of tapestry weaving. There has been a workshop on the site since 1440 when Jean Gobelin practised his trade independently. During the 17th century, under the patronage of royalty, Flemish weavers were imported and the Royal Factory of Tapestry and Carpet Weavers was established in 1662. Guided tours are available at certain times on weekdays.

HALLES (LES)

A market was established here as early as the 12th century and the site gradually became more important until, in the mid-19th century, it evolved into a vast covered structure predominantly concerned with the sale of food and flowers. Even the twelve halls, built between 1854 and 1936, eventually became inadequate and the market was transferred to Rungis, near Orly Airport, in 1969. The great covered halls have now been demolished and in their place stands the eminently modern Forum des Halles, a massive pedestrianised complex containing shops, boutiques and cafés. The Grévin Museum, a waxworks museum depicting Paris in the late 19th century, is also located here.

ÎLE DE LA CITÉ

This small island in the River Seine is the oldest quarter of Paris. Nine bridges join it to the two banks of the river. Ancient houses line its many quays, famous for their rows of bookstalls, and its medieval splendour is epitomised by the soaring façade of the Cathedral of Notre-Dame (see page 132) and the Palais de Justice, the former Royal Palace much restored between 1840 and 1914. Other buildings which once formed part of the Royal Palace include the 13th-century Sainte-Chapelle, a tall, delicate church which contains some of the oldest stained glass in Paris, and the Conciergerie, a series of 14th-century Gothic halls where those condemned to die on the guillotine were kept during the 'Terror' period of the French Revolution.

One of Les Invalides' most outstanding buildings – the Dome Church

ÎLE ST-LOUIS

The smaller of the two Seine islands, linked to its neighbour the Île de la Cité (see above) by the Pont St-Louis. Although generally less popular with tourists, the Île St-Louis contains some trendy little shops and cafés and extremely elegant 17th-century houses, notably the Hôtel de Lauzun where official visitors are accommodated. The church of St-Louis-en-l'Île, dating from 1664, contains some fine 17th-century woodwork and statuary and the essence of the island can best be seen in the area of the Quai de Bourbon.

INSTITUT FRANÇAIS

A fine 18th-century building famous as the home of numerous learned societies including the French Academy (Académie Française), an exclusive body of no more than 40 so-called 'immortals' in the world of literature, medicine, etc. Current members include Ionesco and Marguerite Yourcenar (the first woman to be admitted). Among those whose applications were turned down are Molière, Rousseau, Balzac and Proust! In 1694 the Academy produced the first edition of Dictionary of the French Language.

Off-Beat Paris

Some of the more interesting attractions of Paris are slightly off-beat. For example, there is the Père-Lachaise Cemetery (left), a who-was-who of European artistic history. In the hilly field are the tombs of Rossini, Chopin, Corot, Molière, Victor Hugo, Piaf, Oscar Wilde and Bizet, among others.

By taking the Métro to Denfert-Rochereau on a Saturday afternoon, you can explore the Paris Catacombs – complete with human bones in the walls. They were the head-quarters of the French Resistance in World War II. To see anything you need a torch.

A tour of the city's sewers must be one of the most off-beat 'entertainments' in all of Europe. The boat leaves from the Place de la Concorde every Thursday and every first Sunday of the month, summer only. Tours, taking 30 minutes, start at 2 pm, with the last boat leaving at 5 pm. The sewers are well worth seeing, if for no other reason than so few tourists ever view this unusual underground aspect of Paris.

INVALIDES (LES)

This monumental group of buildings, known as Les Invalides, is one of the most famous features of Paris. The main building, the Hôtel des Invalides, was founded by Louis XIV in 1670 to provide quarters for old soldiers. It was designed in the Classical style by the architect Libéral Bruand, with a gold dome added by Jules Hardouin-Mansart. The nearby Alexandre III Bridge offers an impressive view of this edifice.

The two neighbouring churches have much to offer. The Church of St-Louis-des-Invalides, designed by Bruand, contains the organ upon which Berlioz's 'Requiem' was first played in 1837. Its crypt serves as a resting place for a number of famous French marshals and generals including Joffre and Leclerc. The Dôme Church was designed by Mansart and is praised as a great achievement of the Louis XIV era. Its interior is richly decorated and the circular crypt contains the tomb of Napoleon. This area also has some outstanding museums, particularly the Musée de l'Armée (Army Museum).

What to see Church of St-Louis-des-Invalides (17c); Dôme Church and Napoleon's tomb (17c); Hôtel des Invalides (17c); Musée de l'Armée; Museum of the Order of Liberation (formed by General de Gaulle at Brazzaville in 1940); Museum of Relief Maps and Plans (illustrates military fortifications between 1668 and 1870).

THE LOUVRE

Known to almost everyone for Leonardo da Vinci's 'Mona Lisa', the lady with the enigmatic smile, the Louvre Museum houses one of the most magnificent and comprehensive collections of art and antiquities in the world.

It was built in 1200 as a fortress on the north bank of the River Seine and became a royal residence during the 14th century. There followed many years of structural alterations and additions which included the construction of the Tuileries, the Galérie du Bord de l'Eau, the Cour Carrée and the Arc du Carrousel. The latter was erected by Napoleon.

The Grand Gallery was opened to the public in 1793 and since then the Louvre collections have multiplied into a wealth of art treasures which include such famous items as the Venus de Milo, the Nike of Samothrace

(Winged Victory), Van Dyck's portrait of Charles I, the 'Virgin and Infant Jesus with Saint Anne' by Leonardo da Vinci (a cartoon for which is in the National Gallery in London), 'Entombment and Allegory' by Titian, Michelangelo's sculpture 'The Slaves', and the French Crown Jewels. However, no short selective list of exhibits can give a true idea of the scope and quality of the collections. These are divided into the following categories: Egyptian Antiquities; Oriental Antiquities; Greek and Roman Antiquities; the Dutch and Flemish Schools; the French School; the Italian School; the Spanish School; some representatives of the English and German Schools; French Sculpture; Italian Sculpture; Art Objects; Furniture; Graphics.

LUXEMBOURG PALACE AND GARDENS

This 17th-century Palace was built for Marie dei Medici following the death of her husband Henri IV. The architect, Salomon de Brosse, was influenced by the Pitti Palace of Florence highlighted by his use of ringed columns and Tuscan capitals. Since then the Luxembourg Palace has been used as a prison and a parliamentary assembly, and was occupied by the Germans during World War II. Today it is the seat of the French Senate, whose president resides in the adjacent Petit Luxembourg. This building incorporates the chapel and cloister of the convent founded by Marie dei Medici.

The beautiful Gardens lie behind the Palace and provide the largest green open space on the left bank of the River Seine. They contain the Italian-style Medici Fountain (1624) and numerous statues, including the outstanding Delacroix group by Dalou.

MADELEINE (LA)

The Church of St Mary Magdalen, to give La Madeleine its proper name, really began its life as a Greek temple modelled on the Pantheon. This monument was commissioned by Napoleon in honour of the Grand Army but was finally completed in its present form in 1842.

Corinthian columns surround the exterior, which is surmounted by intricate friezes, and there are some fine sculptures inside. There is a magnificent view from the steps down the rue Royale to the Place de la Concorde.

MARCHÉ AUX PUCES

The Marché aux Puces (Flea Market), near the Porte de Clignancourt Métro station, has occupied this site since the late 19th century and today contains a truly staggering array of stalls offering furniture, old clothes, books, records and curios of all kinds for sale. Over 2,000 stalls are spread through a number of streets in the north of the city and are grouped according to their wares: **Biron** – antiques and valuables; **Cambo** – furniture and paintings; **Jules-Vallès** – country furniture and bygones; **Malik** – old clothes, records etc; **Paul-Bert** – oddments including china; **Vernaison** – period furniture and ornaments.

THE MINT

A fine Classical 18th-century building, known as the Hôtel des Monnaies. There are a number of interesting displays, including a section devoted to medals and decorations; but much of the Mint's business, such as the pressing of blanks, etc, now takes place in Pessac (Gironde).

MONCEAU QUARTER

This area contains one of Paris's few parks and the museums devoted to art. The Parc Monceau, laid out in the late 18th century,

originally contained such features as an Egyptian pyramid, a Roman temple and simulated castle ruins; some of these features still remain. The Cernuschi Museum, near the eastern perimeter of the park, contains a fine Oriental art collection donated to the city by the banker Cernuschi. The neighbouring Nissim de Camondo Museum is mainly devoted to 18th-century art.

MONTMARTRE

The hill, or 'Butte' as it is known, of Montmartre originally contained a thriving religious community based in a Benedictine abbey . It was not until the 19th century that artists and writers began to gravitate to the area, giving Montmartre its 'Bohemian' reputation. The Bohemians are no longer in evidence and the Place du Tertre and Place Pigalle, once the haunt of poor and now immortal artists, are now more visited by sightseers and searchers after colourful nightlife.

Montmartre is a maze of steep, winding streets and stairways. Its outstanding building is the Basilica of the Sacré-Coeur (see page 134). The Church of St Peter, the only surviving portion of the Abbey, is one of the oldest in the city, dating from the 12th century.

In October there is a festive grape-harvest at the Montmartre vineyard. Close by is the Museum of Old Montmartre. Other museums are a waxworks (Historial) illustrating Montmartre's history, the Museum of Popular Jewish Art, and the remarkable Gustav Moreau Museum.

MONTPARNASSE

After they abandoned Montmartre in the early part of this century, the 'Bohemians' made Montparnasse their home. Artists and writers still congregate here and Montparnasse is noted for its lively nightlife, but since the 1960s the area has been developed and the new Maine-Montparnasse Complex, consisting of cafés, restaurants, shops and offices, has been established. The most prominent feature of the new development is the Maine-Montparnasse Tower, at 688 feet one of the tallest office blocks in Europe, and a magnificent view of the city may be obtained from the observatory on the 56th floor. The area also contains the Postal Museum; the Bourdelle Museum, in the former house of Bourdelle, the 19th-century sculptor; and the Paris Institute, devoted to medical research.

Artists and pavement cafés entice tourists to spend money in Montmartre's famous Place du Tertre

PARIS AND THE NORTH

NATIONAL ARCHIVES

The National Archives have been kept in the Soubise Palace, a fine Louis XV style building, since 1808. It has since become necessary to use the neighouring Hôtel de Rohan, dating from the same period, as an annexe. The documents occupy some 175 miles of shelving and the most famous of them, such as the Edict of Nantes (1598), are on display in the Historical Museum of France in the Soubise Palace. The Cardinal's Apartments, in the Hôtel de Rohan, contain some fine decorations, including Aubusson tapestries, and are used for temporary art exhibitions.

NOTRE-DAME CATHEDRAL

The Cathedral of Notre-Dame, dominating the Île de la Cité (see page 130) has been called the religious focal point of France. It is certainly one of the most beautiful, and most famous, churches in the country. Built between the 12th and the 14th centuries to a finely balanced Gothic design, the cathedral has a magnificent west façade consisting of three ornate doorways below twin towers which can be ascended to obtain a splendid view of the city and the river. The vast interior is equally fascinating with its rows of medieval chapels, rose windows and a fine treasury. The Cathedral Museum, containing most of Notre-Dame's historical documents since the 17th century, stands close by. One of the best views of the east end of the cathedral can be obtained from the John XXIII Square.

OPÉRA

This magnificent opera house, designed by Charles Garnier, was opened in 1875. Since then it has remained the world's largest theatre, covering an area of 11,000 square metres. The stage is enormous but the auditorium seats only 2,200.

There are a number of statues near the entrance hall, including the outstanding Paul Belmondo copy of 'Dance' by Carpeaux (the original is in the Louvre). The interior of the opera house is very lavish but may only be seen by attending a performance. It is particularly noted for the splendid great staircase and the richly decorated auditorium.

There is also an Opéra Library and Museum situated in the Emperor's Pavilion.

Notre-Dame's towers, flying buttresses and elegant spire provide a stunning contrast to its simple interior (below)

PALAIS D'ART MODERNE (Palais de Tokyo)

This palace, built for the 1937 World Exhibition, contains several art museums. Its grounds contain numerous statues by Bourdelle, the most outstanding being his 'France'.

What to see The Donations (exhibits of canvases belonging to the Georges Pompidou Centre including Braque, Dunoyer de Segonzac and Rouault).

Fairly close to this palace are other specialist museums: the Guimet Museum of Oriental Art on the north side of the Place d'Iéna; and a costume museum in the Palais Galliera.

Museum of Experimental Art (holds different exhibitions based on a central theme, style or artist); Museum of Modern Art of the City of Paris (20th-century exhibits of the Paris school including Dufy, Rouault, Soutine and Utrillo. It also contains the biggest picture in the world – Dufy's 'The Good Fairy Electricity' (600 square metres) and Jean Lurçat's tapestries; temporary exhibitions of present-day art are also an important aspect); Orsay Museum (exhibits by Post-Impressionist artists born before 1870 including Gauguin, Maillol, Seurat and Signac).

PALAIS-ROYAL

This 17th-century palace was originally built for Richelieu by Le Mercier. It was first known as the Cardinal's Palace and took the name of Palais-Royal when the widowed Anne of Austria moved here from the Louvre. Today it houses the office of the Council of State and is not open to the public. The exterior of the palace may be viewed and it is particularly worth seeing the main courtyard and the building's splendid central façade. Near here is the only surviving part of the Cardinal's Palace – the Valois side gallery. This is also known as the Prow Gallery due to its nautical decoration and is now occupied by the Ministry of Cultural Affairs. The delightful garden with its colonnades contains the toy cannon, known as the Palais-Royal cannon, which is fired every Saturday at midday.

PANTHÉON

The 18th-century Panthéon, built to fulfil a vow of Louis XV, is now one of the most famous sights in Paris. It stands on the site of the former church of St Genevieve and was designed by Soufflot. His vast

Treasures of a City

Paris is a major world centre for art and antiques but don't expect many bargains – these days it is an expensive city.

To see what high prices truly are walk into any of the art galleries on the Faubourg St-Honoré or the Louvre des Antiquaires, next to the Louvre Museum. The dealers at these galleries explain that anyone who has to ask the price of an item could not possibly afford to buy it!

More fun is the Marché aux Puces (Flea Market) on Saturdays, Sundays and Mondays near the Métro stop Porte de Clignancourt. Here more than 2,000 stalls sell anything from old clothes to priceless Chinese vases. More interesting for 'finds' are the smaller antique shops on the Left Bank, where you will also come across some of the city's more fascinating art galleries. Pictures and prints, antique books, antique toys, even antique bathroom fixtures, can be found by poking your nose past the dusty windows.

The New Hotel Drouot houses the salerooms where most of the Paris auction houses work and the excitement goes on all day.

An ancient Egyptian obelisk, two fountains and eight statues decorate the Place de la Concorde

construction is in the shape of a Greek cross. In 1791 the Constituent Assembly ruled that the Pantheon was to become the burial place for the great men of France. During the 19th century it served again as a church but reverted to a burial chamber once more in 1855 when Victor Hugo was buried here. Its architectural structure is quite magnificent with twenty-two columns supporting the porch. The pediment is particularly outstanding with its famous carving by David d'Angers (1831) depicting France distributing palms to her notable citizens.

The interior walls of the Panthéon display numerous late-19th-century paintings including the splendid works by Puvis de Chavannes, 'Scenes from St Genevieve's Life' and 'Saint watching over Paris' and 'Bringing Food to the City'.

There are conducted tours around the crypt where tombs of many distinguished Frenchmen, such as Voltaire, Rousseau and Louis Braille, may be seen.

PARADIS (RUE DE)
The rue de Paradis is famous for its shops of splendid French glass, porcelain and china tableware. One of the most notable attractions is Baccarat the glassmaker's, which is next to a fine glass museum. The street also contains a small poster museum situated in the former Choisy-le-Roi China and Porcelain house.

PÈRE-LACHAISE CEMETERY
This cemetery dates from 1804 and was designed by Brongniart. It was named after Louis XIV's confessor Father La Chaise and today is the largest in Paris. The last stand of the Paris Commune occurred here on 28th May 1871 when its survivors were shot against the Mur des Fédérés (Federalists' Wall).

PLACE DE LA BASTILLE
The Bastille was a prison for political offenders where the 'Man in the Iron Mask' and Voltaire were detained for some time. It was stormed in July 1789 when the remaining seven prisoners were set free – an act which marked the beginning of the Revolution. Although the building was destroyed its plan may be seen on the paving stones of the square. Today the Place de la Bastille is dominated by the bronze July Column (171ft high). This is crowned by the figure of Liberty and commemorates the Parisians killed in the uprisings of July 1830 and February 1848.

PLACE DE LA CONCORDE
The Place de la Concorde is one of the largest and most beautiful squares in France. It was originally designed for, and named after, Louis XV but in 1792 it became known as the Place de la Révolution. The guillotine was erected here. Its victims included Louis XVI, Marie-Antoinette, the Girondins and Robespierre. In 1795 the square was renamed the Place de la Concorde.

The decoration of the square was completed by the architect Hittorff during the reign of Louis-Philippe.
What to see Hôtel Crillon (designed by Gabriel – now a famous luxury hotel); Hôtel de la Marine (designed by Gabriel – now the Navy Headquarters and Ministry for the Quality of Life).

PLACE DE LA RÉPUBLIQUE
This large square was designed by Haussmann in the mid 19th century to replace the smaller Place du Château-d'Eau. It is situated at the junction of seven important roads and has a barracks for 2,000 men on its north-eastern side. The square's monument is the 'Statue to the Republic' by Morice (1883). On its base are fine bronze reliefs by Dalou depicting the history of the Republic from its beginning until 1880.

PLACE DES VOSGES
The Place des Vosges, situated on the south-eastern edge of the Marais, is the oldest square in Paris. It was completed in 1612 and became known as the Place Royale – its present name was not acquired until the 19th century. The square developed into one of the most fashionable parts of Paris and today its houses have retained their arcaded and symmetrical appearance. Several of the houses are connected with famous people, including Victor Hugo. The largest house is the King's Pavilion on the south side.
What to see King's Pavilion (south side); Queen's Pavilion (north side); No 1 bis (Madame de Sévigné was born here in 1626); No 6 (home of the poet Victor Hugo from 1833 to 1848 – it is now a museum displaying souvenirs of his life); No 17 (home of the preacher Bossuet); No 21 (home of Richelieu from 1615 to 1627).

PLACE VENDÔME

This square, designed by Jules Hardouin-Mansart, is a fine example of 17th-century architecture. It was conceived as a setting for a statue of Louis XIV which was demolished during the Revolution. In 1810 its place was taken by the Austerlitz column whose bronze spiral was made from the remains of 1200 cannons captured at the battle of Austerlitz

The arcaded buildings around the Place Vendôme are uniform in design and contain some of the most notable bankers and jewellers. A number of the houses are also associated with well-known people, the most famous being number 12 where Chopin died in 1849.

SACRÉ-COEUR

This white edifice was built in fulfilment of a Catholic vow to raise money following the Franco-Prussian War of 1870. It was designed in the Romanesque–Byzantine style by Abadie and erected between 1876 and 1910. The basilica is now a famous pilgrimage centre and its interior depicts the devotion of France to the Sacré-Coeur (Sacred Heart). Its belfry contains the Savoyarde bell which, at 19 tons, is one of the heaviest in the world. The dome is worth ascending as it commands fine views of the interior and an extensive panorama of Paris and its surroundings.

ST-ÉTIENNE-DU-MONT (Church)

The present church was built between 1492 and 1626 to replace a smaller church dedicated to St Stephen. It highlights the transition from Gothic to Renaissance and is the only church in Paris to possess a rood screen (constructed 1521–1535). A modern gilded-copper shrine contains a number of small relics of St-Genevieve, who is venerated here. Other features of St-Étienne-du-Mont include the graves of Pascal and Racine (both 17th-century) and its stained glass dating from the 16th and 17th centuries.

ST-GERMAIN-DES-PRÉS (Church)

This Romanesque church dates from the 11th century and is the oldest in Paris. It was formerly part of a Benedictine abbey which was suppressed at the Revolution – a period when the church was converted to the manufacture of

The Tuileries Gardens' symmetrical patterns of terraces, avenues, ponds and fountains epitomise Le Nôtre's formal style

gunpowder. There have been many alterations to the structure of St-Germain-des-Prés including the addition of an 18th-century presbytery and a 19th-century steeple. One of the main attractions of its interior is the recently excavated St-Symphorian Chapel where St-Germanus, 8th-century Bishop of Paris, is buried. In addition a number of tombstones may be seen, such as those of Descartes and Montfaucon.

Close by is the Eugène Delacroix Museum, in the house where this influential Romantic painter of the 19th century had his studio.

ST-SÉVERIN (Church)

The present church dates from the 13th century and is a fine example of Flamboyant Gothic architecture which was employed here until 1530. Its main feature is the splendid double ambulatory whose ribbed vaulting is very detailed. The church also has some lovely stained-glass windows, such as the one depicting the Tree of Jesse (16th century) behind the organ. There is a small garden near the church which was once a burial ground with an adjacent charnel house. In 1474 Louis XI offered his freedom to a man condemned to death, if he survived an operation to remove the gall stones from which he suffered. The surgeon who

wished to carry out the experiment operated in this burial ground – the first time gall stones had been removed from a living person. The patient survived and was freed.

SALPÊTRIÈRE HOSPITAL

The Salpêtrière Hospital was founded by Louis XIV (1656) on the site of a gunpowder factory. It was known as the General Hospital for the Poor of Paris and its inmates eventually included beggars, the mad and prostitutes; from the 18th century on it acquired a reputation for humane and advanced psychiatric techniques. The buildings were enlarged by Le Vau and Le Muet (1667) in an austere style which resembles that of Les Invalides. In 1670 Libéral Bruand designed the St-Louis Chapel whose ground plan took the form of a Greek Cross. Since then the Salpêtrière Hospital has amalgamated with the Pitié Hospital to form the University Hospital Centre.

SORBONNE

The Sorbonne, world-famous as the seat of the University of Paris, dates from 1253 when St-Louis' confessor Robert de Sorbon founded a small theological college. This soon gained recognition and it was here in 1469 that the first French printing press was established. The present

buildings, apart from the church, date from 1885 to 1901 when large scale rebuilding occurred. They now contain vast educational facilities including 22 lecture halls, 16 examination halls, 240 laboratories, a physics tower and a library.

The church was built in the early 17th century in the Jesuit style and contains the white marble tomb of Cardinal Richelieu which was designed by Le Brun and carved by Girardon in 1694.

TUILERIES GARDENS

The formal Jardin des Tuileries is situated beside the River Seine. Its name derives from the 15th century when tiles – or 'tuiles' – were made out of the local clay soil. During the 17th century part of the garden was beautifully laid out by Le Nôtre and this has survived, just as he designed it, to the present day. The garden contains many fine statues including works by Nicolas Coustou, Le Pautre and Coysevox. In particular the latter is noted for his splendid 'Fame on a winged horse' and 'Mercury on a winged horse'. Terraces line the gardens and it is worth visiting the Bord de l'Eau Terrace which commands a view extending to the Seine and the Louvre. There is also a first-rate national collection of Impressionist paintings by artists such as Cézanne, Degas, Monet, Renoir, Gauguin, Manet, Rousseau, Seurat, Toulouse-Lautrec and Van Gogh, housed in the Jeu de Paume Museum; while the Orangery is used for temporary exhibitions and the magnificent series of paintings by Monet of the waterlily pool in his garden.

UNESCO HEADQUARTERS

The international UNESCO (United Nations Educational, Scientific and Cultural Organisation) building, opened in 1958, was designed by three architects – Breuer (American), Nervi (Italian) and Zehrfuss (French). It consists of three main buildings – the largest is Y-shaped and houses the secretariat, another contains committee rooms and conference halls and there is also a secretariat annexe. The interior is sumptuously decorated by international works of contemporary art and includes frescoes by Picasso (Spanish), the statue 'Figure in Repose' by Henry Moore (English), mosaics by Bazaine and Herzell (French) and a Japanese garden by Noguchi.

VERSAILLES

The Palace of Versailles, situated 20 kilometres south-west of Paris, is one of the most popular attractions in France. It originated as a small château built for Louis XIII and was enlarged on a massive scale by Louis XIV (17th century). He commissioned Le Vau as architect (later succeeded by Mansart), Le Brun as decorator and Le Nôtre as landscape gardener who, together, created the magnificent edifice which became the envy of the western world.

The interior is sumptuously decorated and is best-known for the Hall of Mirrors. This contains 17 mirrors and was used for great celebrations such as the wedding reception of the future Louis XVI and Marie-Antoinette. The Treaty of Versailles which formally ended World War I was signed here on 28th June 1919. Other features include the Diana Salon (part of the Grand Apartment) where the bust of Louis XIV by Bernini may be seen, Mansart's Chapel with its elaborate gold and white decoration, and the Royal Opera House designed by Gabriel.

Le Nôtre's gardens extend over 250 acres and contain many statues, of which Neptune is the largest. There are several fountains whose day and floodlit night performances are restricted to certain times of the year.

The two Trianons (châteaux) are another important feature at Versailles. The Grand Trianon, used by Louis XIV as a retreat, is now the château where France receives her visiting heads of state. The Trianon-sous-Bois wing is reserved for the French President and is not open to the public. The Petit Trianon, established by

Attractions at Versailles include the Parterres d'Eau where statues represent the rivers of France

Louis XV, was given by Louis XVI to Marie-Antoinette.

What to see
Château Chapel; Grand Apartment (including Diana Salon); Hall of Mirrors; Hercules Salon; King's Private Suite; King's Suite; Madame de Maintenon's Suite; Marble Court; Queen's Private Suite; Queen's Suite; Royal Opera House; Royal Stables; Museum of French history.
Gardens Bosquet des Marronniers (chestnut grove); Buffet d'Eau (lake); Étoile Royal (Royal Star); Fountains; Grand Canal; Grand Trianon; Groves – North and South; Orangery; Parterres d'Eau; Parterres du Midi; Parterres du Nord; Petit Trianon and hamlet.

VINCENNES

The medieval château at Vincennes, to the east of the city, was constructed by the Valois family. During the 17th century Le Vau added symmetrical royal pavilions, a triumphal arch and colonnades which gave it a Classical air. It has a splendid keep, which was converted to a state prison and has prisoners' graffiti on the walls (early 16th century to 1784). Several of its prisoners were famous and included Cardinal de Retz, Diderot, the Great Condé and Mirabeau. The Sainte-Chapelle has mid-16th-century stained-glass and splendid stone rose windows.

The extensive parkland (Bois de Vincennes) adjoining the château has much to offer with its delightful Paris Floral Garden, Zoological Garden, lakes and museums. A 'Throne' or 'Gingerbread Fair' is held on the Reuilly Lawn every spring, a tradition dating from the monks of St-Anthony's Abbey (957).
What to see
Château Keep; Sainte-Chapelle; Tour du Village (tower).
Bois de Vincennes Breuil School of Horticulture; Buddhist Centre; Indo-Chinese Memorial Temple and Tropical Garden; Lakes; Paris Floral Garden; Zoological Garden; African and Oceanian Art Museum; Transport Museum.

Coffee ~ with a view

The pleasure of café life in Paris lies in watching the world go by while relaxing with coffee or something stronger – and no-one will rush you along to free the table. The bill includes a service charge and there is no need to give an additional tip.

Watching people can be a full-day occupation on the Right Bank, where prices are steep. The livelier cafés are on the Left Bank, especially around the Latin Quarter and the St-Germain-de-Prés neigh-

bourhood. The Deux Magots and the Flore are very much what cafés in Paris are expected to be. In Montparnasse the Coupole and the Select, both large restaurants but with pavement tables, rate highly with regular café-goers.

Working-class cafés fill up early in the day with people drinking cheap red wine, and stay open late as teenagers take over. During the day artists and poets holding court at their habitual tables mingle with the city's tourists.

Paris City Plan

Driving and Parking in Paris
Paris's astonishing traffic statistics show that there are nearly a million private cars in the city, on less than 750 miles of road. It is not surprising, then, that driving in Paris – especially for motorists accustomed to driving on the left – can be nerve-racking. All things considered, public transport is a much better method of getting about, but if you do use a car you must be aware of the numerous parking restrictions in the city.

As in many French cities, parking within the 'blue zone' is strictly controlled and a parking disc (*disque de contrôle*) must be displayed inside the windscreen. These discs can be obtained from hotels, garages, *Offices du Tourisme* or police stations. The disc clock must be set to show the time of your arrival. The time limit, which applies from 9am to 12.30pm and from 2.30pm to 7pm on weekdays, is 1 hour. From 7pm to 9am no disc is necessary.

Parking meters operate within the 'grey zone' and are closely supervised by wardens (in mid-blue uniforms). The meters take 1f and 50c coins, and cost about 4f an hour. Paris also has some 30 underground garages with room for over 30,000 cars. They charge about 3f an hour. At night, street parking is free, but central Paris is usually very busy in the evening and you may have difficulty in finding a space.

In Paris and the surrounding departments it is forbidden to leave a vehicle parked in the same place on any public road for more than 24 hours at a stretch. It is also forbidden to park a caravan almost everywhere

in the city. Trailers and caravans may not be towed in the blue zone between 2pm and 8.30pm (excluding Sundays and public holidays). As in some other French towns, cars in Paris may only sound their horns in an emergency.

The Boulevard Périphérique
Completed in 1973, this 22-mile, toll-free dual carriageway encircles Paris, keeping through traffic out of the congested city centre. However, traffic on the Bd Périphérique itself is nearly always heavy, and the interchanges can be confusing, so driving on the Bd Périphérique needs extra care and forethought.

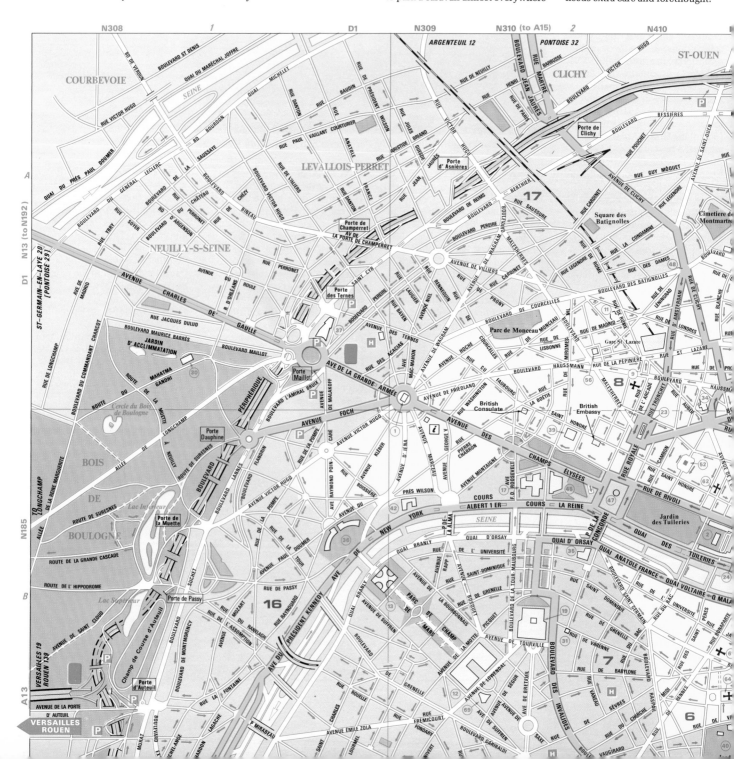

All routes radiating from central Paris (some of them linking up with autoroutes) cross the Bd Périphérique at one of the *Portes* or gateways. Signs above the nearside (right-hand) lane indicate the next *Porte* ahead, and you should move into this lane immediately after passing the *Porte* before the one at which you wish to leave the Bd Périphérique. Often, very little warning is given, and it can be confusing unless you are alert.

The main direction signs are 'Lille, Bruxelles' for Autoroute A1, 'Metz, Nancy, Strasbourg' for A4, 'Lyon' for A6, 'Chartres, Orleans' for A10/11 and 'Rouen' for A13.

The Métro and Buses

The Paris Métro is probably the world's best underground network and the easiest to use. The stations, always clearly marked, often have large electric route maps with rows of push-buttons. You simply push the button for the stop you want, and lights indicate which train to take and where to change. Pocket Métro maps are available, free, at all stations. The Métro runs from 5.30am until about 1am.

The cheapest way to buy tickets is in a book of ten, known as a *carnet*. These can be obtained at Métro booking offices, on buses, at tobacco counters and at shops displaying the

RATP (Paris Public Transport System) sign. The Métro fare is standard, regardless of distance.

Carnets can also be used on buses, but here the number of tickets needed varies according to the distance. In general, buses run from 6.30am to 9pm, though some lines operate later. Some routes may be reduced or altered on Sundays and public holidays.

Special tourist economy tickets are available which entitle you to four or seven days' unlimited travel by either Métro or bus. They may be bought, on production of your passport, at larger Métro stations and RATP offices.

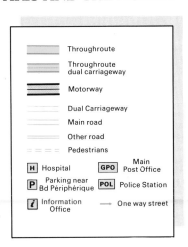

	Throughroute	
	Throughroute dual carriageway	
	Motorway	
	Dual Carriageway	
	Main road	
	Other road	
	Pedestrians	

H Hospital	GPO Main Post Office
P Parking near Bd Périphérique	POL Police Station
i Information Office	→ One way street

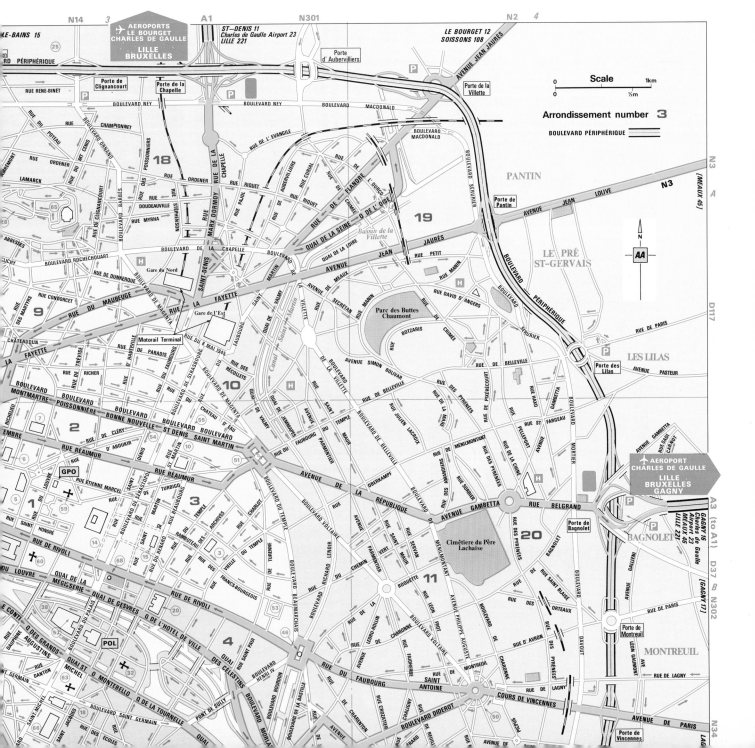

This Symbol marks junctions which should be approached with special care.

INDEX TO NUMBERED PLACES OF INTEREST

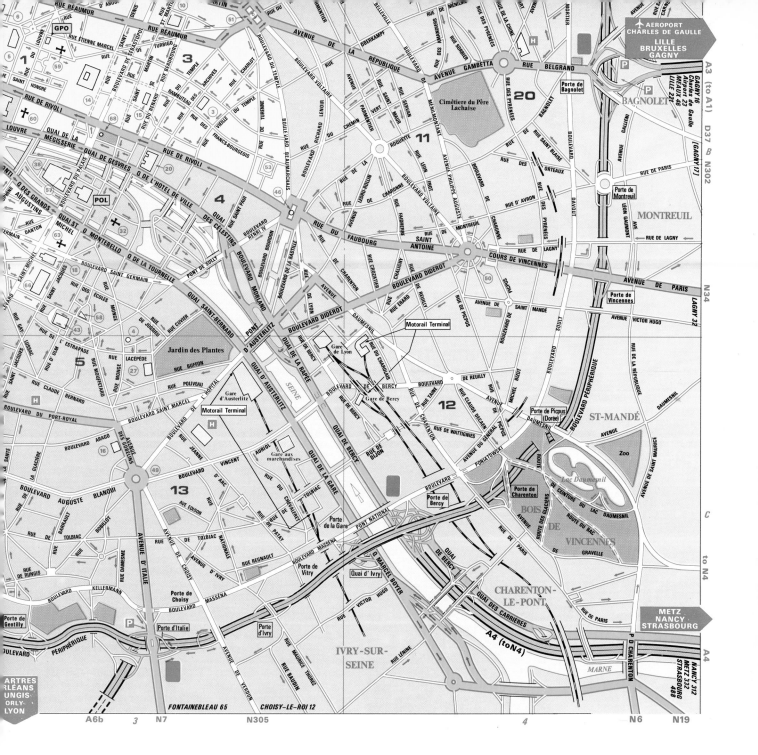

Places of Interest NORTH

Rodin's famous commemorative statue of the 'Six Burghers of Calais' stands outside the town's impressive Hôtel-de-Ville

ABBEVILLE (Somme)

Abbeville, situated on the River Somme, was severely damaged during both World Wars. Despite this, several of its old buildings have survived including the fine Gothic church of St-Vulfran with its Flamboyant façade and Renaissance doorways. There is also a Renaissance house in the rue des Capucins (number 15) and an 18th-century château (Bagatelle). The 'Boucher de Perthes' museum contains prehistoric finds and medieval works of art.

What to see Bagatelle (Château); Church of St-Vulfran (Gothic); Musée Boucher de Perthes; Rue des Capucins; Vimeu countryside.

AMIENS (Somme)

Amiens, the old capital of Picardy, lies on the banks of the River Somme, presenting the visitor with a pleasant mixture of ancient riverside streets and the modern development which followed extensive war damage. The two extremes of architecture are epitomised by Amiens' most impressive buildings, the 13th-century Gothic cathedral and the modern Perret tower (Tour Perret), some 26 storeys high. The Museum of Picardy is mainly devoted to local art. The town's connections with the novelist Jules Verne, who spent the last years of his life there, are commemorated in the Centre de Documentation Jules Verne.

Amiens has a well stocked zoo, set in pleasant parkland, and Les Hortillonnages, a series of market gardens lying on marshland on the eastern outskirts and accessible by boat, are well worth a visit.

Amiens is renowned for its good food, and local specialities, such as duck paté and the Picardy Pancake (ficelle picarde), can be sampled at many of the town's restaurants.

What to see Cathedral of Notre-Dame (13c); Church of St-Germain (15c); Church of St-Remi (15c restored); Hortillonnages (market gardens) and Marché sur l'Eau; Musée d'Art et d'Histoire Regionale (local art and history); Musée de Picardie (a major art and archaeology museum); Parc Zoologique (Zoo).

ARRAS (Pas-de-Calais)

Despite extensive war damage sustained between 1914 and 1918, Arras retains much of its original medieval Flemish character. The former abbey church is now the cathedral which stands near the Fine Arts Museum (Musée des Beaux-Arts). Other places of interest include the fine citadel, established by Vauban in the 17th century, and the 18th-century law courts (Palais-de-Justice).

What to see Abbaye St-Vaast (18c); Cathedral (18c); Church of St Nicholas-en-Cité (19c); Citadel (17c); Hôtel-de-Ville (Town hall – 20c in Flamboyant style); Musée des Beaux-Arts; Palais-de-Justice.

BEAUVAIS (Oise)

Although much of the town was destroyed during 1940, Beauvais' most important building, the Cathedral of St-Pierre, remained virtually unscathed. This fine example of 13th-century architecture was never completed to its original plan but contains many outstanding features such as its 13th- to 16th-century stained-glass windows, its 15th- to 17th-century tapestries, its medieval treasury and its 19th-century astronomical clock. The Galerie Nationale de Tapisserie, adjoining the cathedral, contains a display of the tapestries for which Beauvais was once famous. There is a regional museum (Musée Départmental de l'Oise) in the former Bishop's Palace, which dates from the 16th century.

What to see Cathedral of St-Pierre (13c); Church of St-Étienne (12–17c); Galerie Nationale de Tapisserie; Musée Départmental de l'Oise.

BOULOGNE-SUR-MER (Pas-de-Calais)

An ancient town which has become a leading commercial and passenger port and the country's foremost fishing port. The oldest quarter of Boulogne, the Ville Haute, is enclosed by formidable ramparts dating originally from the 13th century and embellished with towers, gateways and a 13th-century castle. It contains the Basilica of Notre-Dame, a 19th-century church built over a fine 11th-century crypt. The local museum has a collection of Greek pottery and a section devoted to Napoleon, whose connections with the town are commemorated by the Monument de la Légion d'Honneur on the north-eastern outskirts (marking the spot where the first Légion d'Honneur decoration was awarded).

What to see Basilica Notre-Dame (19c); Church of St-Nicolas (13–18c); Colonne de la Grande Armée (viewpoint); Hôtel-de-Ville (18c town hall); Museum.

CALAIS (Pas-de-Calais)

A popular seaside resort which is also one of the leading Channel ports. Calais suffered severe war damage but, despite extensive restoration, has retained vestiges of its medieval defences which withstood siege by Edward III of England for several months during 1346. Rodin's famous 19th-century statue, 'The Burghers of Calais' (Les Bourgeois de Calais), stands outside the town hall. This commemorates the six merchants who were forced to surrender themselves to Edward wearing nothing but their shirts. The gentle inland valleys offer pleasant rural byway excursions, and there are fine sandy beaches to the west.

What to see Church of Notre-Dame (13–17c); Citadel (16–17c); Hôtel-de-Ville (15c town hall); Musée des Beaux-Arts et de la Dentelle (Fine Arts etc).

CHANTILLY (Oise)

A quiet little town which, on account of its famous race-course, is spoken of as the Newmarket of France. The stables can be visited.

Within the château are many galleries forming the Musée Condé containing important works of art charmingly displayed – statues, stained glass, a library – but chiefly paintings including masterpieces by Raphael, and drawings by Leonardo da Vinci and Perugino.

Formal gardens surround the château and include a chapel, an 18th-century hamlet, and the Jeu de Paume (18th-century tennis court), now a museum.

COMPIÈGNE (Oise)

This historic town, where Joan of Arc was finally captured in 1430, lies in the Oise Valley on the edge of the Forest of Compiègne. Its most important building is the magnificent Royal Palace, dating originally from the 14th century, but rebuilt and enlarged by Louis XV and a favourite residence of Napoleon. The state apartments are open to the public and the palace also contains a museum devoted to the Second Empire of Napoleon III and an Automobile Museum. The formal gardens of the Petit Parc are also open daily. The town hall (Hôtel-de-Ville), dating from the early 16th century, has a unique belfry where three wooden figures, known as 'Picantins', strike the quarter hours.

What to see Compiègne Forest; Church of St-Antoine (13–16c); Church of St-Jacques (13–15c); Hôtel-de-Ville (16c town hall); Musée Vivenel (Greek pottery, folkore etc); Palace (14–19c).

FONTAINEBLEAU (Seine-et-Marne)

There has been a royal residence within the Forest of Fontainebleau since the 12th century. The palace was extensively enlarged between the 16th and the 18th century and now covers a considerable area; it is built to a pleasantly irregular pattern around five courtyards. Much of the sumptuous internal decoration was commissioned by Napoleon, who lived there during the upheaval of his abdication.

Barbizon, on the edge of Fontainebleau Forest, gave its name to a school of mid-19th century painters: Rousseau, Millet, Corot, Daumier, Diaz. The houses occupied by Millet and Rousseau are museums.

Napoleon was responsible for Fontainebleau's lovely grounds

LILLE (Nord)

A highly industrialised town, Lille is one of the foremost textile centres in the world. It is also an important commercial centre and has a fine university. Despite a great deal of modernisation the older part of the town has retained a distinctly Flemish appearance which is particularly noticeable in the area around the Place du Théâtre where the ornate façade of the Old Stock Exchange (Ancienne Bourse) has been virtually unchanged since the mid-17th century. The town is overlooked by Vauban's imposing 17th-century citadel, surrounded by pleasant gardens.

What to see Ancienne Bourse (17c); Cathedral of Notre-Dame-de-la-Treille (19–20c); Citadel (17c); Church of St-Maurice (14–19c); Hospice Comtesse (15–18c hospital); Hôtel-de-Ville (20c town hall); Musée Industriel-et-Commercial; Museum (important fine art collections of many schools).

MALMAISON (CHÂTEAU) (Hauts-de-Seine)

Acquired in 1799 by Josephine Bonaparte, the Château became her favourite residence; she died here in 1814.

It remains a beautiful museum of art of the Napoleonic era, containing furniture, fabrics, musical instruments, carpets and works of art owned by Napoleon's family and entourage.

MEAUX (Seine-et-Marne)

An old-established town on the River Marne, Meaux has become a thriving agricultural centre well-known for the manufacture of cheese. Fragments of the old ramparts, some of which date back to the 4th century, have been preserved, but Meaux's main places of interest are to be found around the fine Gothic cathedral and include the 12th-century chapter house and the palace, which contains a museum of local art and history.

What to see Ancien Évêché (12–17c Bishop's Palace); Cathedral of St-Étienne (12–16c); Vieux Chapitre (12c chapter house).

NOYON (Oise)

A Gallo-Roman town, Noyon became a religious centre in the 6th century. Its fine cathedral, begun in 1150, is remarkable as an early Gothic building adjoining a 16th-century arcaded library. A museum has been established in the restored house in which Jean Calvin, the famous Protestant reformer, was born in 1509.

What to see Bibliothèque du Chapitre (16c library); Cathedral (12–14c); Musée Jean Calvin; Musée du Noyonnais (local archaeology).

PROVINS (Seine-et-Marne)

An old fortified town which grew exceedingly prosperous during the Middle Ages as a centre for trade fairs and is today noted for the cultivation of roses. The old quarter (Ville Haute) is still partially enclosed by well preserved 12th- to 13th-century ramparts and contains most of Provins' antiquities. These include the Tour de César, a well-preserved 12th-century keep, and a fine 13th-century tithe barn (Grange aux Dîmes).

What to see Caves (beneath Hôtel-Dieu); Church of St-Ayoul (12–16c); Church of St-Quiriace (12–17c); Grange aux Dîmes (13c); Tour de César (12c).

RAMBOUILLET (Yvelines)

A pleasant town, in attractive forested surroundings, famous for its château which has been the summer residence of the President of France since 1897. Dating originally from the 14th century, the château has undergone a great deal of restoration and expansion. It stands in extensive parkland which contains such unusual features as a national sheep farm (Bergerie Nationale), founded by Louis XVI, and the Queen's Dairy (Laiterie de la Reine), built by the same monarch for Marie-Antoinette

ST-GERMAIN-EN-LAYE (Yvelines)

This elegant town surrounded by forest is famous for its Renaissance château in which is housed the Museum of National Antiquities. Here are collected some of the most important prehistoric finds from many parts of France. The Municipal Museum contains paintings by artists of the Flemish and Dutch schools.

ST-OMER (Pas-de-Calais)

A busy town on the River Aa, surrounded by many canals and waterways. St-Omer was badly damaged during both World Wars but some interesting old buildings have remained virtually intact. Among these is the Basilica of Notre-Dame, which contains numerous medieval works of art, and the 17th-century former Jesuit chapel, which is now in use as a school. Pleasant public gardens have been laid out on the site of the town's old fortifications. An agreeable diversion during the summer months is a boat-ride along the *watergangs*, canals through the marshlands.

What to see Ancienne Chapelle des Jésuites (17c – now a school); Basilica Notre-Dame (13–15c); Hôtel Sandelin Museum (fine arts); Musée Henri-Dupuis (birds, shells etc); *Watergangs* (canals).

Index

Acknowledgements

The publishers would like to thank the following organisations, photographers and picture libraries for the use of photographs:

J Allan Cash	Van Phillips
Colour Library International	PIX
Robert Estall	Peter Roberts
Mary Evans Picture Library	Barrie Smith
French Government Tourist Office	SPECTRUM
Robert Harding	Marian Street
Denis Hughes-Gilbey	Richard Surman
Larry Dale Gordon (Image Bank)	TOPHAM
Mansell Collection	VLOO
PHOTOBANK	Thomas Wilkie
PICTUREPOINT	John Woolverton

Picture research by Sally Howard

Invaluable assistance with research facilities was provided by the following organisations, who are gratefully acknowledged by the publishers:

The French Government Tourist Office

Hertz Europe Ltd

Fédération Nationale des Logis et Auberges de France

SNCF (French Railways)

LOGIS
DE FRANCE

GW00362609

£4·00

WOMAN'S OWN

BOOK OF

HOUSE PLANTS

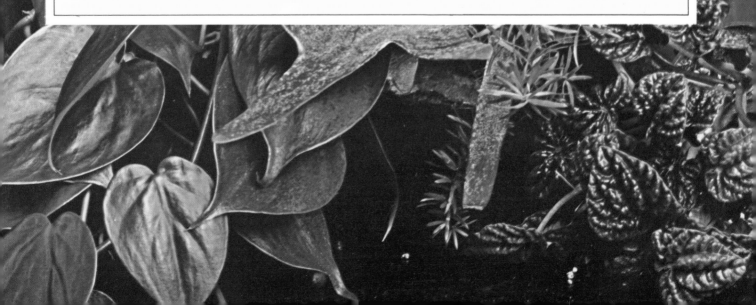

WOMAN'S OWN

BOOK OF
HOUSE
PLANTS

WILLIAM DAVIDSON

TREASURE
PRESS

ACKNOWLEDGEMENTS

The editor would like to thank Mr and Mrs L. Liebster for
allowing us to take photographs of houseplants in their home and
Carol Bowen for lending Bryony

Line artwork by Kevin Maddison

Colour photographs by: *Pat Brindley* (p 15, p 18, p 51 *top*, p 106,
p 126 and p 134 *bottom*); **Harry Smith Horticultural Photographic
Collection** (p 19 *top and bottom right*, p 22, p 42, p 78, p 82, p 83,
p 122, p 127 *top* and p 135); **Peter Stiles** (p 127 *bottom right*); **Michael
Warren** (p 14 *top*, p 55, p 79 *top*, p 107 *bottom* and p 119) and
Paul Williams (endpaper, title page, introduction, p 23, pp 46–47,
p 50, p 54, pp 78–9, p 86, pp 110–111, p 114, p 123 and pp 130-131).

First published in Great Britain in 1969 by
The Hamlyn Publishing Group Limited

This revised edition published in 1980

This edition published in 1988 by
Treasure Press
59 Grosvenor Street
London W1

Copyright © The Hamlyn Publishing Group Limited 1969, 1980

All rights reserved. No part of this publication may
be reproduced, stored in a retrieval system, or transmitted,
in any form or by any means, electronic, mechanical, photocopying, recording or otherwise, without the permission of
the Hamlyn Publishing Group Limited.

ISBN 1 85051 269 8

Printed in Hong Kong

CONTENTS

The popularity of houseplants has now reached such proportions that it is unusual to visit a house in which no plant at all is grown. One can confidently predict that this current enthusiasm will continue for many years, especially as the proportions of modern living rooms with their often rather severe outlines and large windows are particularly well suited to a plant display of some kind. Once bitten by the bug of house-plant growing, the tendency seems to be to utilise every possible corner of the house – so beware!

This book is designed for those who want to know something about the culture of plants indoors without necessarily delving too deeply into their background and nomenclature. For information I have drawn on over 20 years of experience of growing, exhibiting, talking, advising – in fact, almost 'living' houseplants. And, above all, I have kept in mind the end-less stream of questions that have been asked over the years.

Though I have not knowingly sought information from the book of any other author, I feel sure that many of my acquaintances will, however, recognise some of my material as their personal opinions. For this I apologise, if apology is necessary.

I am often asked the simple question, 'What actually is a houseplant?' The answer is equally simple: 'Any plant that forms a permanent part of room decoration'. So, my Granny, in the far north of Scotland, will be pleased to know that her 'shamrock' (oxalis), humble though it is, can lay claim to being a houseplant.

Perhaps I should point out that I have not set out to give brief information on the largest possible number of plants but have endeav-oured to discuss fewer plants more fully, and provide more general advice on plant culture indoors. Well-grown houseplants, attractively displayed, can add greatly to the pleasures of the home.

CHAPTER 1
Selection and display

Eventual success with houseplants depends very often on the quality of plant initially purchased. Average indoor conditions, on the whole, leave much to be desired when seeking the ideal environment in which to grow plants of any kind. Consequently it stands to reason that a plant of inferior quality, when introduced to room conditions, will quickly deteriorate, whereas the robust plant with a vigorous, healthy root system, and free from pests, will have a much better chance of survival.

Sales outlets

Where once the sale of potted plants was the prerogative of the florist or the nurserymen, we now see them retailed in all sorts of unlikely places such as supermarkets and department stores, where they seem to vie with dresses and shoes as potential purchases for anyone having cash available. Although these surroundings may not at first sight appear very appropriate for such things as Swiss cheese plants and creeping figs, most store managers have learned a lot as the business expanded and many care for their plants extremely well. However, one must still exercise a little care when making a selection – the most important requirement would seem to be that the plants themselves should have a cared for look. Some retailers treat the plants in much the same way as the other merchandise placing the plants in dark corners or draughts, and forgetting that they must be watered. Look over the plant's display area before deciding to purchase. Plants must have a suitable place while they are in the store, and they must also have essential attention in respect of watering, even feeding. With a little care, plants in a well-lit, well-

heated and ventilated store can do infinitely better than the same plants placed in a flower shop, for example, that may lack these modern facilities.

You will find good and bad in all houseplant sales outlets, therefore a watchful eye must be kept when purchasing them. If you are a beginner then it is a good idea to take someone along who knows something about it and let them decide until you acquire a bit of skill in detecting good from bad.

Amongst my colleagues I hear a lot of criticism about the way some department stores handle houseplants but, to my mind, rather than harm the houseplant trade it simply puts plants within the reach of many people who would otherwise not have bothered to buy them. Some people who fight shy of entering a flower shop or visiting a garden centre will happily pick up a plant while attending to the family shopping. I can see no objection to purchasing healthy plants from competent staff in premises that are in most instances splendidly suited to the care of houseplants.

More and more garden centres are also cropping up, and needless to say more and more of them are selling indoor plants – some doing a fine job of caring for them while others do not seem to have the first idea of where they should begin. For my sins, I run quarterly training courses at the nursery for people in our trade in an effort to educate them in the needs of plants, and these have without doubt been successful in improving standards at many establishments. Alas, they appear to have little effect on the very busy people in some areas of our trade – they still manage to forget watering, feeding, pest control, shading the glass, and numerous other essential needs of potted plants while they are in transit from the grower to the eventual purchaser.

A simple arrangement of houseplants is often the most effective
Far left, top An old copper kettle makes an unusual container for a small Fittonia argyroneura
Far left, bottom An occasional table is used to give a fatshedera plant a prominent position. The upright shape of this plant is contrasted with the spreading leaves of the *Platycerium alcicorne*
Left A garden trug is an attractive container for a selection of flowering and foliage plants. An arrangement of this type can be changed around as frequently as desired

Choosing a good quality plant

Regardless of the supplier, it still applies that one must have an eye for a plant and one should never forget that the quality of the purchased plant can make all the difference to its eventual performance indoors. Check the plant over when purchasing, and do make a thorough check of the foliage should there be any suspicion of pests being present; there is no point in introducing unwanted visitors that may well in time damage other plants in one's collection. There are, however, other ways of detecting good from bad; and one of the most important points is to ensure that plants are actively growing, and not stunted or limp at the tips. Even in winter, greenhouse-grown pot plants should make a reasonable amount of growth, though there are a few exceptions, such as the rubber plant (*Ficus elastica robusta*).

If a plant has a fresh, crisp appearance this is another point in favour of purchase. Staked plants should look as if the growth is actually climbing the stake, and one ought to avoid plants that are hanging limply around their support. Hard-baked or thoroughly saturated composts are both signs of mismanagement on the part of the supplier, and are two more reasons for directing your purse and your footsteps to the next shop along the road.

Well-furnished plants

The professional grower is always impressed on seeing what he terms 'a well-furnished plant'. By this he means a plant of full appearance with leaves all the way down the stem; and, given the choice, he would invariably select the smaller, well-furnished plant in preference to the tall, leggy one. Production of such a plant takes more time and requires frequent pinching of leading shoots to encourage a bushy appearance, so one should expect to pay a little more for it. Missing, yellow, or damaged leaves are further indications of indifferent culture and handling.

Defects to look for in flowering plants

With flowering pot plants it is also important to look for the same defects that one might expect to find in foliage plants: yellow and missing leaves, an untidy appearance and so on. Equally, or perhaps more important, is the need to buy plants that are not 'blown' or in full flower, though it is also important that flowering plants should not be too backward when purchased. The aim should be to select plants with a reasonable amount of colour showing and plenty of young buds still to open that will give you pleasure in the months to come. There are exceptions, though; the pleasure of seeing a friend's face light up on being presented with something as exciting as an *Azalea indica* in full bloom can make the lasting qualities of the plant seem unimportant.

Always try to buy a well-furnished plant with leaves well down the stem or a bushy appearance

Plastic pots

Much controversy still reigns over the pros and cons of plastic pots compared to clay ones. A few years ago I would have unhesitatingly selected the plant growing in a clay pot in preference to an equally good, often better plant growing in a plastic pot. Nor does it seem so long ago that the rather conservative race of people generally referred to as gardeners, or growers, were shaking their heads disapprovingly at the thought of growing difficult or temperamental plants such as hydrangeas, cyclamen or poinsettias in plastic pots. However, as we all know, these plants are now almost all grown in the lighter pot, and it would seem that the clay pot with its many drawbacks is dying a comparatively rapid death. Have no qualms about selecting the plastic pot; most plants do equally well in them and many do very much better.

A slight change in growing technique is necessary for plants in plastic pots, in that they require very much less water than similar plants growing in clay pots. Some years ago a meticulously controlled experiment was carried out with clay and plastic pots in order to estimate the growth difference of plants grown in identical conditions. It was found that the different pots had very little effect on the plants. Where a mixed batch of pots was watered according to the requirements of the clay pots, the plastic ones became much too wet, and when the treatment was reversed, the compost in the clay pots became much too dry. In every other respect the clean, light and easily handled plastic pot gave a very good account of itself.

When growing African violets (saintpaulias), the plastic pot has a marked advantage over the clay, as the latter absorbs moisture that will quickly rot through any leafstalks that may rest on the rim of the pot. An aluminium foil, or silver paper protective cover, kneaded around the edge of the clay pot is essential in order to prevent leafstalks becoming wet.

Taking your plants home

Purchasing a suitable plant is one thing, but taking it from the shop to the home unprotected can often undo all the good work of the nurseryman. So when acquiring plants during the colder months insist on adequate wrapping. When making your choice, do not pass over the clean plant that has been carefully wrapped. Plants, as a rule, are reared in warm greenhouses and, though they quickly adapt themselves to cooler indoor conditions, a short

Knead aluminium foil round the edge of a clay pot to prevent the stalks of African violet leaves taking up moisture and rotting

spell in below freezing conditions will often prove fatal. The damage may not be apparent until some time later.

Mention of cold conditions suggests a further precaution when making one's purchase. Generally speaking, there are few shops where space is not a permanent problem, and this is frequently made obvious by the number of plants standing outside on the pavement. This may be all very well for the hardier type of indoor plant during the summer months, but the sight of a *Begonia rex* propped against the outside wall of a shop in the middle of March is enough to chill the blood. Need one be warned not to buy from the box outside, or from the inconsiderate person who placed it there?

Is it difficult to grow?

Of the various houseplants available, the majority are comparatively easy to manage and with reasonable care will give several years pleasure, while others are more trying and will test the skill of the most competent houseplant grower. Several nurserymen are wise enough to attach labels to their products with clearly printed advice regarding each particular plant, and stating whether they are easy or difficult to manage indoors. When purchasing plants needing higher temperatures, like codiaeums (crotons) and dieffenbachias, it should be realised that these are expendable but will give great pleasure, if only for a few months in some cases. Keen plantsmen, however, seem to manage many of them very well once the plants have settled down in their new environments. It should not be forgotten that when compared with an expensive bunch of flowers, the exotic foliage plant is indeed good value for money.

The conventional carboy is just one type of container that can be used to create a miniature garden with a controlled environment
Far left A sweet jar, an unheated propagating tray and a glass have all been used for this purpose
Left The traditional Wardian case invented by Dr Ward for delicate plants
Bottom left Although a complete contrast in appearance this modern 'bubble' terrarium performs much the same function as the Wardian case
Bottom right An old fish tank has been used to create a moist environment for small ferns

Displaying houseplants

Good display of house plants can make all the difference to their effectiveness as an ornamental feature in the home. And one of the best ways of achieving this is to group the plants in some sort of container, either sinking the pots into damp peat or removing the plants from their pots and setting them in compost. When a planting-up of this kind is attempted it is important to use slow-growing plants with similar cultural requirements and not to use too many – they must have space to expand.

To be really effective choose plants with different heights, leaf shapes and colours but keep the height in proportion to the depth of the container.

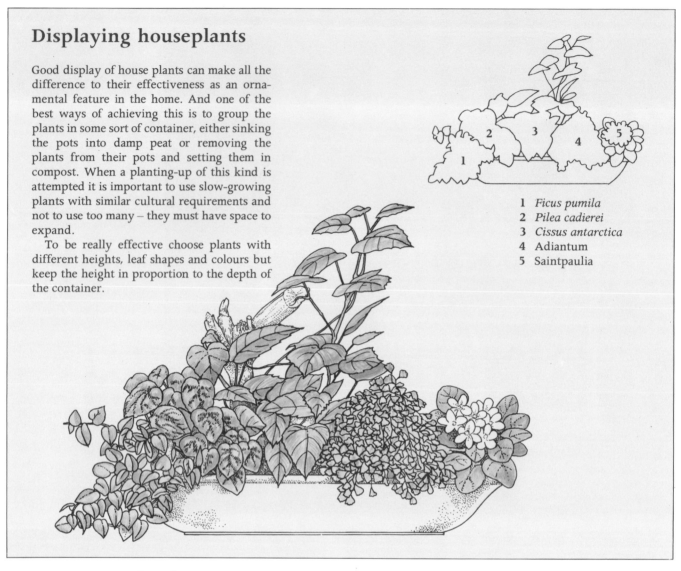

1 *Ficus pumila*
2 *Pilea cadierei*
3 *Cissus antarctica*
4 Adiantum
5 Saintpaulia

Containers & display

Suitable containers of adequate size are one of the most important aids to plant display, be it a piece of ornamental pottery for a single pot, or an elaborate container for a group of plants. When purchasing an outer decorative pot for a plant already in your possession take the simple precaution of either measuring the plant's pot before setting out on your errand, or, better still, take an empty pot with you of similar size to the one in which your plant is growing. Where possible, containers should be slightly larger than the pot in order that a layer of moist pebbles can be placed in the bottom of the decorative pot for your plant to stand on.

When selecting or making display containers, keep in mind the thought that the height of plants is almost invariably governed by the dimensions of the pot in which the plant is growing. The following approximate guide to relative sizes may be helpful: a $3\frac{1}{2}$-in diameter pot for a plant about 15 in to 18 in tall; 5-in pot for a plant about 20 in to 26 in tall; a 7-in ($3\frac{1}{2}$ ft to $4\frac{1}{2}$ ft) tall; and a 9-in pot for a plant about 5 ft to 7 ft tall. Plants in larger pots should always be seen before finalising purchase; otherwise, you may, for example, purchase a 4 ft tall monstera plant only to find that the spread of the plant is much too large for the position earmarked for it.

The use of larger containers accommodating a number of plants poses the question of whether one should employ the free-planting method, or simply plunge plant pots to their rims in moist peat. If the first method is adopted the container should be almost filled with compost and the plants placed on the compost in suitable positions to simplify the actual planting operation which follows. I would suggest that one or two spaces are left for flowering plants; do this by inserting an empty pot or two into the compost. These can be easily removed and replaced with a flowering plant at almost any time. When the plants are freely planted, growth will be much more vigorous, but there will be less opportunity for rearranging them.

If plants are left in their pots, probably the best plunging medium is moist peat, as plants are easily arranged in this and can be tilted at just the right angle for the finished effect. If the dark peat is found to be objectionable, a scattering of gravel on the surface of the peat will improve the appearance. Where plants with differing water requirements are free-planted in the same container it is wise to strike a happy medium when watering, and, if anything, one should err on the side of dryness rather than making the soil over-moist.

One should not be afraid of getting one's hands dirty occasionally when working with plants, even if it is only to prod a finger into the soil to test its water requirements. Nevertheless, it would be regrettable if a potential houseplant owner were to be put off by my references to soil, peat and the like. Take heart, there are many other ways of displaying plants, and inspection of the wide variety of plant stands and containers available in almost any good department store or florist's shop will provide ample inspiration. If space is limited, the standard type of plant trough can be used to get the maximum number of plants into the minimum amount of space. However, a well-arranged plant table always appeals to me as providing a clean and effective display that is easily maintained.

Plants in rooms

We have a lot to learn about plant display in a large living room of around 20 ft by 10 ft and our continental neighbours provide us with good examples.

Taking a typical block of flats (where indoor plants mean so much to those without gardens) almost anywhere in the country as a yardstick, I am afraid that the way houseplants are displayed compares most unfavourably with similar homes on the other side of the North Sea. Recently I had the pleasure of spending a holiday in Amstelveen, a suburb of Amsterdam, where I lived in a box-shaped room, with a large plate glass window, in a box-shaped block of flats. During the day these flats had little to commend them, other than immaculately tended gardens, compared to similar developments here. However, during darkness, when the room lights were switched

on, the place became a fascinating fairyland for me. My wife and I walked around and unashamedly stared into many of the delightful rooms with their diffused lights and remarkable range of superbly grown houseplants. I got the feeling that our Dutch hosts derived a certain amount of pleasure when someone stopped and paid them the compliment of admiring their contribution to the general charm of the neighbourhood. Need one add that a tour of a similar area here would be a pretty dismal business – and it could all so easily be changed, with a little effort.

Ingredients for success
Doubtless the bare minimum of curtain draped around the windows of Dutch homes during the day is one reason for them being able to grow plants of infinitely better quality than most of us here. I include myself, as I have been fighting a losing battle with my wife over the years to have windows freed from light obstruction. Alas, privacy is still more important. Of all the considerations when arranging plants indoors, perhaps the most important is to ensure that they have a light position in which to grow.

A further possible reason for our continental neighbours' success with plants is that they always seem to have plenty; seldom less than twenty in the average living room. There seems little doubt that plants do better when grouped together, be they in the greenhouse or the home, and the single plant with a room to itself rarely prospers. Like ourselves, plants seem to need company, and soon deteriorate in solitary confinement.

The continental grower is more fortunate than his British counterpart in that there are many more occasions, other than the usual ones, for the giving of flowers and plants as gifts. Birthdays and Christmas are important present-giving times, but it is also quite common for the continental housewife to find a welcoming array of plants and flowers awaiting her on return from her annual summer holiday. Plants play such an important part in room decoration that it is not uncommon to find specially designed plant windows in many homes; these are positioned where plants will not be exposed to strong midday sun. Such windows have special tiled sills, which are deeper than usual and are often provided with suitable drainage, so that there is no concern when water is spilt.

An extension of this idea is the plant room, where the bare minimum of furniture is used and plants are given pride of place. These rooms are not unlike the Victorian conservatory, except for the fact that they are integral

continued on page 24

The
Kitchen

Kitchens are usually very good places in which to grow houseplants. Conditions of warmth, humidity and light are all beneficial to the great majority of plants. However in many kitchens the temperature falls dramatically at night, particularly in the winter, so avoid plants which need a consistently high temperature. A variegated rubber plant in an old casserole dish looks fitting in kitchen surroundings **(below)**. A small fern and *Scindapsus aureus* complete the arrangement. Various plants have been carefully arranged in a family kitchen to make it look attractive without interfering with the cooking and eating **(right)**. Notice especially the trailing *Scindapsus aureus* on the right of the picture, grown on the hydroponic system, the small cacti on the windowsill and the pretty hanging basket which, of course, takes up no valuable surface space.

parts of the house with large plate glass windows, carpeted floors and other such comforts.

Plants as a special feature
In 1978 I was given sole charge of designing and arranging Rochford's Chelsea Flower Show display. The design was simple, the plants of superb quality, and everything went right on the day. The exhibit was awarded a Gold Medal at the show, and later in the year it was awarded the much coveted Lawrence Medal for the best exhibit shown to the Society during the course of the entire year.

The design was simple and all the plants were arranged so that they appeared in what I thought could well have been a natural setting. All too often one sees plant arrangements where the plants are put in hopelessly unnatural settings. The first lesson to be learned is that plants must never be overcrowded, and should not be fitted into an impossible location simply because it is pretty, or whatever.

Climbing plants   Recently I was asked to recommend plants for placing either side of an arched opening between two rooms. The suggestion was that a single plant in an attractive container should be placed on either side and that the plants should be soft and flexible rather than rigid, the idea being that they would grow up and be trained around the archway eventually creating a green arbour effect. In the end the chosen plant was the weeping fig, *Ficus benjamina*; two were placed at either side of the entrance. As this plant gets older the stems become less flexible, but in the early stages they can be tied in to provide a very pleasing weeping effect.

More of a clinging plant, but equally useful in providing cover for a wall as a climbing plant is grape ivy, *Rhoicissus rhomboidea*; there is also the newer version with serrated leaves, *Rhoicissus ellendanica*. If a more rampant green-foliaged climber is wanted then there can be no better choice than *Tetrastigma voinierianum*, but it is not the plant for the limited space of a small room.

Hallways   For a wide step, or for the more spacious entrance hall there are some fine plants that can be placed as individual attractions. Best known of these is probably the Swiss cheese plant, *Monstera deliciosa*, with its attractive serrated green leaves and bushy though reasonably compact habit of growth. Of a duller shade of green with fans of oval-shaped fingered leaves attached to stout petioles *Schefflera digitata* is a splendid upright plant. With both of these some of the lower leaves will almost inevitably be lost in time;

Monstera deliciosa or Swiss cheese plant is ideal for a light, spacious, draught-proof hallway

this is natural in most plants as they age. To help refurbish the lower and denuded portion of the stem, it is a good idea to introduce a small new plant at the base when the larger one is being potted on. For similar locations, particularly in cooler temperatures, one could consider *Aralia sieboldii* (syn. *Fatsia japonica*), which is reminiscent of the Swiss cheese plant.

A fireplace display   During the summer months the disused fireplace is a favourite position for indoor plants. When such a position is chosen for plants, take the precaution of blocking off the chimney vent with a piece of cardboard, otherwise they will quickly succumb to the draughty conditions. Unless the room is particularly well lit it is better to confine one's choice to the hardier varieties when decorating the fireplace, preferably to the green-leaved sorts. The fireplace is often the ideal place for arranging a temporary display of plants for a special occasion, when other space may be at a premium.

A group of small plants

Should a solitary plant be considered inadequate then one can go in for a collection in a larger container. Make sure that the plants you choose are compatible with regard to soil and atmospheric requirements, and mix leaf shapes and colour as well as size when forming the group. Water-grown plants, that survive very well with no soil whatsoever around their roots, could well be the ideal answer for a mixed grouping.

Small, individual plants are not so easily managed if they are to form an effective display, and for maximum effect it is often better to place such plants in a glass case of some kind – an old fish tank (even a new one!) being most suitable. The plants will grow extremely well as they are shielded from draughts and can create their own micro-climate. Such containers seem to me to be much more satisfactory than more conventional bottle gardens that always appear overcrowded and are difficult to get into to perform essential chores.

As I do my rounds I see an ever-increasing number of small greenhouses that are well suited for indoor use and the care of more tender houseplants. Plants in these are immediately accessible, and at minimal cost one can provide the temperature that the plants require without the cost of heating the entire room. Even a single light bulb will offer a surprisingly pleasant amount of warmth in a closed, glassed area indoors, and the additional light will also improve the performance of the plants as well as enhancing them visually. Small marantas, fittonias and selaginellas are fine for enclosed cases, as are African violets (saintpaulias) and smaller ferns.

Plants for dark corners

Time and time again I have been asked for advice on the most suitable plant for a dark corner. My reaction is to suggest the dear old cast iron plant (aspidistra) which will tolerate the most trying conditions without batting an eyelid, or, should we say, shedding a leaf.

For the slightly less dark areas of a room there are some fine plants to choose from, and one of the finest is the old favourite, the nephrolepis fern. These ferns are available in many splendid varieties, and have large fronds of greenery that will radiate from the pot in all directions. Keep them moist, sprayed over and in the shade and they will give endless pleasure as pedestal subjects.

Philodendron scandens and *Rhoicissus rhomboidea* are also fine trailing plants for shady corners. A plant that has been giving me considerable pleasure and very little bother in recent years is *Scindapsus aureus*. It is especially useful for providing contrast in areas of solid green leaf on account of its very attractive golden-yellow variegation.

In lighter and cooler locations the ivies will do well, and an old indestructible (surviving in almost any location) is the spider plant (*Chlorophytum comosum*). This is particularly attractive as a hanging plant when the young plantlets begin to spread in all directions thrown out on long stalks from the parent. For the more ambitious, though not such a difficult plant in my experience, is *Columnea banksii* which has pretty naturally trailing evergreen leaves and the added bonus of highly coloured orange flowers during March and April.

An indoor greenhouse creates a warm, moist micro-climate allowing delicate plants to be grown with much more reliable results

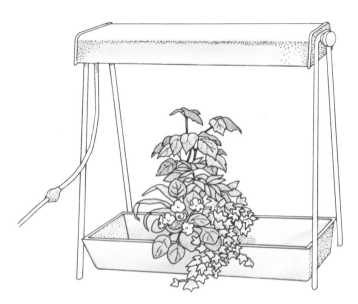

A tabletop lampstand provides light-loving plants such as African violets with the extra boost they need, particularly in wintertime

Artificial lighting

When arranging groups of plants or individual plants indoors, particular care must be taken that the lighting is adequate. A plant stood in a dark corner contributes little to the appearance of the room, yet the same plant artificially lit improves out of all recognition. Use light to enhance the appearance of your plants in the same way as the shopkeeper does to brighten his wares; though with plants, softer lighting is more effective.

Plants at party-time

Here I might well add a further note of warning; at party time plants will be much safer if they are transferred to an upstairs bedroom. Guests who are having just one more drink pressed on them are not above emptying the unwanted alcohol into the convenient receptacle provided by a plant pot! The damage does not become apparent until some time later and the plant's sudden failure usually remains a mystery.

Water-grown plants

The advantage of growing plants by this method, variously referred to as hydroponics or hydroculture amongst other names, is that the amount of water available to the roots of the plant can be fairly accurately controlled. The container in which the plant is growing is provided with a water-level indicator, which makes the task of filling up to the desired level

a reasonably simple operation. With soil-grown plants on the other hand there is always an element of doubt – has the plant had too much, or has it had too little?

There are numerous adaptations of the principle but the majority of plants that are growing in water started their life as conventional soil-grown subjects which, once they were well established, had all the soil washed from around their roots and anchored in the water with special clay pebbles. Those made from London blue clay and known as hydroleca are probably the best type available.

The advantages of these clay pebbles are that they are lightweight, attractive in colour and can absorb about one-third of their own weight of water. When plants are converted from soil-growing to water-growing they are placed in containers that have additional drainage holes in the base to allow maximum movement of water around the roots. When the water level of the container is correctly charged it does not mean that the base of the plant is totally immersed in water, only that the lower three or four inches of the pot, in fact, contain water.

Watering and feeding

When the indicator drops to the minimum mark there is virtually no water around the roots of the plant, but this condition is beneficial rather than harmful, so it is advisable to allow the indicator to remain on the minimum indication for at least three or four days before the reservoir is re-charged. When topping up, ordinary tap water must be used so that the very special fertiliser in the pot can be activated by the chemicals in the water and thus do its work effectively. Known as the ion-exchange fertiliser it is bonded on to polystyrene granules, and as the acidity of the water changes so the fertiliser becomes available to the plant in exactly the right amount. When plants are purchased they will have directions accompanying them which will indicate the frequency with which the fertiliser should be replenished and the amount that is required for the particular container. Because of the chemical interaction between water and fertiliser it is not possible to overfeed plants, but they can be starved of nourishment if one neglects to re-charge with fertiliser at the appropriate time.

All sorts of plants can be grown by means of the hydroponic system, some doing better than others, with flowering plants being the most difficult to manage. Almost all foliage houseplants will succeed, with the aroids, monsteras, philodendrons and similar plants growing at an infinitely quicker pace than the same plants growing more conventionally in soil.

Grouped plants

Besides individual plants in single containers, groups of plants in large troughs (frequently seen in office interiors) will also do splendidly. The important requirement here is that all the individual pots planted in the large container, regardless of the size of the plants, should be placed at the same depth. One can then set the system up with a single water level indicator that will work perfectly as all the pots are sitting in the same level of water.

In winter, for all types of containers the water should be maintained at a slightly lower level than during the summer growing months. Also, in winter it is advisable to use water that is tepid rather than cold, and the growing temperature for the plants should be maintained at a slightly higher average – somewhere in the region of 18°C (65°F).

Changing containers

Transferring plants to larger containers is only necessary if the existing one is very much out of proportion to the size of the plant. The transfer is simply done by lifting the plant out of its existing container and placing it in the larger one, adding sufficient pebbles to ensure that all gaps between the plant roots and the new container are filled in. Be certain that the water indicator is properly located, which means having it at the same depth as it was in the original container.

Converting from soil to water

Besides buying plants that are properly set up for immediate growing there are many kits on the market that will allow you to convert your own plants from soil to water growing. Directions are provided with all of these and some are much more satisfactory than others. However, it is important to ensure that the plants selected for conversion are healthy and well-rooted in the soil, they will then settle to the new growing method much more readily. The other important rule is to ensure that all the soil from around the roots of the plant is removed. This will entail holding the root ball of the plant under running water so that all the roots are exposed and clean. Advice among different kit manufacturers will vary, but the above is important, as is the need for keeping plants warm and shaded while the conversion is taking place.

Having set everything up and got the plants under way it will be found that water-grown plants are very much easier to grow than soil-grown plants.

A cross section of a plant grown on the hydroponic system

CHAPTER 2
Routine culture

Feeding

Beginners with houseplants often launch out with the best intentions, purchasing the best plants, suitable containers, and so on, yet, after a month or two, the plants have much smaller new leaves than they should have, lose their lower ones, and take on a generally hard appearance. Why? In the majority of cases, it is because feeding is being neglected.

The efficient nurseryman sends out established plants, be they in the smallest 'tots' or the larger 10-in size pot. From the time they have become established in their pots, large or small, the plants will have received regular feeding with a balanced fertiliser. Should this supply of nutrient suddenly stop when the plant leaves the nursery, a gradual process of deterioration will take place; hence the smaller and harder leaves.

For the sake of convenience most nurserymen use easily applied liquid fertilisers, though the wise ones occasionally ring the changes and give applications of powdered fertiliser during the growing season.

Simple rules

There are a few simple rules to follow when feeding houseplants. One should ensure that the compost in the pot is moist before applying fertilisers as dry roots are very easily damaged, particularly so if one is misguided enough to use plant food in excess of recommended requirements. Always follow the manufacturers' directions for they have experimented carefully in order to arrive at the correct strength and rate of use for their products. Some plants do not benefit from additional feeding, and advice on this matter is given under the descriptions of individual plants.

Roots are a very important part of almost every plant and any damage caused to the roots will inevitably be reflected sooner or later in the foliage. Damage can frequently be traced to the fact that the soil in the pot has lain wet and sodden for much too long, excluding essential oxygen and causing the roots to rot and die.

By the same token, plants that are fed to excess will also suffer root damage and the inevitable deterioration of the foliage. When a plant is being fed, unless it is very clearly a vigorous subject, the fertiliser manufacturer's feeding directions should be followed. Growth in winter is usually very much slower than in spring and summer, if there is any at all, so caution should be exercised when feeding. Some plants do not require any feeding at this time of year.

On the whole, winter feeding is an unnecessary extravagance, but if a plant produces new leaves in winter it will need a fertiliser that has a low nitrogen content to encourage the production of firm rather than soft leaves. Your sundriesman or florist will be able to advise you on the most suitable one to use.

It is worth experimenting with various fertilisers to see which ones the plants like best. In experimenting you will find out that there is tremendous variety in cost as well as performance.

Foliar feeding
Plants with very vulnerable root systems, the more delicate ferns for example, will respond better to a foliar feed. This is sprayed on to the foliage and assimilated by the plant through the leaves.

When to change the diet
Besides changing the method of feeding in this way, there may also be a need for altering the fertiliser given to the plant at a certain time. For example, many of the flowering pot plants, such as gloxinias, will perform very much better if they have a change of diet as they are about to come into flower. While

leaves are being produced it is necessary to feed established plants with a fertiliser containing a high proportion of nitrogen which will encourage leaf development, and to change to a fertiliser containing a higher proportion of potash at the first sign of flower buds. Therefore a collection containing a mixture of flowering and foliage plants should be fed with fertilisers of differing composition. It all sounds terribly complicated but, in fact, it is a simple matter to purchase what is wanted as all the fertiliser manufacturers clearly list the composition of the feed on the containers.

Tablet fertilisers

Fertilisers in tablet form are also excellent for potted plants and have the advantage of being easy and clean to use. Here again, one should resist the temptation of overdoing it – it is so easy to push into the pot more tablets than recommended by the manufacturer.

Watering

The failure of nearly all the plants that eventually find their way to the dustbin can be traced to the over-indulgent plant enthusiast who is ever ready with the watering can. Strangely enough, it is misguided kindness on the part of the plant owner to feel that the plant needs a little something almost every time he or she has a cup of coffee. Much of the damage can also be attributed to the oft-repeated advice, 'Drop it in a bucket of water, wait until all the bubbles stop coming up and your plant will be sufficiently moist'. To my mind, 'completely waterlogged' would be a better interpretation of the plant's condition.

This treatment may be all very well for the dry azalea, hydrangea, or even the houseplant of the aphelandra type which has been allowed to become very dry, but for the majority of plants it is not advisable. In the greenhouse, however, where moisture in any shape or form is a blessing on a hot day, plunging pots in a bucket of water can have its advantages.

As I travel around the various horticultural shows meeting the gardening or houseplant-growing-public, I am increasingly aware of the need for some sound advice on the subject of watering. Inquirers often say they have purchased a particular plant and would appreciate being told exactly how often it will require watering. I get the impression that an exact answer such as 10.15 a.m. on Tuesday and 3 p.m. on Friday would be quite acceptable. But such a reply would, of course, be ludicrous. Plants are very much like human

beings, and no two identical plants reared in similar conditions would require exactly the same treatment in respect of food and liquid nourishment.

So what is the answer? First, there is little doubt that it is best to err on the side of dry conditions rather than wet, and, with the average houseplant, to allow the compost to dry out a little between waterings. Bear in mind that roots in a permanently wet compost become lazy and inactive, there being no need for them to forage in search of moisture. An active root system is the perfect anchor for a well-furnished plant, healthy roots are much more capable of withstanding the indifferent treatment that many indoor plants are often subjected to.

How to tell when plants need water

Often, one is advised to tap the pots with a tool made by fixing a cotton reel on the end of 2-ft cane to test the plants' water requirements. A dry pot will give a resonant ring and a wet pod a dull thud. This piece of advice, handed down through gardening books, may apply where the experienced gardener is concerned, but the mind boggles at the thought of the average owner of a few indoor plants performing this percussion exercise, and trying to decide whether it should be one or two egg-cupfuls of water.

Better by far to give plants a good watering by filling the space between the rim of the pot and the compost each time the soil takes on a dry, grey-brown appearance. If the soil is very dry do this twice, allowing the first lot to soak in before giving the second watering. Err on the side of dryness by all means, but guard against excessively dry soil; the mixture must never be so dry that the compost is coming away from the side of the pot. Should this happen, subsequent watering will result in water finding its way between soil and pot too rapidly, thereby preventing the root ball from becoming moistened which is, after all, the prime object of watering.

A sluggish soil that drains slowly, or not at all, quickly becomes sour. Remedy this by removing the root ball from the pot in order to unblock the drainage holes; it may be necessary to place a few pieces of broken flower pot (crocks) over the drainage holes of clay pots. Plastic pots are amply provided with drainage holes, and only the presence of worms in the soil would cause the drainage holes to become obstructed.

Automatic watering

In recent years the principle of watering plants by means of capillary action has gained many

*A capillary watering unit
is invaluable to the
houseplant-owner at
holiday time*

devotees, and much work has been done towards perfecting this method of watering. The plants are stood on a permanently moist base and take up water according to their needs. It is particularly useful if one leads a busy life and cannot attend to the water requirements of plants as often as one should. Equally, it is a boon in the conservatory or greenhouse that is left unattended for most of the day while one is out at work. Capillary watering also presents a method of ensuring that plants have ample moisture at their roots while owners are on holiday. This is particularly useful as houseplants always present a problem at holiday time.

Many plastics' manufacturers have developed trays that need little more than a supply of water from a 'header' tank or bottle, and a 2-in layer of sharp sand or special fibre matting in the tray to become almost foolproof capillary units. The water level in the reservoir tank should be topped up periodically; after initial experiments it becomes a simple matter to adjust the apparatus to ensure that the sand or matting is maintained at the ideal degree of moistness for the plants' needs.

A makeshift capillary unit can be made simply by filling a shallow baking tin with sand and keeping it moist by means of a watering-can. The sand, for best results, should be kept quite wet, but avoid getting the sand into a puddled condition as the plants would suffer from waterlogging and would quickly deteriorate.

Thin-based plastic pots are ideal for capillary watering, as the compost in the pot and the wet sand come into direct contact, thus ensuring that water is drawn up from the sand immediately. Holes in the bottom of clay pots should be plugged with a piece of fibre-glass padding which will act as a wick, so bridging the gap between compost and sand. The plant pots must be gently pushed into the sand when placing them in position. It is important that the soil in the pot should be watered before placing it on the sand to encourage the capillary action. Further watering of the soil should not be necessary.

Lighting

Although some plants will tolerate lower light levels it is generally considered that a minimum of 800 lumens is necessary if plants are to do reasonably well. Better results are possible if a slightly higher level of light can be maintained. The difficulty however is in converting lumens into everyday terms – for example, how many 60 watt light bulbs does one require in order to produce the required light level? Although I have never had a satisfactory answer, it is generally considered that a level of light sufficient to work by is about right for plants. Many plants, African violets (saintpaulias) in particular, will grow perfectly well without any form of daylight if there is adequate artificial lighting for their needs, but it is essential that the lights be left on for at least twelve hours in each twenty-four.

There are specialised light fittings purporting to simulate normal sunshine that one can purchase for placing above plants so that they not only look better, but also grow better. However, for everyday needs the majority of plants will do well in rooms that are bright during the day and augmented by normal room lighting in the evening.

If you are lighting your plants take care not to scorch the leaves. Lights should not be placed too close to plants, particularly spotlights which generate a considerable amount of heat.

Potting on

One other aspect of houseplant culture that may be taken as routine is the need to transfer plants to larger containers when the soil becomes exhausted. The appearance of a few wispy roots through the bottom of the pot does not necessarily indicate that the plant is in need of fresh soil. The actual root ball must be inspected by removing the plant from its pot, and if the roots are well matted you may then consider that potting on is necessary. An emphatic plea – plants should not be knocked out of their pots any more than is absolutely necessary. A friend describes it as resembling a surgical operation from which the plant requires time to recover.

The potting on operation is best performed in March or April when the roots are starting into active growth and will quickly get on the move into the new compost.

Pot sizes

Pots are available in many sizes, but in the business of growing plants commercially the larger sizes are generally 5-, 7- and 10-inch; thereafter plants go into a tub of one kind or another.

The potting sequence is geared to the sizes of pot that are generally available: you transfer a plant from a 5-in pot to a 7-in pot and when it has outgrown the 7-in pot you simply put it into a 10-in container. Once established in pots of this size, the majority of indoor plants will be happy for many years if regular feeding is not neglected.

Potting composts

The potting mixture itself is not so critical as we are sometimes led to believe. Experience has shown that almost all houseplants prefer a light, open soil of a spongy texture. To arrive at this, without suggesting ingredients that are often difficult to acquire, use a mix consisting of two-thirds John Innes No. 2 potting compost (or No. 3 for larger pots) and one-third clean peat. Naturally enough, some plants will

need a different mixture; these will be dealt with in the notes on individual plants.

With the increase in popularity of indoor plants there has been an inevitable increase in the supply and range of ancillary items that are available to improve the performance or

A simple method of potting on: use the existing pot as a mould to make a hole in the new soil exactly the right size for the rootball of the plant

appearance of the plant. One pleasing result of this activity is that there is now a much wider range of potting mediums from which to choose – soil for acid- and lime-loving plants, soil for cacti and soilless composts.

Soilless composts

The last mentioned are composed almost entirely of peat with added nutrients. Much experimentation has gone on in perfecting these soilless mixes, and they are excellent for a wide range of indoor plants, provided one ensures that the feeding of the plant is never neglected. It is also important that these composts are never allowed to dry out excessively as they are difficult to re-wet satisfactorily. Perhaps I am a little old fashioned, but I am still a little hesitant when it comes to using soilless mixes for larger plants that are to stay in the same pot for a long time. I feel that such plants require a percentage of loam in the potting mixture, but for smaller plants the soilless mixes offer quite considerable advantages.

A technique for beginners

For the experienced gardener potting is a simple enough task, but the beginner may well approach it with some misgiving. The novice might benefit by adopting the following method; instead of potting the actual plant, take a pot of the same size as that in which your plant is growing and use if to form a mould in the slightly larger container. It is then a simple task to remove the plant from its pot and drop it into the perfectly shaped hole, having first removed the empty pot.

Potting on larger plants

Most growers of indoor plants will happily tackle the task of potting on small plants into larger pots but tend to be less adventurous when it comes to moving large plants on into more roomy containers. Yet the principles involved are very much the same – the new pot should be only a little larger than the one the plant is growing in, and both the plant and new compost should be moist. Spring is the best time to tackle the job. However, the actual time of year is not critical if the growing conditions are favourable.

Potting of larger plants can be undertaken in exactly the same way as that described for smaller plants – you simply make a mould in the new compost with the pot that the plant is growing in, and then place the root ball of the plant in the perfectly shaped hole. However it is of the utmost importance to ensure that the soil is well firmed around the root ball before giving a thorough watering.

Cleaning the leaves

Many indoor plant growers have a fetish for cleaning the leaves of their charges when, more often than not, the plant would be much happier if it were left alone. Wiping the leaves of plants with a soft, damp cloth is quite adequate most of the time; care must be taken not to handle tender new leaves. There are all sorts of concoctions on the market for imparting a gloss to the leaves of indoor plants, but all of them must be used sparingly and with a degree of discrimination. You must never use leaf cleaning sprays or liquids when temperatures are low, or if plants are likely to be exposed to direct sunlight immediately afterwards. When making use of any leaf cleaner for the first time it is advisable to test it on one hidden leaf first in case it damages the leaves in any way.

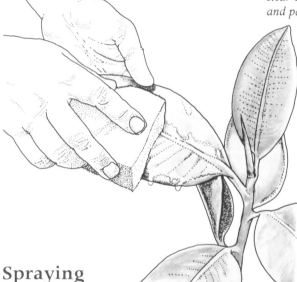

Large-leaved plants need an occasional wash with clear water to remove dust and particles of grime

Spraying

Many indoor plants, particularly those that prefer high humidity such as ferns, will relish an occasional fine spray of water on their leaves. Besides offering beneficial humidity, the presence of moisture will deter red spider mite which thrives in hot, dry conditions. When spraying plants with water, and especially when treating with an insecticide, particular care must be taken to ensure that the undersides of leaves are thoroughly wetted.

A further word of warning, particularly important where aerosol sprays are much in use, is that one should at no time expose plants to housefly sprays, furniture polish aerosols, or hair lacquer sprays. In fact, indoor plants must at all times be protected from all forms of spray other than those that are specifically intended for use on plants.

CHAPTER 3
Types of container

The makers of fancy pots, troughs and such like have not been slow in keeping abreast of the general increase of interest in houseplants in recent years. A wide range of designs and materials are available for this purpose.

When selecting containers the appearance is, of course, important, but it is also essential to ensure that they are of adequate size and that they are watertight. To obviate the possibility of water seepage damaging furniture, one should take the precaution of placing a cork mat under the container until it is obvious that dampness is not likely to be a problem.

Wooden containers

In spite of all the new materials, plant troughs and boxes made from good quality timber still hold their own and blend perfectly with almost any kind of foliage. Such boxes can be made watertight by inserting a metal liner, or, more cheaply and simply, by using drawing pins to tack a double thickness of polythene to the inside of the box. When using any form of wood preservative for treating boxes prior to planting, care must be taken to ensure that the material is not harmful to plant life.

In most cases it will be advisable to fit legs to the container or to place it on a table where plants may benefit from the maximum light available, only larger plants should actually be placed on the floor. The fitting of castors enables one to move plant boxes back into the warmth of the room in the evening where the plants will be much more comfortable than they would be if left in the cooler window position.

Dish-type containers

I find that dish-type containers of fairly generous proportions (deep enough to accommodate a 5-in pot) are excellent for temporary plant arrangements. The owner of a dozen or so plants will derive much pleasure from displaying them in a group as a change from lining the windowsill or decorating the wall. If the container is first filled with peat, newspaper, or sphagnum moss, which is kept moist, this will ensure that plants remain firmly in position when inserted. One precaution is necessary: do not allow the plants to be too congested. There must be sufficient space between each for them to be individually appreciated. Displays of this kind can be dismantled and rearranged weekly and will permit the use of flowering pot plants when they are in season, thus providing an extra touch of colour.

Plant troughs

The majority of houseplants seem to enjoy the company of each other, and grow better when they are grouped together. However, the large plant that is well-established will happily endure solitude in its individual corner.

Plants grouped together in a plant trough, provide a pleasing focal point in the room, besides affording the plants more agreeable conditions in which to grow. Where possible, plants ought to stand on, or be plunged in, a moisture-retaining material of some kind. Sphagnum moss, moist peat, or even wet newspaper can be used for this purpose. So that watering needs can be attended to, care must be taken to ensure that the pots are plunged only to their rims and no further. Moist pebbles, or one of the light-weight aggregates such as Lytag, provide an ideal base for standing pots on. Though pebbles must be kept wet to give a moist atmosphere around plants, it will be detrimental if the plant pot is actually allowed to stand in water.

Other suggestions

Try exploring local junk and antique shops for suitable containers such as pretty china washing bowls. It is also possible to obtain antique or reproduction versions of the Victorian jardinière which consists of an elegant pedestal topped with a matching bowl.

Copper soup tureens and old brass coal scuttles, if they can be acquired, are also excellent for setting off groups of indoor plants.

Self-watering pots

Houseplant owners who are obliged to leave their plants unattended for any length of time may well gain from purchasing one of the variety of self-watering pots and troughs that are on the market. Not all of these give the desired results, but the majority, having overcome their teething troubles, are now thoroughly reliable. With these devices,

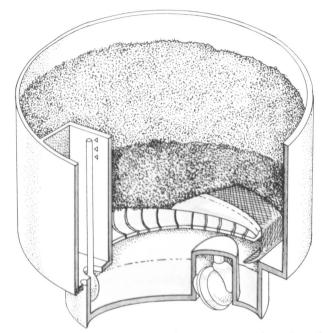

An automatic watering pot. Being clean and easy to move about, these are ideal for office arrangements

Junk shops and markets will prove to be fertile hunting grounds for unusual plant containers

watering is simplified to the point where one merely tops up the water supply at intervals to a clearly marked level. Such containers are also ideal for the plant grower who is at a loss to know what to do with indoor plants when going on holiday. Recently, I heard about a rubber plant that grew in a self-watering pot from a height of 2 ft to 9 ft in the space of three years. This remarkable rate of growth was, it seems, achieved with the minimum amount of attention.

Tall containers

Strawberry pots, made of clay with carefully placed holes in their sides for plants, can be especially attractive when planted up with a collection of different ivies with something more colourful such as a geranium planted in the top of the pot.

Tower pots are similar, but slightly more elaborate; these are plastic cylinders with bays for plants in their sides that can be stacked one top of the other. The cylinder is filled with compost, and as this is being done plants are introduced through the gaps in the side of the container. In limited space this is an excellent way of growing all sorts of indoor plants to make the most of their varied colours and habits. Tower pots are also suitable for growing strawberries in a limited space such as a patio or balcony.

Spiral planters look attractive from any angle but watering must be done carefully

Wall brackets

One sometimes sees photographs of interiors in magazines in which exotic houseplants are displayed to perfection. On seeing the latter, the reader may be tempted to set forth and purchase an exotically-coloured codiaeum (croton) for placing in a wall bracket where it will blend perfectly with the general decor. The hot, dry atmosphere that plants will have to contend with when pinned to the wall will, in most instances, result in quite rapid deterioration.

If neglected for only a short time the leaves of the wall plant will quickly take on a dry, toasted appearance. When positioning wall brackets it is particularly important to ensure that they are not directly over room heaters; the hot dry air from these would lessen the plant's chance of survival. Tiny pots dry out very rapidly, so ensure that you buy brackets which will accommodate a pot of at least $3\frac{1}{2}$-in diameter so that the plants in them can be thoroughly watered.

Wall brackets, in my opinion, are not suitable for the majority of houseplants, except for the real toughies, such as ivies, trade-scantias, *Philodendron scandens* and *Rhoicissus rhomboidea*. Less hardy plants should be placed where their needs can be more readily administered to, and, unless of trailing habit, the majority of smaller plants are really seen to best effect when one looks down on them.

Wall brackets are decoratively pleasing but only reasonably hardy plants should be used in them

1. *Sit the hanging basket in the top of a large pot to make watering easier*
2. *Line the basket with sphagnum moss and fill the bottom with compost*
3. *Carefully place some of the plants through the sides of the basket and firm their roots into the compost*
4. *Fill the remainder of the basket with compost*
5. *Position the final plants in the top of the basket remembering to allow room for them to grow and develop naturally*
6. *A hanging basket planted-up with colourful summer-flowering plants will provide a long-lasting source of pleasure for a patio or conservatory*

Hanging baskets

Many of the easier houseplants will benefit from a short 'holiday' in the garden during the summer months. In this connection the hanging basket is ideal in that it can be planted and put in position outside in the garden or on the balcony and can be quickly moved to a sheltered spot should the weather become inclement.

Planting up a hanging basket

The basket you choose should have a reasonably close mesh and not be rusted or damaged. Fresh, moist sphagnum moss should be used to line it. Place the basket in a large empty pot for support and then tease out the moss to make an even lining without gaps. Fill the basket with the chosen compost (preferably peat-based) and firm it into position as you go along. If desired, small trailing plants, such as ivy, tradescantia and lobelia, can be planted through the sides of the basket so that a fuller effect is achieved when the planting is complete. When the basket is filled with firmly compressed compost the principal plants can then be introduced. This is simply done by making large enough holes in the compost to receive the root ball of each plant in turn. One should avoid the temptation to plant too thickly, as plants in baskets that are kept moist and fed regularly will usually make rapid progress.

If the basket is intended for the conservatory, patio, or the greenhouse there is a very wide range of plants to choose from: lobelia that will trail down, petunias in an incredible range of colour, geraniums both upright and trailing, ivies and fuchsias. Although they may be included with other plants I find that fuchsias are much more satisfactory when individual varieties, such as *Fuchsia* Cascade or *F.* Marinka (both natural trailing types), are the only plants in the basket. For indoor use, however, one should confine the choice of plants to those that are known to do well in the home – fuchsias for example would be of no value as there is not sufficient light indoors for these plants to retain their flowers.

Although one must agree that the conventional moss-lined basket is probably best, excellent results can be had by lining the basket with black polythene prior to filling with compost and planting. Some form of drainage is essential, so use a skewer to perforate the polythene after planting. Where drips may be a problem there are baskets available with built-in trays.

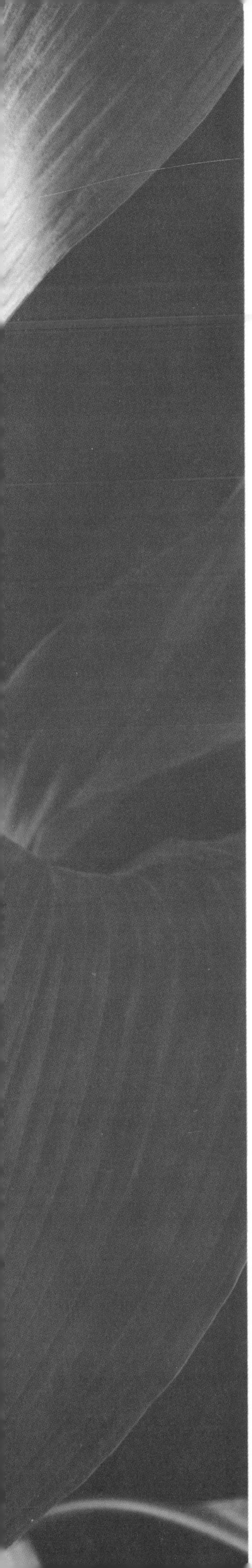

CHAPTER 4
Easily grown houseplants

*O*ver the years the majority of the plants referred to in this chapter have proved successful in all manner of conditions, and almost all are available from a general nurseryman. Purchase of some will, however, necessitate a special order to your supplier, and the possibility of having to wait until a batch of plants becomes available.

Growing conditions and cultural directions for plants in this group can be generalised; where special treatment is required this is stated in my notes on individual plants. On the whole, a light position and a temperature in the region of 16°C (60°F) is advised. Information on general care (watering, feeding and such like) will be found in the chapter on Routine culture.

To make reference easy, the plants in this section have been grouped together in their families. There is also a comprehensive index at the back of the book.

Araceae

Aroid family

Plants belonging to the family *Araceae* are frequently referred to as aroids, and they are to be found almost everywhere in the world in one form or another. The arum lily is one of the best known members of this botanical grouping.

If houseplant growers were to be deprived of any particular family of plants, for some reason or other, one feels that the aroids would be their greatest loss. From this single family we get easy plants, difficult ones, flowering plants, and many of the bolder ones so much relied upon for display and general decoration. Almost all of the pot-grown members prefer a temperature in excess of 16°C (60°F) and the atmosphere is rarely too humid for them. Yet

one recalls the disastrous cold winter of 1962–63 when many plants were obliged to suffer lower temperatures than were previously thought possible. Although many succumbed, a surprising number pulled through. We learned that when low temperatures were unavoidable the plants tolerated the conditions much more satisfactorily when the soil in the pot was kept almost bone dry. One batch of *Philodendron bipinnatifidum* that we were growing, when treated in this way, survived temperatures that were, on many nights, down to 1°C (34°F).

Monstera deliciosa borsigiana
Swiss cheese plant

Really mature plants of monstera would in some cases be large enough to fill a small living room, leaving very little space for inhabitants or furniture. Do not be alarmed, when confined to smaller pots indoors, the leaves remain a manageable size.

Often I am asked what one should do with the freely produced aerial roots of this plant. The answer is to tie them in loosely with string and wind them around on top of the soil in the pot. Make a hole in the compost with a pencil and direct the tip of the root into it; this will keep the young roots under control.

One must be patient in order to appreciate the reason for the name *deliciosa*, as there is nothing about the plant itself to suggest the reason for it. Mature plants of monstera will in time produce exquisite, creamy-white inflorescences (flowerheads). These are very short lived and eventually develop into fruits of the most unappetising appearance. To sample the fruit at its best one must be patient and leave it on the plant until the outer protective covering begins to disintegrate. Even then it is possible to eat only a little of the fruit at a time, with its elusive pineapple-banana flavour; in Australia it is called the

continued on page 44

The
Living Room

The living room probably offers more scope for growing
houseplants than any other room in the house as it is likely
to be both light and warm. Plants on a windowsill look fine
during the day but on winter's evenings bring them into
the room rather than leave them trapped in the cold air
between window and curtain. A fireplace arrangement
makes a good feature for a living room (below) as long as
draughts can be excluded. Blinds rather than curtains
make a room beautifully light (right) so that a wide range of
plants can be grown.

fruit salad plant. I find that it is best to stand the fruit in a jug and to eat a little with a spoon each day as the outer green covering goes through the natural process of peeling itself away from the pulp-like fruit underneath. Do not let the appearance of the edible part put you off – your courage will be well rewarded.

Monstera leaves can be cleaned in the same way as those of other glossy-leaved plants, though great care must be taken not to handle young leaves, which are very easily damaged.

Philodendron bipinnatifidum

This plant is best suited to the more spacious room where its large leaves will have an opportunity to extend to their full spread. Though sometimes offered for sale, smaller plants are not very satisfactory, as the leaves do not show their true character until the plants are growing freely in pots of at least 7-in in diameter.

Surprisingly enough, I once saw this plant being used as a hanging basket subject in one of the reception areas of a continental airport. It is comparatively easy to grow so maintenance was little bother, and the plant effectively relieved the emptiness of the high ceiling.

There are several similar philodendrons with leaves radiating from a central crown on petioles 2 ft or more in length. These will develop aerial roots in time and, as an alternative to tying them together on top of the pot, the roots can be directed into a container of water and allowed to take in moisture from this source. It is also a good way of interesting young children in plants for they will be intrigued to see the root action. When a plant is treated in this way it will be found that the compost in the pot requires comparatively little water.

Philodendron Burgundy and P. hastatum

These two plants are both typical of the aroid family in their cultural needs. Both benefit if their supporting stakes are clad with a 1- or 2-in layer of fresh sphagnum moss. If the moss is kept moist, the freely produced aerial roots will quickly find their way into it, and the plant will grow much better as a result. Keeping mossed stakes moist indoors does, however, present a problem. This may be overcome by standing the plant in the bath, or outdoors (on a fine day), and thoroughly soaking the moss with a hand spray. Many of the other aroids will also benefit from the use of similar mossed stakes. These stakes are easily prepared by binding the moss to the stake with plastic-covered wire of neutral colour; plastic wire is preferable to metal wire as it is non-corrosive.

Philodendron scandens, the popular sweetheart plant

Damp sphagnum moss bound firmly to a stake with rust-proof wire is the best form of support for moisture-loving plants

Philodendron scandens
Sweetheart plant

By far the best known of the philodendrons is *P. scandens*, or the sweetheart plant; this is mainly because of its ability to withstand ill-treatment. It would be nice to say it remains unscathed, but low temperatures and mis-handling soon give the leaves a dry, paper-like appearance instead of their natural glossy green. The American common name, bath-room plant, gives a clue to the conditions it likes – a hot and steamy atmosphere. Bath-rooms with a minimum temperature of 16°C (60°F) are ideal; it would be unwise to subject *P. scandens* to the temperature fluctuations of the average bathroom which is often very cold for most of the day. Fluctuating temperatures are more damaging to plants than those that are constant, even though slightly below the recommended level.

Araliaceae

Aralia family

Plants belonging to the *Araliaceae*, the aralia family, are native to both tropical and temperate parts of the world and include many with ornamental foliage and attractive habit.

Fatsia japonica and Fatshedera lizei variegata

When considering this family we are immediately faced with a plant that masquer-ades under two names – *Fatsia japonica* and *Aralia sieboldii*. Like the ivies, which also belong to this family, the aralias are dual-purpose plants in that they may be planted out in a sheltered spot in the garden when they have outgrown their allotted space indoors or as an alternative to throwing them in the dustbin. The green form of *Fatsia japonica* is an 'easy doer' that will, with proper attention, make a substantial plant, though this will take some time in room conditions.

In common with almost all variegated plants, *F. japonica variegata* is a slightly more difficult plant that is inclined to have brown leaf edges if neglected. Larger plants of this variety will remain more compact and attractive if they are potted into standard John Innes No. 3 potting compost.

Before discussing the ivies, I must mention a man-made plant, fatshedera, which gets its name from its two parents, fatsia and hedera. Having enlarged ivy-shaped leaves on the upright stem, the fatshedera is an excellent choice for the back row of a group of plants. *Fatshedera lizei variegata*, the variegated variety, is a more colourful plant, but inclined

continued on page 48

Overleaf A varied collection of easily grown houseplants
1 *Sansevieria trifasciata laurentii*
2 *Chlorophytum comosum*
3 *Rhoicissus rhomboidea*
4 Two varieties of peperomia
5 *Billbergia windii*
6 *Philodendron scandens* and *Pilea* Moon Valley
7 *Maranta leuconeura erythrophylla*

Fatshedera lizei

to have brown leaf edges if the compost is kept permanently wet.

For those with an experimental turn of mind it is interesting to try grafting one of the more decorative small-leaved hederas onto the top of a fatshedera, thus giving a fascinating plant that will never fail to interest visitors. To perform the grafting operation it is necessary to have a reasonably healthy fatshedera plant about 3 to 4 ft in height, which should have its growing tip removed. The stem should be attached to a cane to keep it erect. With a sharp knife cut down twice into the stem just above the leaf joint for about 1 in. Prepare four wedge-shaped ivy tip cuttings from firm pieces, and insert these into the cross-shaped cut made in the top of the fatshedera. Tie them very firmly in position with raffia or adhesive tape, place a polythene bag over them and tie the bag in position. The bag will prevent the cuttings drying out and will consequently help them to bond much more readily. When the cuttings begin to grow the bag must be removed and when the ivy pieces have developed several new leaves the tips should be pinched out to encourage a bushy appearance.

1. *The growing tip of the plant is removed and a cross cut made into the stem*
2. *The ivy tip cuttings are placed in the cross cut*
3. *The cuttings are bound tightly into place with raffia and the whole graft is covered with a polythene bag*

4. *The resulting plant when ivy growth has matured and the leaves of the original fatshedera plant have been stripped off*

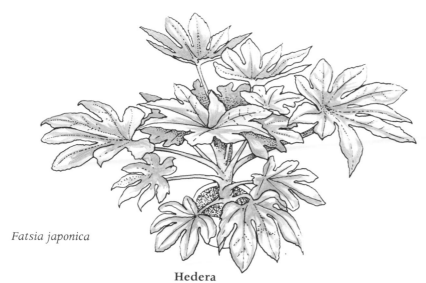

Fatsia japonica

Hedera
Ivy

In spite of flowering plants, exotic foliaged ones and new introductions, the hederas, or ivies, still retain their popularity, and can well form an interesting specialised collection of plants. In fact, a collection of ivies would give a pleasing display all the year around. There are about 25 different kinds to choose from, though only about 15 are readily available.

We hear many opinions to the contrary, but it has been my experience that all the ivies offered for sale as houseplants also make excellent garden plants. Success in establishing them out of doors depends to some extent on the planting time. Give the soil time to warm up, then, about the middle of May, plant them out. On walls, in the rock garden, or dotted around in the shrub border they will be a continual source of pleasure. By far the most spectacular is *Hedera canariensis* and, when planted against a sheltered wall, there can be few climbing plants that give a better year-round display. Some I planted a few years ago were reluctant to produce anything more than the odd bit of straggling growth until two substantial York paving stones were placed on the soil immediately in front of them. The cool, moist root run under the stones seemed to be exactly what the doctor ordered. Grown in this way there should never be any shortage of cream and green material for flower arrangements.

Even when the last spark of life appears to have deserted your ivy, put it in the garden instead of the bin – the results, nine times out of ten, will surprise you.

But the subject is indoor plants, to which I return. Of the larger-leaved ivies probably *H. canariensis* and *H. maculata* are the most popular; others, such as the varieties Ravenholst and Gold Leaf, have fallen out of favour. Indoors, ivies all require similar conditions for success – the most important being a light, airy room and a modest temperature in the region of 13°C (55°F). Hot and dry conditions encourage red spider mite; the browning of leaf edges is by way of being their trade mark.

Almost all growers of houseplants list a good selection of hederas, so there would not seem to be any need for repeating them all here. However, some of my particular favourites are worthy of special mention.

Hedera helix Adam has grey-green variegation and tiny leaves which are perfectly shaped and compactly arranged on the stem to the point where they overlap on particularly good specimens. Because of the tightly matted leaves, care must be taken not to get the centre of the plant too wet, or wet at all for that matter. It will also pay to periodically check over the plants and remove any dead leaves that would be liable to rot if left in the centre. The compact leaves and distinct variegation make this variety a great favourite with florists as the final touch to brides' bouquets.

Stocks of the variety Little Diamond vary considerably in quality, so care must be taken when making one's selection to ensure that the individual leaves are, as the name suggests, diamond shaped. Good stock should also have naturally twisting stems, and such plants are particularly suitable for grafting on top of fatshedera, as previously described.

I am including the variety Glacier not so much for its attractiveness as for its lasting qualities. For inclusion in an arrangement of plants, to trail over the edge of the container and break its line, Glacier is ideal. It is also particularly suitable for use as a trailing plant in window-boxes out of doors and does not seem to mind harsh weather.

The small-leaved ivies almost all branch freely when the growing tips have been removed; this should be done occasionally to keep the plants compact and tidy. One of the exceptions is Jubilee (commonly named Golden Heart on account of its gold-centred leaves with a green perimeter), and for this reason it is not often grown commercially. In full sun in the rock garden, however, it can be relied upon to give a good year-round display, for although there is a tendency to wander, growth is easily snipped back and kept under control.

The easily grown *H. canariensis* is quite the best of those with bolder leaves. One of its drawbacks is its unwillingness to branch when the growing tip is removed. Instead it continues to grow from the leaf bud immediately below the position where the tip was taken out. So, in order to keep the plant within bounds, the growth should be wound back and forth

continued on page 52

Despite their exotic appearance most bromeliads are not difficult to care for. Often the colourful bract will last for many months so, although they are by no means cheap, they are good value for money
Left The stunning bract of *Guzmania lindenii*
Above right *Neoregelia carolinae tricolor*
Right *Aechmea rhodocyanea*

around itself. When twisting the stems, take the simple precaution of bending them in a gentle arch, for if the growth is bent at too acute an angle the flow of sap is checked and the part beyond the fractured stem invariably dies off.

Bromeliaceae

Bromeliad or pineapple family
Named after the Swedish botanist, Bromel, members of the *Bromeliaceae* or pineapple family, are much neglected. If only on account of their durability, they deserve to be more popular.

It is always a problem to decide whether the bromeliads should be included among the flowering plants or the foliage plants, but as most of them take several years to produce flowers (some as many as fifteen) I feel that they are with us longer as foliage rather than as flowering plants, and have included them here.

Billbergia
Billbergia is surely one of the easiest of all indoor plants to care for, the most popular varieties being *B. nutans* with narrow leaves and *B. windii* that has broader leaves. There

Billbergia nutans

are several others that display very exotic bracts, but all for only a few days duration. All have the typical elongated funnel-shaped bracts of the billbergia from which emerge more bracts of exotic colouring.

Both *B. nutans* and *B. windii* will form solid clumps of rosettes in time, which can be divided at any time to provide new plants. Plant divided pieces into small pots filled with peaty compost and they should produce greenish coloured bracts in a surprisingly short time. Plants with their roots bound in a clump of sphagnum moss and attached to a tree branch in the greenhouse can present a most impressive sight when the pendulous bracts appear. Given reasonable temperature and conditions they are dependable plants.

Cryptanthus
Earth stars
Beginning with the smallest members of the family, there are the cryptanthuses and tillandsias; the latter has an exciting range of bract shapes and flowers, mostly in shades of blue, but these are short-lived. For the bottle garden there can be no better choice than the compact cryptanthuses that can remain undisturbed for long periods without attention. These are grown primarily for their colouring, and, perhaps more particularly, for their fascinating shapes that have earned for them the apt common name of earth stars.

The flowers of the cryptanthuses are, on the whole, insignificant and barely emerge from the tightly overlapping leaves of the plants. In common with other members of the family, offsets will be produced at soil level when flowering has finished. When large enough these offsets can be removed by bending them to one side, and can be planted up individually in small pots filled with a peaty mixture. Rooting will be considerably speeded up if the pots are stood on a bed of peat which has an electric soil-warming cable running through it.

Cryptanthus tricolor, unfortunately rather a costly plant, is of striking appearance, particularly when the cream and green striped leaves take on a reddish tint. Both the colouring and appearance of *C. tricolor* is greatly improved when the plants are grown in a natural way on an old log or piece of bark, instead of in the more conventional pot. These 'mobiles', as they are called, have a certain fascination when suspended in mid-air on a length of clear nylon fishing line. Only close inspection will convince admirers that the 'object' is not floating in space.

Mobiles are easily made by knocking plants from their pots and placing a wad of fresh sphagnum moss around the exposed roots; the

light and dark shades of grey, form an urn-shaped rosette, the centre of which must be kept topped up with water. From the centre of the 'urn' the bold pink bract emerges, and from the bract striking blue flowers eventually appear. The cost of these plants often discourages the would-be purchaser, but it should be borne in mind that they very rarely take less than four years to produce a bract. With the assistance of carefully measured chemicals and gases, plants can be induced to flower in less time; the results, however, rarely match up to the naturally produced product.

Ideally, aechmeas should be purchased when the bract is a little above the water level in the urn. Records show that, when purchased at this stage, it is quite possible for them to remain colourful for up to 12 months. As the bract begins to fade and die, so too, does the rosette from which it came; this is common to all bromeliads. When the main rosette is no longer attractive it should be cut away with a sharp knife, care being taken not to damage the new young shoots that will by then be sprouting from the base of the parent plant.

moss ball is then tied securely to the chosen anchorage. Nails can be driven into the bark or log and used for tying the plants, and these can subsequently be concealed by an additional bit of moss wedged in around them. Needless to say, mobiles are better suited to the greenhouse or conservatory where drips resulting from watering will not be a problem. Water the plants by saturating the moss with a fine syringe when necessary, or by plunging the plant and anchorage in a bucket of tepid water.

Some of the tillandsias will also be perfectly happy if attached to a log in this way, though care must be exercised to ensure that only those with small, compact rosettes are selected.

Epiphytic plants grow well if their roots are wrapped in sphagnum moss and bound to the branch of a tree or piece of bark

Larger Bromeliads

Space permits mention of only a few of the larger bromeliads, *Aechmea rhodocyanea*, *Guzmania lindenii*, *Neoregelia carolinae tricolor* and *Vriesea splendens*. All are spectacular plants that should give little difficulty if a minimum temperature of 16°C (60°F) can be maintained.

Aechmea rhodocyanea
Urn plant
Aechmea rhodocyanea is a very fine plant, and one that the uninformed look at with amazement, wondering whether it is real or not. They might well wonder, for a mature plant with a well-developed flowering bract has few competitors in the 'exotic honours' field. Large, strap-like, recurving leaves, banded in

Aechmea rhodocyanea

There is much argument as to whether or not one should remove these shoots and pot them up individually, or leave them to develop still attached to the parent rosette. I can only quote the experience of a keen gardener of my acquaintance, who was in fact the part-time gardener at my local railway station. He left the cluster of five 'pups' on his plant, and two years later he had the most magnificent specimen with four heads at the

continued on page 56

Far right This plant display has been put together to contrast many different leaf shapes and colours. It includes *Begonia rex, Maranta leuconeura kerchoveana* (rabbit's tracks), *Philodendron scandens* and heptapleurum
Top right Coleus is easy to propagate and provides a wealth of colourful plants
Bottom right Two plants with interesting leaf markings: *Peperomia magnoliaefolia and Pilea cadierei*

peak of perfection, all in full colour at the same time. What is more, they were still in the same soil. Why did number five fail to develop? There is always a 'why' in gardening!

In the greenhouse, healthy plants will produce side growths that develop quickly and may have bracts in as little as one year, but this is the exception and two years at least must be allowed under normal circumstances.

With all larger bromeliads it is important that the 'urn' be kept topped up with water, preferably clean rain water which should be completely changed periodically to prevent it becoming stagnant.

Guzmania lindenii

Another bromeliad which is spectacular when the head of dark red bracts appears is *Guzmania lindenii*. It needs a warm, but lightly shaded position and, as with other bromeliads, the compost should be only just moist but the vase in the centre must be filled with water.

Other good kinds include the much smaller *G. lingulata minor* with orange-coloured bracts and a new sort, *G. Orangeade*, with orange bracts and pale green leaves.

Neoregelia carolinae tricolor

Neoregelia carolinae tricolor is another spectacular and thoroughly reliable plant which I first saw growing in an airport restaurant where the amount of natural day-light was negligible. In fact, the neoregelia was one of only two survivors from the original planting – in spite of the fact that the 'urn' seemed to provide a convenient receptacle for discarded cigarette ends.

The saw-edged overlapping leaves will brighten any display with their cream and green variegation; strong sunlight will give an overall russet flush to the leaves. Mature plants eventually have bright red centres, and at the same time the rather insignificant flowering bract appears in the middle of the urn, barely emerging from the water that must always be present. A word of caution, as the flowers appear the water in the urn takes on an unpleasant odour and should be changed more frequently than usual. The compost in the pot must be kept moist, but never saturated. Many of the bromeliads will tolerate comparatively dry root conditions provided the water level in the urn is maintained, but the lower leaves of the neoregelia become brown and shrivelled if the soil is excessively dry for any length of time.

Vriesea splendens

The vrieseas include some of the most interesting plants in the family. In particular there are *Vriesea hieroglyphica* and *V. fene-stralis*, both of which have astonishingly intricate leaf markings. These I mention only by way of interest, knowing that they are difficult to acquire, and that only the true expert could ever hope to succeed with them indoors.

Vriesea splendens is a plant that is generally available and relatively easy to care for. It should have a light position in the room. An interesting feature of this plant is the way in which the transverse light and dark bands of colour on the leaves gradually blend into a greenish-brown overall colouring as the spear-shaped red bract increases in size.

Compost for bromeliads

Bromeliads, on the whole, have rather poor root systems, so when potting it is important to ensure that a light, open compost is used. One successful mixture consists of the following ingredients: one-third pine needles, one-third oak or birch leafmould, and one-third peat. If all those materials are not at hand, prepare a mixture which conforms to this specification as nearly as possible, bearing in mind the need for an open, spongy compost.

Commelinaceae

Spiderwort family

The *Commelinaceae* or spiderwort family is native to tropical and subtropical regions and includes the tradescantias, which will be familiar to many readers.

Zebrina pendula

Tradescantia Quicksilver

Tradescantia
Wandering Jew

There is always a soft spot for one or other of the tradescantia tribe, first introduced to this country some 300 years ago and still as popular as ever. Most are easy to care for, while others are a wee bit difficult; almost all of them root like the proverbial weed when propagated from cuttings. For the beginner there can be no better choice than tradescantias, and the many varieties available will ensure a pleasing range of colour throughout the year.

In the easier range there are the varieties Silver, Gold, *tricolor*, *purpurea* and the lovely Quick Silver, which has altogether larger and more colourful leaves. *Zebrina pendula*, formerly named *Tradescantia zebrina*, with silver, green, purple and grey leaves, is another in the easy range. Slightly more difficult are *T. blossfeldiana variegata*, *T. quadricolor* and the related *Setcreasea purpurea*, the purple heart.

Many are the complaints we hear of tradescantias turning green in colour and losing their bright appearance; much of this is due to inadequate light and too much moisture at the roots. The old adage that tradescantias should be kept dry and starved in order to preserve the variegation has never proved itself in my experience; such treatment results in thin, weedy growth that may be variegated but is certainly never attractive. Stand them in the lightest possible window, feed them regularly and pot them on as required is the best advice for obtaining healthy and variegated plants. Also, when green shoots appear on the plant they should be ruthlessly removed, as these contain much more chlorophyll and so grow more rapidly, leading to a completely green plant in time.

One is often shown a tradescantia with the proud comment that the plant is four, five or even six years old; and, quite honestly, they almost all look as if they are at least that age. To get the best out of these plants, new ones should be started each year in order to provide fresh, vigorous growth. Select the most colourful growths, about 4 in in length, and put five or six around the edge of a 3½-in pot filled with John Innes No. 2 potting compost or a soilless equivalent. Rooting them first in a normal propagating mixture is a complete waste of time. To keep the plants compact, the cuttings should have their growing tips removed almost as soon as they have rooted.

Where space permits, it may be worthwhile preparing a hanging basket of tradescantias. Do this by selecting half-a-dozen potfuls of the most colourful plants and space them out evenly in a basket that has been lined with black polythene and filled with John Innes No. 2 potting compost or a soilless equivalent. It is important that the polythene should have several holes made in it so that excess water can drain away easily. Tie in some of the longer shoots underneath the basket and pinch out the growing tips periodically to improve the shape of the plant; weed out those green shoots as they appear. The *tricolor* and Silver varieties make particularly good subjects for use in baskets.

Setcreasea purpurea
Purple heart

Setcreasea purpurea belongs to the same tribe as the much more common tradescantias, but it is a much more difficult plant to track down when it comes to purchasing as well as being marginally more difficult to care for.

The striped leaves have a base colour of olive green, and are an attractive purple on the undersides; the small white flowers of the plant are insignificant. Useful as a hanging plant, it will quickly develop masses of long, trailing growth in conditions offering reasonable light and warmth. New plants can be raised from cuttings a few inches in length taken at almost any time of the year. Plants should be fed regularly while in active growth, and the soil should never be allowed to become wet and sodden.

Compositae

Daisy family

The *Compositae* or daisy family provides us with many of our most colourful and adaptable garden plants, and the potential of many as pot plants has not been neglected. Both of the plants mentioned here are grown primarily for their foliage, as their flowers are comparatively insignificant.

Gynura sarmentosa

Gynura sarmentosa
Dead nettle

This plant attracts the eye, especially when the sunlight picks out the velvety purple colouring of the topmost leaves. Reasonably easy to grow, *Gynura sarmentosa* may in some conditions be genuinely described as rampant, though it will present problems when culture is at fault. It abhors wet conditions and seems to enjoy a warm, sunny position. As houseplants go, this dead nettle is unusual in that it produces orange-coloured flowers fairly freely. Alas, they are in no way an attraction, and they should be removed while still in bud on account of their abominable odour. Cuttings are little trouble to root, so it is better to propagate a few fresh young plants periodically and to dispose of the older ones when the new have rooted.

Senecio macroglossus variegatus
German ivy or Cape ivy

Deceptive, in that it is frequently mistaken for an ivy, *Senecio macroglossus variegatus* is recognised as something different when one touches the thick, fleshy leaves. The shape of the leaf is more or less triangular, and the plant is a natural climber, twining itself around any convenient support. It is comparatively easy to please if given a light position and if the watering-can is used sparingly. Be particularly careful not to water freely during the winter months. The orange-coloured daisy flowers are attractive, but rather inconspicuous against the cream and green background of the foliage.

Euphorbiaceae

Spurge family

The members of the *Euphorbiaceae*, the spurge family, occur as both garden and houseplants and include an important genus of succulents. The brightly coloured Christmas flower, the poinsettia, is a well-known example, although it has a very different appearance from the plant listed here.

Ricinus communis
Castor oil plant

With leaves similar in shape to *Fatsia japonica* (with which it shares the common name of castor oil plant) *Ricinus communis* is an annual plant grown from seed that will reach some four to six feet in height, depending on treatment. To improve germination the seed should be soaked in warm water for several hours before sowing. Sow seed in the spring in peaty compost and pot on as necessary – the larger the eventual pot the larger (usually) the

Ricinus communis

plant. Reddish, palmate leaves are carried on upright stems, and make the ricinus an attractive plant either for indoors or as a centre piece in the summer flower border.

Liliaceae

Lily family
The *Liliaceae* or lily family is known to everybody and, like many other plant families, it includes subjects which bear little superficial resemblance to each other. If a sansevieria plant is placed next to a hyacinth in flower, the uninitiated would find it difficult to believe that they are botanically related. However, see *Sansevieria trifasciata laurentii* in flower in mid-summer and the similarity is immediately made clear. The pale green, faintly scented flowers of this sansevieria are frequently looked upon as something of a phenomenon, but they are, in fact, quite freely

produced on mature plants. Occasionally the small sansevieria will also oblige with a flower and the owner may with some justification feel that his plant deserves more than a passing glance.

Aspidistra lurida
Cast iron plant
The cast iron plant, *Aspidistra lurida*, is the toughie to outlast all toughies, and there is a keen desire by many to see the return of the aspidistra to the nurseryman's list. Sad to say, the aspidistra, besides being durable, is also lamentably slow-growing when compared to the more modern houseplant. The cost of growing them today would be prohibitive and beyond the purse of most would-be purchasers.

When I asked an old gardener how he cared for his 60-year-old cast iron plant that was growing in good health, he supplied the following rather surprising answer: 'Every springtime I knock it out of its pot, remove about one-third of the soil (roots and all) from the lower part of the root ball. Then I put a crock over the hole in the bottom of the pot, add an equivalent amount of soil to that which was removed from the root ball, and place the plant on top of it. After watering in, the plant never looks back'. Drastic, but effective.

Aspidistra lurida

Chlorophytum capense variegatum
Spider plant
This is another favourite houseplant that can be propagated without difficulty. Grass-like in appearance, chlorophytums produce plantlets on long stalks that can be rooted in ordinary soil by pegging them down in much the same way as one would layer a strawberry runner. Plants are sometimes reluctant to produce these little ones but it has been my experience that, when large enough, all chlorophytums produce young plantlets, and very fine they are when seen trailing from a hanging basket. For success, keep them well watered, well fed, and pot them on into slightly larger containers annually in the spring. Other than that, all they ask for is a light position and a moderate temperature. Browning of the leaf tips presents a minor problem, and is usually caused when plants are inadequately fed or are in need of potting on.

Sansevieria trifasciata laurentii
Mother-in-law's tongue
This plant seems to thrive on neglect, and is decidedly happier when the soil is very much on the dry side, particularly in winter. Cold

or wet conditions or a combination of the two are the worst enemies of this plant, but it will thrive in warm, sunny situations.

When purchasing, it is wise to select plants that have young shoots growing up at the side of the pot; one can then be reasonably sure that they are well-established.

As the rhizomes increase in both size and number they will break the pot in which they are growing, be it clay or plastic, and this is a positive sign that the plant is in need of fresh soil around the roots. Use John Innes No. 2 potting compost or a soilless potting compost and pot firmly. As older plants tend to become top-heavy it is wise to use heavier clay pots rather than plastic pots.

Marantaceae

Maranta family
It would be bold and foolish of me to include the entire maranta tribe – members of the *Marantaceae* – in this easily-grown section, but there are two that seem to qualify: *Maranta leuconeura kerchoveana* and *M. leuconeura erythrophylla*.

Maranta leuconeura kerchoveana
Rabbit's tracks or prayer plant
On reading the above heading one cannot help but feel that common names are, in their way, something of a blessing. For good measure this plant has two: rabbit's tracks, which it gets from the smudged brown spots on the attractive green leaf, and prayer plant. The reason for the second name is not obvious until the leaves are seen to fold up together like hands in prayer as darkness descends. This is a somewhat eerie sight when first seen by torchlight in a darkened greenhouse; leaves that were perfectly flat during the day having folded together showing only their reverse sides. One gets the feeling that every movement one makes is being watched!

Maranta leuconeura erythrophylla
Herringbone plant
Maranta leuconeura erythrophylla does, fortunately, have a common name, herringbone plant, which is a less tongue-twisting alternative for the layman. Understandably enough, this plant is also sold as *Maranta tricolor*. It is a particularly exciting plant that has come on the scene comparatively recently. At first sight the predominantly brown leaves, with quite fantastic stripes and patterns running through them, suggest a delicate stove (very warm greenhouse) type of plant. Limited experience has shown that it propagates

Maranta leuconeura kerchoveana. Inset shows leaf detail of M.l. erythrophylla

readily, and is more durable than almost any other plant in the entire family. However, do not run away with the idea that it is a tradescantia type of plant; it will require a minimum temperature of at least 18°C (65°F) and careful watering for success. When potting marantas, the addition of extra leafmould or peat to recommended composts is essential, and it should be firmed lightly. Exposure to strong, direct sunlight for any length of time should avoided, as it will quickly result in the leaves losing their colour and the plant taking on a generally hard appearance.

Moraceae

Fig family
The members of the *Moraceae* – it is a large family containing 55 genera – are mostly native to the tropics. In this family I am concerned only with the genus *Ficus* (the figs), a collection of plants of considerable importance to the houseplant enthusiast.

Ficus elastica robusta
Rubber plant
The rubber plant, *Ficus elastica robusta*, has, over the years, become the epitome of a houseplant. It would be virtually impossible to answer here all the questions that are asked about rubber plants, unless many other houseplants were to be excluded from the chapter. Also, since so many different species of ficus are cultivated in the home, I have

decided to give general information on ficus culture rather than a catalogue of ficus names with specific cultural instructions.

Of all the questions that are asked, the most frequent is, without doubt, the one concerning loss of leaves. When plants lose their lower leaves it is, in most cases, due to overwatering, although it is quite natural for older plants to shed leaves as they increase in height. During the winter months water should be given sparingly as the plants are dormant and, therefore, need much less moisture. Rapid defoliation suggests other possible causes such as: overfeeding; insecticides used incorrectly; the use of harmful oil-based leaf-cleaning agents applied too frequently or at excessive strength; or coal gas fumes.

Considerable harm is also done by potting plants at the wrong time of the year, or when, in fact, potting is unnecessary. The layman is frequently misled into feeling that the obvious answer to the appearance of yellow lower leaves is to purchase a larger pot and transfer his ailing plant to it. Potting on (in effect, removing the plant from one pot and putting it into a pot one size larger) and disturbing roots that are probably damaged anyway, is a positive way of writing the plant's death warrant. Sick plants should be carefully nursed back to health by placing them in a draught-free corner where an even temperature of about 18°C (65°F) can be maintained. Above all, water must be given sparingly to give new roots an opportunity to get on the move.

Some ficus owners are plagued by their plants losing leaves, while others are casting worried glances at the top of the plant as it makes its way inexorably towards the ceiling. It was at one time a standing joke to suggest cutting a hole in the ceiling so that the plant could also be admired in the bedroom above!

For plants that are getting too tall and running out of head-room, one of three solutions is suggested. First, ask your nurseryman if he will be prepared to accept it in exchange for a smaller one, with suitable cash adjustment, naturally. Secondly, consider lopping off the top of the plant – probably a more practical suggestion. Do this with sharp secateurs; cut straight through the main stem about 1 in above a leaf joint at the height you wish your plant to be. The cut will exude latex that will dry up in time or it may be sealed by rubbing it over with a little moist clay soil or ordinary compost. The plant will subsequently produce four or five new shoots from the topmost leaf joints, so giving it the appearance of a standard specimen, like a standard rose or fuchsia.

The third suggestion is for the more adventurous, and involves an operation known as air-layering, see page 158. The foregoing information applies to healthy rubber plants, and one should not be too optimistic when treating ailing plants in this way.

Indoors, the rubber plant has a growing season that extends, more or less, from March through to October, during which time it will put on an average of one leaf per month — many more where conditions are favourable. However, some plants will go through the entire summer and develop no new leaves at all, and for no apparent reason. Occasionally, if the plant suffers a setback it will stop growing for a time; until, in fact, conditions are again to its liking. At these times it is particularly important to ensure that the winter watering procedure is practised, that is, giving water only when it is obviously required.

Temperature is quite important if plants are to develop leaves of normal size; over 18°C (65°F) the leaves will be larger than normal and inclined to droop, under 7°C (45°F) much smaller leaves will result. Plants that have been subjected to widely fluctuating temperatures will show this by producing large or small leaves, depending upon the temperature prevailing at the time these leaves were about to open.

Piperaceae

Pepper family
This family contains a group of plants known as peperomias. There are many different species and varieties the majority of which are compact and low growing. Those with variegated leaves need ample light in order to retain their attractive colouring while those with darker leaves become hard in appearance when exposed to excessive sunlight.

The best-known peperomias
Best known of the peperomias are *Peperomia magnoliaefolia*, with fleshy leaves, cream and green in colour; *P. hederaefolia*, with metallic grey leaves; and the attractive dark green, crinkle-leaved species, *P. caperata*. The last two are not difficult to propagate if this is done by leaf cuttings in the manner of saintpaulias (African violets).

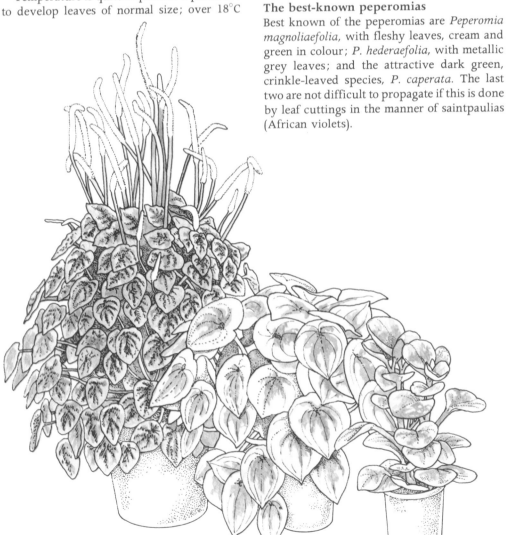

Three types of peperomia

With the variegated sorts it is necessary to take a cutting with part of the stem attached to the leaf if a variegated plant is to result from the propagation. Cuttings prepared from leaves only will result in green growth. Yet the leaves of *P. sandersii*, with dark stripes of green on the grey background, can be propagated by cutting the leaf into sections, and the resultant growth is invariably identical to the parent leaf in both colour and pattern.

Peperomia rotundifolia is the most recent to be tried as a houseplant. It has plain green, rather uninteresting leaves, but it has an advantage over most indoor plants in that it regularly produces its clean, white flowers. When the flowers fade, cut back to a sound pair of leaves, so that fresh growth may be encouraged.

Proteaceae

Protea family
The *Proteaceae* or protea family is a large group of plants containing many large shrubs, which were particularly popular over 100 years ago when large conservatories were fashionable and could provide the plants with the protection that most of them require.

Grevillea robusta
Australian wattle or silk oak
Here again we have two common names for the same plant – the Australian wattle and the silk oak. It is a fast-growing green plant, that quickly adapts itself to most reasonable growing conditions. It is easily reared from

seed, and besides being an attractive indoor plant it plays an important part as the centre-piece of bedding schemes in many public parks during the summer months.

Rapid growth is a drawback in some respects, as grevilleas will outgrow their headroom in a matter of two or three years, if conditions are to their liking. Ideally, by the time it reaches the ceiling the keen houseplant grower should have a younger plant growing on, ready to take the place of the larger one. It is not everyone who has the heart to destroy over-grown, healthy plants, so finding a suitable home for the monster becomes a problem. The garage showroom, or the hotel manager will often take these off your hands and give them a home where overhead space is improved by the presence of the silk oak.

Saxifragaceae

Saxifrage family
The plants of this family are well known to everyone. The production of new plants from small plantlets is a characteristic feature and is clearly shown in the houseplant members of the family.

Saxifraga sarmentosa
Mother of thousands
Saxifraga sarmentosa, an attractive trailing plant with small pink and white flowers, makes rapid growth, and ease of propagation ensures that it will retain its popularity. Mother of thousands, as it is called, is seen to best advantage when placed in a pot or small orchid-type slatted-wood basket and suspended from the window lintel. Small plantlets snipped from the parent plant establish themselves readily.

Tolmiea menziesii
Pick-a-back plant
Described as a hardy perennial herb, *Tolmiea menziesii* is also a fine indoor plant that is very much neglected in this respect. Outdoors the foliage will die back in winter, indoors it will remain evergreen.

This is a particularly easy plant to care for, and has the amusing common name of pick-a-back plant, which it gets from the way young plantlets are formed and carried 'on the back' of older leaves. These young plantlets root with ease in ordinary compost if they are inserted with the parent leaf still attached.

Avoid overwatering, especially during the winter months, but keep moist and well-fed at other times once plants have become well-established.

Grevillea robusta

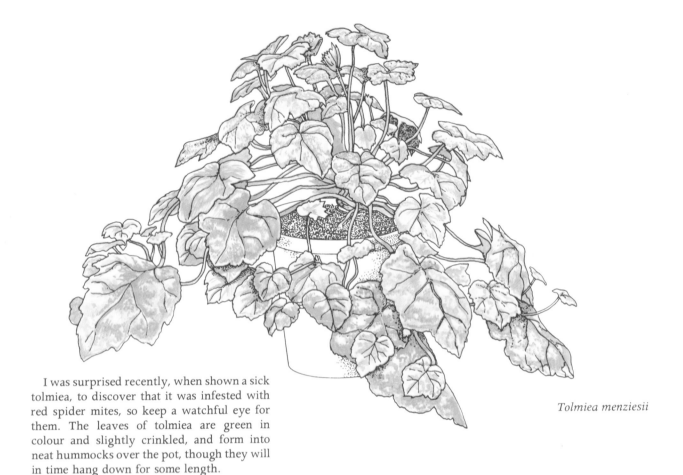

Tolmiea menziesii

I was surprised recently, when shown a sick tolmiea, to discover that it was infested with red spider mites, so keep a watchful eye for them. The leaves of tolmiea are green in colour and slightly crinkled, and form into neat hummocks over the pot, though they will in time hang down for some length.

Urticaceae

Nettle family
Apart from the well known weeds the nettle family contains several good garden plants and two important genera of houseplants.

Pileas
Aluminium plant
The nettle family's two main contributions to the modern houseplant scene are the attractive variegated plants *Pilea cadierei* and *P. cadierei minima*. The latter is rapidly gaining in popularity over its larger-leaved forbear. These have aluminium-coloured leaves (hence the common name aluminium plant) and are comparatively easy to care for; only when the compost is well filled with roots are they inclined to become hard in appearance and less attractive. Like tradescantias, they are simple to propagate, so it should be the rule to raise new plants from fresh cuttings periodically. Regular pinching out of the growing tips is necessary if growth is not to become leggy. Remember a small, bushy, 'well-furnished' plant is much more attractive than an ungainly, sprawling large one.

Pilea cadierei (**above**) *and Pilea Moon Valley* (**below**)

Pilea mollis
Pilea Moon Valley

Pilea mollis is much better known by its common name of *P.* Moon Valley, and is one of our most attractive smaller foliage plants. These plants may be used to good effect as individuals on the windowsill, as part of a group planting, or may be seen at their best when several small plants are gathered together in a shallow dish. The rough texture of the leaves and their attractive golden-green colouring make these very attractive plants. They are not difficult to manage if given reasonable warmth and light. Occasional pinching out of the growing tips will keep plants compact and bushy.

Coleus
Flame nettle

Coleus in their many brilliant colours are invariably a good purchase, as they are inexpensive and not in the least difficult to manage. Plants grown from seed are available in the spring and will usually require potting on into slightly larger containers soon after purchase. Use a fairly rich compost and pinch out the growing tip of the plant after it has been potted – this will encourage the plant to branch and form an attractive bushy shape.

Coleus, showing a variety of leaf markings

Select the best colours when purchasing young plants, or if you wish to grow the plants from seed, again select and retain only plants of better colouring. Plants of particular merit can be retained to grow on the following year, or new plants may be easily raised from seed sown in the spring. In time coleus tend to become untidy and overgrown, and it is then a good idea to propagate new plants from the topmost stem sections; pieces with three or four leaves attached will be about the right size.

Besides the run of the mill sorts that are raised from seed there are also many excellent named varieties available from nurserymen that have splendid colouring, and in some cases seem to have a superior habit of growth.

Vitaceae

Vine family

A characteristic of the vine family or *Vitaceae* is that the majority of the members of the family are climbers and produce tendrils which help them to attach themselves to supports.

Cissus antarctica and Rhoicissus rhomboidea
Kangaroo vine and grape ivy

The two important contributions made by the vine family to present-day house plant displays are the kangaroo vine, *Cissus antarctica*, and the grape ivy, *Rhoicissus rhomboidea*. The first-mentioned is reasonably easy under most conditions, though it does not approve of hot, dry rooms, particularly if the compost in the pot is allowed to become too dry. Under these conditions, the leaves take on a crisp, dry appearance, and the plant does not recover very readily. Yet its close relative, the grape ivy (there is also the larger-leaved *Rhoicissus rhomboidea* Jubilee) is probably the most durable of all indoor plants. Of climbing habit, it has naturally glossy leaves.

A few years ago an observant Danish nurseryman detected a variation in one of his plants – a piece with shallow-indentations along the margin of the leaf. The rogue piece was nursed along with more than a little care, and we now have a new variety freely available called *Rhoicissus ellendanica*, which is a combination of the nurseryman's wife's name, Ellen and danica for Denmark.

Although the indentations distinguish it from the grape ivy, the leaves have the same attractive glossy appearance of the parent, and it is equally easy to care for which means that it is one of the plants best suited to indoor growing.

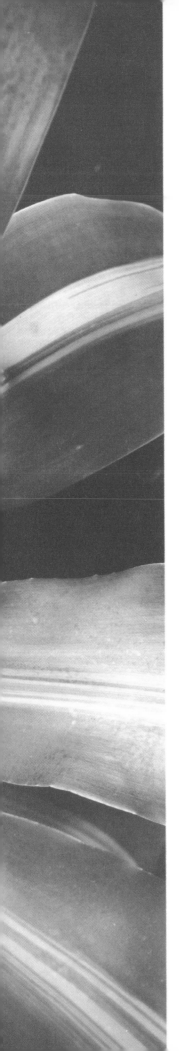

CHAPTER 5
Distinctive houseplants

When gathering together a collection of plants it is wise to include a few that are out of the ordinary, be it for their flowers, leaf colour, or simply because they have an unusual shape.

Because of their habit of growth or their colouring many plants can claim to be distinctive, some easy to care for while others will prove more testing. Whatever their merits in respect of culture, there is little doubt that the inclusion of a selection of distinctive plants will enhance the appearance and prove more interesting in almost every collection of indoor plants. Some of the plant varieties mentioned will in all probability prove difficult to acquire, but obtaining material is all part of the challenge when it comes to growing more distinctive plants.

Acorus gramineus variegatus
Easy

Of the grassy-foliaged plants available, the golden-leaved acorus is one of the best, being compact, colourful and easy to grow. With almost any other houseplant it would be fatal if it were allowed to stand in water for any length of time, but the acorus is rarely too wet, and will often do better if the pot is partly submerged in water. It is a particularly fine plant for a bottle garden.

Aglaonema
Moderately difficult

In the past few months I have been agreeably surprised at the way in which a plant of *Aglaonema pseudo-bracteatum* has tolerated indifferent treatment and the smoky atmosphere of a club bar. In its favour, no doubt, is the constant minimum temperature of 17°C (63°F) that is maintained for 24 hours a day. Aglaonemas are difficult to purchase, but there seems to be much interest in the new variety Silver Queen which is short and compact with silver-grey leaves and which is likely to become more easily available in time.

Mealy bug is a troublesome pest that is difficult to eradicate and it will attack the roots as well as the leaves of this plant. A thorough drenching with malathion insecticide diluted according to the manufacturer's instructions is effective if the bug is detected in time.

Araucaria excelsa
Norfolk Island pine. Easy

Araucaria excelsa, popular in the past, is slowly coming back into favour as a decorative houseplant. In common with many of the Victorian potted plants, it is slow growing and therefore, by definition, costly. In a cool room, where the temperature need not exceed 10°C (50°F), its tiered green leaves seldom fail to please. Water moderately, as the leaves quickly lose their crisp appearance if the compost is permanently wet; likewise, leaves are spoilt if the temperature is excessive. It is usual for new plants to be raised from seed, but this is a slow business. Sow seed in John Innes No. 1 potting compost or a soilless seed compost in February or March.

Begonia
Moderately easy

The rex types of begonias, with their intricate and colourful leaf patterns, are the best known. For indoor use, I find that some varieties of *Begonia rex* are better than others and, in particular, those with smaller leaves are easier to care for. After a time plants become unsightly when the rhizomatous growth extends beyond the edge of the pot, and lower leaves are lost in the process. Although it presents considerable difficulties, I have known enthusiasts succeed when attempting to root leaf cuttings in pans of moist peat on a window sill (for further details see page 162).

Besides the rex types there are many other equally interesting and attractive fibrous-rooted begonias, and one finds it difficult to understand why these delightful plants are not more popular. These range from the tiny

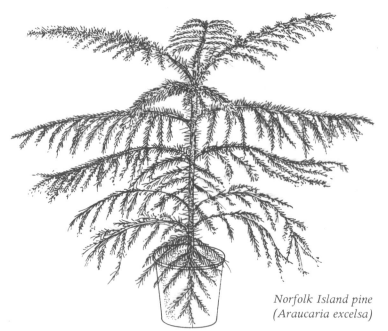

*Norfolk Island pine
(Araucaria excelsa)*

light and dark green leaves of *B. boweri*, which develops into tight hummocks of over-lapping leaves. Also among the smaller leaved sorts there is the slightly larger plant, *B.* Cleopatra, with bronzed foliage and typically lopsided begonia-shaped leaves. Of upright habit and growing to roughly six feet there is *B. maculata* with speckled grey-green colouring. All of these produce flowers, but they are insignificant when compared to the foliage.

Slightly more difficult to propagate than the *B. rex* varieties, *B. masoniana* (known as iron cross) is, however, a superior plant, both in respect of durability and usefulness. With its distinctive iron cross marking in the centre of each leaf, it is particularly easy to use in small bowl arrangements, and equally useful for blending with other plants in larger displays.

Caladium
Difficult
These aroids, available in many colours, have the most delicate foliage of all indoor plants. Indeed, the leaves of the most popular kind, *Caladium* Candidum, are almost transparent, yet it is one of the easiest to care for indoors. Last year I tried one for the first time, and felt I had had full value when it lasted for four-and-a-half months in an unheated room.

Corms are started into growth in warm peat beds in the greenhouse in the early part of the year, and the plants are on sale from the end of April. When the leaves die back naturally in the autumn one should be able, in theory, to allow the compost to dry before storing the corm in a minimum temperature of 16°C (60°F) until February, when the compost is gradually given more water to encourage fresh

growth. This I have done, and I await results but am not too hopeful, knowing that it can be difficult to overwinter caladiums even in a greenhouse where the conditions are almost ideal.

My plant responded to a watering programme that allowed the soil to dry a little between bouts with the watering-can. When a plant has been purchased, it is advisable to support the larger leaves with thin canes, as they become top heavy and the petioles bend very easily, restricting the flow of sap to the leaves and causing them to die.

Calathea
Difficult
Many calatheas are difficult indoors, and some downright impossible. Probably the easiest is *Calathea louisae*, which has less colourful leaves than many of the others. *C. insignis* and *C. ornata* Sanderiana are both very striking plants that will catch the eye in any collection. These, however, should be treated as being expendable and should not be expected to live for more than a year or two at the most. Calatheas will not tolerate direct sunlight at any cost; and warm, humid conditions must be the aim when caring for them.

Comparatively slow growth and difficulty of culture tends to make calatheas costly and scarce.

Calathea louisae

Citrus mitis
Calamondin orange. Moderately easy

Citrus mitis is a winner all the way, but it can be somewhat aggravating to see yellow, chlorotic leaves develop – as they often do – when the correct cultural needs of the plant have been supplied to the letter. The Calamondin orange, as it is commonly called, is short and compact, without the spines normally associated with citrus plants. It has the considerable advantage over *C. sinensis*, the more common species, of bearing fruit on comparatively small plants.

Citrus mitis

In America these dwarf oranges are extremely popular, and to encourage sales the story goes that no cocktail bar is complete without its real live orange tree from which oranges can be plucked and used for flavouring. Having seen both, it would seem that the American product is very much better than our home-reared plants; success across the Atlantic owing much to the abundant sunshine available in California for ripening one-year-old wood that will bear fruit the following year. Providing the plants with the maximum amount of sunshine during the summer months, when they can be put outside, is one way of encouraging them to flower and fruit. Guard against over-watering, as the weak root system quickly dies in wet conditions. Cuttings root with little difficulty, and these will sometimes fruit as little as 12 months from potting. The fruits resemble tangerine oranges and peel in much the same way, but are somewhat bitter.

Codiaeum
Croton. Difficult

There seems to be no limit to the range and variety of colours to be found in codiaeum (croton) leaves, and these colours will improve considerably if the plants are exposed to the maximum amount of light available. In common with most plants of ornamental appearance, the codiaeum is a stove (very warm greenhouse) subject, so it must have an adequate temperature – 18°C (65°F) or more. Both low temperatures and dry conditions will result in leaf drop and the soil need only be very dry on one occasion for leaves to fall a week or two later.

Keep feeding codiaeums while they are actively growing, and pot them on annually into slightly larger containers; John Innes No. 2 potting compost, well firmed, is the growing mixture to use. Red spider mite is a troublesome pest and a watchful eye (assisted by a magnifying glass) should be kept on the underside of leaves for signs of its presence.

Codiaeum reidii is recognised by keen plantsmen as one of the finest pot plants at present in cultivation. Mature specimens, growing in ideal greenhouse conditions, may have leaves as much as 18 in long and 9 in across. These leaves are beautifully patterned and are predominantly orange-pink in colour. Not easy to grow indoors, it will, however, be well worth purchasing, if only to provide a spring and summer display.

The variety Mrs Iceton has smaller leaves almost like a rainbow in their range of colour. It requires maximum light for best results. Much confusion exists over the proper naming of codiaeums and this plant is no exception, there being two other names to my knowledge – Annie Bier and Volcano. When it is seen almost erupting into colour, one realises that the last-mentioned name is not inappropriate. A point in favour of Mrs Iceton, not shared by many codiaeums, is the way in which foliage that has almost completely reverted to green will regain its exotic colouring as soon as the drab days of winter are left behind.

With bright yellow colouring, *C.* Eugene Drapps, will in ideal conditions develop into a giant some 8 ft in height to become a truly distinctive plant. Although not often sold by varietal name it is easily detected in the retailer's collection by its very colourful appearance. Combining elegance with distinction, *C. warrenii* has leaves little more than an inch wide and some twelve inches in length, and forms into a neat clump if the growing points are periodically removed.

Possibly the most popular of all codiaeums,

Codiaeum Mrs Iceton

C. holuffiana, with yellow to orange colouring, is generally sold in very large quantities during the summer months.

Dieffenbachia
Dumb cane. Moderately difficult

All of these may safely be described as delicate plants that will require a minimum temperature of not less than 18°C (65°F), both by day and night. In the greenhouse, some varieties

Dieffenbachia picta exotica

attain a maximum height of about 5 ft by which time they will have lost many of their lower leaves and will be producing young plants at soil level from the base of the parent stem.

When the plant is no longer attractive, the main stem can be cut back almost to soil level, and the top portion may be propagated as a very large cutting; but unless conditions are good, one should not be too optimistic about the results. The bare stem of the plant can be cut up into pieces about 4 in in length, each with a node or joint, and laid on their sides partly buried in fresh peat. Keep the peat at about 18°C (65°F); it is surprising the way in which some of these tough old stumps will develop into new plants.

Dieffenbachia has the unusual common name of dumb cane, which it gets from the fact that speech becomes difficult for a day or two should one inadvertently get the sap on one's tongue. However, since dieffenbachias smell so abominably when cut, such an event is most unlikely.

One of my personal favourites among the dieffenbachia tribe is *D. oerstedii*, which has dark green, almost black, leaves of roughly oval shape with a striking mid-rib, ivory white in colour, that runs the entire length of the leaf. *Dieffenbachia bauseii* is another fine plant with an almost white stem and dark, speckled, light green leaves – a plant guaranteed to improve any collection. With cream and green leaves *D. picta* is probably a little easier to acquire, while its improved form, *D. picta* Superba, with brighter cream colouring will require that little extra care and attention if it is to succeed.

Since the introduction of *Dieffenbachia amoena* from America about fifteen years ago it has gained many admirers. The bold, dark green leaves require space in which to spread so spacious surroundings are the answer. Water should be given with care, as excessive moisture will result in the main stem splitting at the base and eventually rotting. *D. arvida exotica* has been with us about the same length of time as *D. amoena* and is, if anything, more popular. Being more compact and slower growing than the latter it is much better suited to average room conditions.

Foliage plants are becoming increasingly popular for use in planted bowls, and florists frequently include one or two exotic plants, such as *D. exotica*, in order to catch the customer's eye. As a result, I am often asked how such arrangements should be cared for – a problem indeed. I find, however, that it is invariably better to place the container in a room temperature that will suit the more delicate subjects. While the majority of easier plants will tolerate the higher temperatures it will be found that the delicate plant will quickly succumb in colder conditions. In respect of watering, one should always aim at the happy medium, at all costs avoiding overwatering as many of these bowls have no drainage so an excess of water just collects in the bottom of the container.

Dizygotheca elegantissima
Difficult

Belonging to the same family as the hederas, or ivies, *Dizygotheca elegantissima* is, however, a much more trying plant to care for, wet and cold conditions reducing it to a bare stalk in a

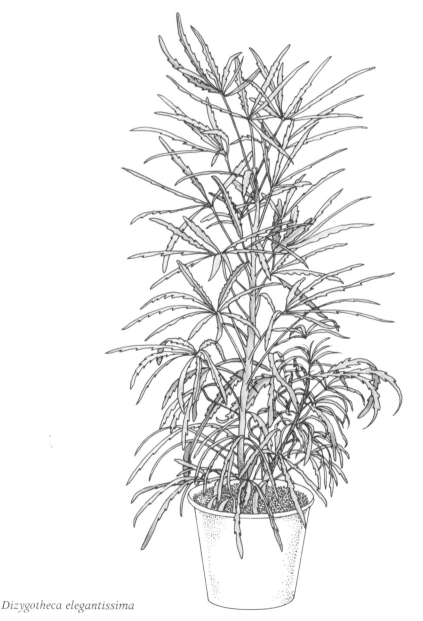

Dizygotheca elegantissima

very short space of time. A temperature of 18°C (65°F) is required for successful cultivation, the soil being kept moist, but never saturated. Surprisingly enough it adapts itself very well to the modern technique of capillary watering. Plastic pots are used when plants are watered in this way as the thin base permits the compost in the pot and the sand to come into direct contact.

Mature plants of eight years or more in age lose much of their fine-leaved, elegant appearance as they develop into small trees, the leaves becoming much coarser and larger in the process. There is little fear of having them push the roof off indoors though, as growth becomes much slower, and even an expert would have difficulty in keeping plants for more than a few years.

Dracaena
Easy and difficult

Several species of dracaena are available and the best known is probably *Dracaena terminalis*, a somewhat difficult plant which is prone to brown leaf tips as a result of root failure. A light position is preferred, and it is especially important that soft water should be given in preference to hard tap water. The stiff red leaves are much prized by the enthusiastic flower arranger, but to me it seems almost criminal to strip leaves off this aristocrat among plants for such a purpose.

Dracaena sanderiana has grey and white narrow leaves on slender stems, and presents something of a problem in respect of culture. Excessively wet compost allied to low temperatures will almost certainly result in browning of the leaf tips. Although plants with single stems may appear unimpressive, I find that when planted in groups of a dozen or more they are indispensible for display work. Should one own a number of these plants it will be found that a much more pleasing effect can be achieved by potting several together; three plants to a 5 in pot is about right. Overgrown plants can be cut back and will develop new shoots from the old stem, as well as from soil level.

A dracaena of distinctive appearance is *D. godseffiana* Florida Beauty, a variety with oval leaves borne close together on low growing stems and heavily spotted with cream.

A distinctive plant of easy culture, *D. volckaertii*, has narrow, dark green leaves borne on a slender stem, making it an excellent plant as a background subject in a group of plants. Keep the soil on the dry side and offer a reasonably light location with a temperature in the region of 16°C to 18°C (60° to 65°F).

Much shorter and more compact, with

Dracaena marginata

Ficus elastica tricolor

Ficus elastica tricolor is an attractive plant, similar to the ordinary rubber plant, but with variegated leaves of pink, cream and green. When first introduced it was hailed as being a plant of good temperament, needing little more care than the green rubber plant. Browning of leaf margins tends to be a problem and is usually associated with wet, cold conditions. It does, however, have the remarkable capacity of growing away clean and strong for a second time when the stems have been cut to stumps of little more than 3 or 4 in in height. So, do not completely despair when plants lose their leaves and are no longer attractive – instead, try cutting them back. Cut back plants will, of course, require only the bare minimum amount of water until such time as new leaves are produced.

Another variegated ficus is *F.* Zulu Shield, which has brightly variegated leaves that are identical in shape to those of the common rubber plant. My personal experience of this plant suggests that it has many fine qualities, not least among them the plant's ability to grow at a reasonable pace if provided with good light (not direct sunlight) and watering that ensures that the soil does not remain wet

leaves of attractive dull red colouring, *D.* Redege will have to be maintained at the higher temperature recommended above if it is to do well. This one is excellent for mixed plantings in tubs or even the larger plant cases.

One of the toughest of the dracaenas, *D. marginata*, has a relative in *D. marginata tricolor*, which has a soft creamy-pink colouring that is most attractive. However, it is a much more difficult plant to care for and will need a temperature in the region of 18°C (65°F) and careful watering that errs on the dry side.

Ficus
Rubber plant. Easy and difficult
Besides the ordinary rubber plant, *Ficus elastica robusta*, (see page 61) there are many other ficus plants available, some easy to care for, others not so easy. At the extreme ends of the scale, in respect of size, there is the stately fiddle-leaved fig. *F. lyrata*, and the creeping *F. radicans variegata*, neither of which is easy to grow. Given ideal conditions, *F. lyrata* reaches tree-like proportions in time, and will tolerate quite severe pruning when established.

for long periods. Less water and feeding are necessary in winter.

Ficus Black Prince has, as the name suggests, very much darker leaves than any of the other rubber plants. Care is very much the same, also the habit of growth, but if anything the plant is a little more temperamental than the other ficuses.

Fittonia
Difficult

Fittonia argyroneura and *F. verschaffeltii* have similar habits of growth, but are easily distinguishable, the first having silvered leaves and the latter leaves which are reddish brown in colour. Both are suitable bottle garden plants and should be given a minimum temperature of at least 18°C (65°F), and a certain amount of humidity. Water should be given in moderation; indeed, *F. argyroneura* has quite astonishing powers of recovery after the compost has become really bone-dry. Leaves suffering from drought will collapse to the point when they will appear to be quite shrivelled and lifeless; yet, after watering, they soon become firm again.

The miniature form of the silver fittonia, *F.a.* Nana, is a recent development. The markings on the leaves are equally attractive but it seems much easier to care for than its parent form. Peaty compost is essential, as is the need for shade and careful watering.

Heptapleurum
Easy

One of the most exciting houseplants to appear recently is *Heptapleurum arboricola*, and its similar relatives *H.* Hong Kong and *H.* Geisha Girl. Tall, erect stems carry palmate leaves that are not dissimilar to its relation, schefflera, which give the plant a most elegant appearance. Grow in light shade at a temperature of around 18°C (65°F) and water and feed in moderation. Plants can be pruned to shape at any time, and are often seen at their best with branching green stems rather than slender single stemmed specimens.

Isolepis gracilis
Easy

Isolepis gracilis (syn. *Scirpus cernuus*) is an adaptable plant. Trouble free, it puts up with wide variations in temperature, and asks for little more than sufficient water to keep the soil moist, and occasional feeding with liquid fertiliser. It is easily propagated by dividing the roots and potting them up individually in any reasonable compost. Although it would appear to be a member of the grass family, it is in fact a miniature bulrush.

Overleaf Ferns grow well when grouped together and, as long as there is no draught, can tolerate the shady conditions of a fireplace. The atmosphere around them must never be allowed to dry out so frequent spraying with a hand mister is important. The variety of leaf shapes and textures available makes them fascinating to collect.

1   *Asparagus plumosus*
2   *Nephrolepis exaltata bostoniensis*
3   *Adiantum cuneatum*
4   *Platycerium alcicorne*
5   *Asplenium nidus avis*
6   A group of small ferns
7   *Pteris ensiformis*

Fittonia verschaffeltii

Maranta picturata
Difficult

Maranta picturata is a difficult plant to grow, and not easy to obtain, but it is a particular favourite of mine – hence my reason for including it. The leaves are light grey, compactly arranged with dark green margins and maroon undersides; they seldom fail to attract attention. A shaded position, with a temperature of 18°C (65°F) and high humidity, will provide ideal growing conditions. Plants are increased by means of cuttings, which are prepared from pieces of growth about 4 in in length with two or three leaves attached. Insert them in 3-in pots of moist peat. They may also be increased by division in the early part of the year and, if one is lucky enough, plants will occasionally have a colony of self-set seedlings around them. However, it must be confessed that a heated greenhouse, with plants standing on a moist peat bed, is almost essential for the latter to take place. As a general guide, if delicate plants require a growing temperature of about 18°C (65°F) one may safely assume that at least 3°C (5°F) more heat will be needed when propagating new plants.

Persea gratissima
Avocado pear. Easy

You buy the pear, plant the stone, and in time you will have the satisfaction of saying that you did it all yourself. Unfortunately, these plants grow rapidly indoors and the larger leaves tend to droop eventually. To keep the plant reasonably compact the leading shoots should be pinched out occasionally. In average room conditions the avocado pear will soon outgrow its allotted space, and the owner is then faced with the problem of what is to be done with it – few of us have the heart to put a healthy plant in the dustbin. Sad to say, I cannot help here, as it often requires a little diplomacy and a chat with the local garage proprietor who may be prepared to accept it for his showroom. At all costs, keep away from your florist and nurseryman, as they have, no doubt, had to say 'No' in the past when asked to provide a home for overgrown avocado pears.

Planting the stone is a simple operation; for details see page 163.

Philodendron melanochrysum
Moderately difficult

The heart-shaped leaves with brown velvet colouring make this plant well worth trying, even though it has the reputation of being difficult. A temperature in the region of 18°C (65°F) and humid conditions are both important.

It is probably an ambitious thought for the indoor plantsman, but hanging baskets filled with these philodendrons can look very striking, and might be worth trying. I well remember the mystified observers in Paris a few years ago, at an international flower show which I attended, when they saw a fine basketful of *Philodendron melanochrysum* twist first one way then the other with no visible means of support, or propulsion. They were not to know that nylon fishing line supported the basket, and the circulating warm air in the building was keeping it on the move. It is odd that, at flower shows, the slightest movement, be it only a drip of water in a pool, will attract more attention than the most exotic plant life in the vicinity!

Scindapsus aureus
Money plant or devil's ivy. Moderately difficult

I often wonder if plants can change or adapt their needs in respect of general care: the reason for asking is that plants of *Scindapsus aureus* were at one time among the more delicate of indoor subjects, yet I now see them growing in all sorts of unlikely places with little discernible effort. However, a steady temperature in the region of 16°C to 18°C (60° to 65°F) is important, and plants should be well watered, although allowed to dry a little before repeating. The same applies for *S. Marble Queen*, but one would not expect an especially good response from this more temperamental plant.

Sparmannia africana
Indoor lime or African windflower. Easy

Sparmannia africana has two common names, the indoor lime, which it gets from the appearance of the cool, green foliage, and the African windflower, because of the way in which the flowers open outwards at the slightest breath of wind.

In ideal conditions it will quickly outgrow its welcome, but one can quite severely prune the branches to shape at almost any time. It is not often grown commercially, as demand is very limited, and growth in greenhouse conditions is frequently rampant enough to become an embarrassment to the commercial grower. A fine plant for a cool, light room, it will give little trouble if regular feeding and annual potting on are not neglected. In common with many of the easier plants, it can be increased readily from cuttings, so it is advisable to start new plants every few years.

Temperature around 16°C (60°F) will suit these, and they should be watered more freely during summer than winter, but never allowed to dry out. Large pale green leaves are a constant attraction, with interesting flowers that appear in summer being an added bonus.

Sparmannia africana

Right Dracaena, calathea
and dieffenbachia are all
plants grown for their
distinctive foliage

Opposite page
Top *Araucaria excelsa*
Bottom left A large-leafed
pink caladium
Bottom right One of the
colourful varieties of
codiaeum

Palms

In their many forms, palms have been among the most popular of potted plants for a century or more, and there does not appear to be any sort of decline in spite of the high cost of cultivation and the subsequent high purchase price.

Howeia forsteriana
Parlour palm. Easy
Queen of the palms as far as indoor use is concerned is *Howeia forsteriana* (much more popularly known as *Kentia forsteriana*) which has segmented leaves held high on stout stems. As individual, or specimen plants for any form of decoration they are unsurpassed, and with reasonable care will continue in fine condition for many years.

Reasonable care entails the maintenance of a minimum temperature of around 18°C (65°F), a light but not sunny location and watering that is done thoroughly, but not to excess. The safest method of watering is to fill the pot with water and allow the surplus to drain away through the bottom of the pot – a few insignificant dribbles indicates that not enough water has been given. It is then essential to allow the soil to dry a little before repeating the watering exercise. Feed estab-lished plants at regular intervals while new leaves are being produced with a weak solution of liquid fertiliser. When potting on use a mixture of peat and leafmould and pot with reasonable firmness. Spring and early summer are the best potting times.

The above advice applies to almost all the palm plants that one may purchase. It is also best to never clean the leaves with any form of chemical cleaner – spray the leaves with water frequently and occasionally wipe with a damp cloth to remove surface dust.

Besides *Howeia (Kentia) forsteriana* there is also the similar plant *H. belmoreana*, but the latter is a very much stronger growing plant that is only suitable for premises that can offer the necessary headroom. The leaves are also coarser in appearance.

Cocos weddelliana
Coconut palm. Easy
One of the smallest and most delicate of palms is *Cocos weddelliana* which is usually bought in pots that have no drainage holes in the bottom. In their early stages these plants do grow better for this treatment, but will do just as well later on if grown in more conventional containers. The foliage of this plant is very fine and delicate, which makes it a very useful plant for mixed displays.

Howeia forsteriana,
popularly known as Kentia

Chamaedorea elegans
also *Neanthe bella.* Easy
The palms seem to be beset with dull names, and in *Chamaedorea elegans* we have a plant that is much more popularly known as *Neanthe bella.* A very slow growing plant that will go on for many years if a careful eye is kept for the presence of red spider mite on the undersides of leaves.

Phoenix roebelenii

Phoenix
Moderately easy
Phoenix dactylifera takes many years to reach maturity, but presents the interesting prospect that it can be raised from a date stone that is subjected to a high temperature of not less than 21°C (70°F) while germinating. Another palm with similar appearance is *P. canariensis* which produces masses of roots and has vicious barbs along the midrib of the leaf. Of similar shape, but more delicate and much more attractive as a plant for a large room is *P. roebelinii.*

Chamaerops
Fan palm. Moderately easy
As the common name suggests the fan palms have leaves that fan out from the petiole, much as the fingers fan out from the palm of the hand. The most popular of these are *Chamaerops humilis* and *C. elegans* (which is more popularly known as *Trachycarpus fortunei*). Both of these require reasonable space if they are to be seen at their best.

Care of palms
Indoors, palms can be very unpredictable in respect of growing performance; in some situations they are difficult to manage, while at other times they are completely trouble free. For example, I know of one *Howeia belmoreana* growing in a 15-in pot that is well over eighty years of age. Why it does so well is a complete mystery as it has to suffer the somewhat harsh treatment every fourth year or so of having its roots severely pruned in order to restrict its top growth. It is virtually a very old and very majestic Bonsai plant – however, it should be added that it is growing within the confines of a heated greenhouse with expert care.

You are seldom likely to walk into a garden centre, and find packets of palm seeds in the racks being offered for sale. Banana and all sorts of other unlikely seeds are often on offer but not palm. The reason for this is that palm seed is almost permanently in short supply, and the small amount available is much in demand by the commercial grower the world over. However, should one be fortunate enough to come across a supply, the seed should be buried in a very porous compost mixture in a temperature of not less than 21°C (70°F). Germination will take six to eight weeks, often longer. One porous mixture that I recall using with a high success rate was very fine coke breeze that was kept well moistened, but because of its composition it could never become excessively wet and cause seed to deteriorate.

Ferns

I, personally, find plants endlessly fascinating and when I cast my eyes on some of the more delicate ferns (maidenhair, for example), both indoors and out, I find it difficult to believe that anything so delicate and beautiful can survive. Yet survive they do, and many of them are very tolerant of the often indifferent conditions that we offer them indoors. But there are the exceptions, and it would seem that the tender adiantum, or maidenhair, does present more than a few problems in the room where the atmosphere is excessively dry.

Above all else, it is essential that the ferns have a shaded location in which to grow, and that there should be plenty of moisture around them. This should not be construed as meaning that the compost in the pot should remain sopping wet. Ideally, the compost should be well drained and kept moist – a condition that lies between wet and dry. With ferns, I feel that it is important to place a collection of

continued on page 84

The
Bathroom

The humid atmosphere makes bathrooms excellent places in which to grow plants. Bathrooms tend to be cooler and often darker than the rest of the house so ferns such as *Asparagus plumosus*, *A. sprengeri* and adiantum (**below**) are ideal. The spider plant, *Chlorophytum comosum* (**right**) can withstand almost any conditions but this position in a jardinière in front of the windows shows off its graceful, arching leaves and stems to their best advantage. Other plants which will grow successfully in a bathroom are the moisture-loving philodendrons, particularly *Philodendron scandens* with its twisting stems and heart-shaped leaves, and also the many varieties of tradescantia.

*Three delicate-leaved ferns: Pellaea rotundifolia (**bottom left***), Asparagus plumosus (**bottom right***) and Adiantum flabellulatum (**behind***)*

plants together in a larger container that is filled with peat, moss or some other moisture-retaining material.

Excessive feeding of ferns is to my mind detrimental rather than beneficial, and I am firmly of the opinion that the vast majority of these plants are far better off with a regular foliar feed only.

Many of the smaller ferns (*Pellaea rotundi-folia, Pteris argyraea, P. cretica,* and *P. ensiformis* Victoriae to name but a few) are excellent plants for use in bottle gardens.

Nephrolepis fern
Moderately easy
There are many variations of the nephrolepis fern, and almost all of them are among the

royalty of the plant business; they have few peers. As an individual plant in a hanging basket or a large pot, they present a splendid sight with their bright green leaves radiating in all directions from the heart of the plant. In a small greenhouse that is heated to around 18°C (65°F), new plants can be easily propagated if the parent plant has its pot plunged in a bed of moist peat, and plantlets on the ends of long runners are allowed to root into the plunging medium.

When purchased, any ferns that appear too large for their pots should be potted on immediately using a very peaty potting mixture. This applies in particular to plants that are in smaller pots of around 3 in in diameter.

Asparagus sprengeri and A. plumosus
Asparagus fern. Moderately easy
With trailing sprays of greenery, *Asparagus sprengeri*, is a most prolific plant that will flourish given the cultural care mentioned earlier. Having more upright and rather more delicate foliage, *A. plumosus*, is a reliable plant that will go on for many years with comparatively little attention. Equally distinctive and quite different to these two is *A. meyeri* which develops stiff cylindrical sprays of greenery. (Although universally referred to as ferns these, in fact, belong to the lily family).

Asplenium nidus avis
Bird's nest fern. Moderately easy
This attractive plant produces smooth pale green leaves that radiate from the centre of the plant, so that it is similar in shape to a shuttlecock. Generally it is a trying plant to grow indoors; an even temperature in the region of 18°C (65°F) is essential, also fairly high humidity.

Contrary to general advice, feeding with weak liquid fertiliser will preserve the pale green colouring of its leaves. When dark brown 'spider's legs' of roots begin to creep over the edge of the pot, it is an indication that potting on is necessary. Use a potting compost that contains lots of peat, leafmould and a little fresh sphagnum moss.

Should the leaves require cleaning, this must be done with a soft sponge and clear water, as they are very easily damaged. Oil-based cleaners will give the leaves a transparent appearance that will in time cause them to rot, so they should not be used.

Pellaea rotundifolia
Button fern. Easy
One of the easiest and most popular ferns is *Pellaea rotundifolia* (button fern), which produces a dense mass of small, very dark green leaves on slender stems. This fern tolerates quite low temperatures, but does enjoy a mist of water sprayed over its foliage.

Adiantum
Maidenhair fern. Moderately easy
When all is said and done, possibly the most attractive, and certainly one of the most useful of all the ferns, is the maidenhair or adiantum. Many of the very pale green-coloured varieties, such as *Adiantum fragrans*, are exceptionally fine with their black wiry stems contrasting sharply and beautifully with the delicate foliage.

Overleaf In this elegant drawing room a few distinctive plants have been used to good effect as an integral part of the interior design. In a spacious room where the shape of a large plant can really be appreciated this is usually more effective than a much greater number of small plants.
1 *Dracaena deremensis*
2 *Howeia forsteriana*
3 *Codiaeum*

Unusual ferns
Among the pteris ferns there are many with quite extraordinary colouring, ranging from silver to almost white. Stiff and upright stems carry the foliage in an elegant manner, making the pteris splendid plants for inclusion in the mixed collection. An even temperature around 16°C (60°F) will suit these plants best.

Propagation of ferns
Many of the smaller ferns that grow in clumps can be increased by teasing the plant apart and planting the segregated pieces as individual plants. Acquiring and sowing spores is by far the cheapest method of increasing the varieties and numbers of your plants; it is not as complicated as it may seem. When the spores have ripened on the reverse of the leaf, the leaf can be carefully removed, placed in a paper bag and allowed to dry. The spores will fall from the leaf and they can then be sown on damp peat in a temperature of around 27°C (80°F).

CHAPTER 6
Architectural plants

Such a grand-sounding heading for a chapter as architectural plants conjures up thoughts of towering office blocks and vast carpeted foyers.

In recent years there has been a tremendous upsurge in the use of plants in offices, virtually hundreds of containers being put to use throughout open-plan interiors. In most cases the plants are maintained by specialist plant contractors who call regularly to ensure that plants are fed, watered, cleaned and generally kept in good order. Presuming that the contractor knows his job, the important requirement as far as plants are concerned is that there should be adequate temperature every day of the week and that there should be sufficient light for plants to grow successfully.

Certainly the term 'architectural plant' does suggest one of fairly substantial proportions, and they are, in most cases, set off to better advantage in more spacious surroundings. This need not imply, however, that they have no place in the home, as most of these plants are, in fact, sold in a variety of pot sizes. Indeed, homes with larger rooms and entrance halls do accommodate many of these larger plants, though sometimes to the exclusion of a piece of furniture.

The available range of specimen indoor plants, be they architectural or otherwise, is limited to comparatively few species and varieties. No doubt many more plants could be listed as having architectural merit, but this seems quite pointless knowing that they are almost unobtainable commercially. Only very few of the commercial houseplant growers are prepared to tie up capital in a long-term investment in specimen indoor plants, many of which take several years to mature. Because of their slow rate of development these plants are almost invariably costly purchases.

On the question of cost, the individual specimen plant may be expensive, but in the proper setting it is much more impressive than a nondescript collection of smaller plants, and in the end need not be much more costly than a selection of small plants. Also, a larger plant will be much easier to care for than a collection of smaller ones, which dry out quite rapidly in warm conditions.

Selecting & positioning

When selecting and positioning such plants, be it in the office or private house their suitability must be carefully considered. In respect of height, there should be a minimum of 2 to 3 ft of head room so that the plant has an opportunity to develop. Where spotlights are used to highlight aspects of interior decor, or the plants themselves, care must be taken to ensure that the plant is at least 4 ft away from the light bulb or reflector. If there is a continual flow of people past the plant or plants, then they should be placed well away from their general route. This is to protect them from being damaged by passers-by brushing against them, and to deter inquisitive fingers from handling the leaves in an effort to decide whether they are real or plastic!

Although architects are very capable people where building design is concerned, many of them are lamentably ill-informed in respect of plants and their requirements. Elsewhere I have discussed the general requirements of indoor plants and their positioning and have no wish to repeat my remarks here, except on one point, namely, the question of plant height in relation to the size of the pot in which the plant will be growing. When visualising a bold plant of some 8 to 10 ft in height or with a wide spread, there is no point in providing a match-box-sized container in which to house the pot, as is so often the case. For larger plants the absolute minimum size of container is one with a diameter of 12 in and a depth of not less than 10 in.

*Philodendron
bipinnatifidum*

One further point on containers; I feel that they should be portable when housing larger plants. This will save a good deal of perspiration if it is decided to reposition the plant. Boxes, or containers, mounted on castors will simplify matters so that a rearrangement of the plants can become a matter of course. Also, it makes life much easier for whoever has to do the cleaning when boxes can be moved around.

Araceae

Aroid family

The *Araceae* and *Moraceae* are the families which provide the majority of plants that can be defined as architectural, mainly on account of their larger leaves and more stately appearance. The aroids, *Araceae*, as well as including many of our bolder plants, also give us some of the most beautiful and delicate-foliaged hot greenhouse plants. Perhaps the most important aroid for this chapter is the well-known *Monstera deliciosa borsigiana*, Swiss cheese plant, (see page 41), sometimes wrongly referred to as *Philodendron pertusum*. The latter is, in fact, a plant with smaller leaves and a more erect habit of growth. Of all the many beautiful green-leaved plants in

cultivation, Mother Nature surely excelled herself when devising the serrated, and eventually perforated, monstera leaf. Positioned where space is ample and temperature adequate the monstera will give lasting service with comparatively little attention.

Philodendron bipinnatifidium
Easy

Another aroid of spreading habit, with green fingerlike leaves is *Philodendron bipinnatifidum* (see page 44). Mention has been made elsewhere of the semi-retired gardener at our local railway station, and his devotion to, and ability with, plants. Perhaps the *P. bipinnatifidum* in the parcel office was his most spectacular plant, and much of the success was due to the aerial roots being allowed to drink up as much water as they required, instead of, as so often happens, being allowed to hang limply in a dry atmosphere. This was made possible by placing the plant pot in one end of a zinc trough and encouraging aerial roots, as they developed, to have a free run in the moist gravel in the bottom of the trough. This, by the way, is an excellent method of encouraging aroids to produce really bold leaves: stand them on the edge of a pool or water tank and give the aerial roots free run in the water. By so doing it will be found that the actual compost in the pot requires only the bare minimum of water.

Unusual philodendrons

Other philodendrons I mention only briefly on account of their scarcity. *Philodendron wendlandii* is a compact green plant with a shuttle-cock arrangement of the leaves that radiate from a low central crown; and Burgundy is an excellent and tolerant variety which will, in time, produce remarkably rich-coloured leaves, as much as 2 ft in length, in no way belying its name. This latter plant will benefit considerably if its supporting stake has a thick wad of sphagnum moss bound to it with florist's wire; keep the moss moist and aerial roots will quickly begin to work their way into the damp material. Similar in appearance to Burgundy but with plain green leaves, *P. hastatum* will also benefit from having its stake mossed; and, for the best results, the temperature should not be allowed to drop below 18°C (65°F).

Moraceae

Ornamental figs

The *Moraceae*, or fig family, provide us with an incredible range of ficus or rubber plants; from the creeping or climbing (if placed against a damp wall in the greenhouse) *Ficus pumila* to the majestic *F. lyrata* (see below). In the architectural group I have not included the upright *F. elastica decora*. Instead, one should endeavour to grow something rather more spectacular by acquiring one of these rubber plants when it has formed itself into a natural tree shape. This they do without help on reaching a height of about 8 ft, or when the growing tip has been deliberately cut out. Planted out into beds filled with good potting compost these plants will grow at a remarkable pace, putting on as many as 50 new leaves on a single branch in the course of one growing season.

Ficus lyrata

Fiddle-leaved fig. Moderately difficult
Ficus lyrata is an unusual and attractive plant, commonly named the fiddle-leaved fig because of its fiddle-shaped leaves. It will develop a sizeable trunk when at home in its surroundings. When well settled in and growing away it will tolerate quite severe pruning, though dark conditions and an inadequate or fluctuating temperature will quickly result in the loss of the lower leaves, and pruning will be more of a dream than a reality.

Weeping fig. Moderately difficult
A ficus of quite different appearance, having nothing of the stiff habit of its relatives, is the elegant weeping fig, *F. benjamina*. This is often rather a perplexing plant when first put in position, as it seems almost inevitable that it will have some yellow leaves until it settles down. These should be removed, if only to improve the plant's appearance, and it will be found that in most cases the plant will establish itself in a week or two.

Besides the well known *Ficus benjamina* (weeping fig) we now have *F. benjamina nuda* that has more pointed leaves which hang much more gracefully. It is said to be more tolerant of indoor conditions, but in my experience it is little different. One of the problems with the weeping figs is that they take unkindly to being moved from one place to another, and have a tendency of showing their displeasure by shedding their leaves until they eventually settle down. The leaves of this plant may also turn brown and fall off if the growing location does not offer sufficient light. Although full sun is harmful, plants should nevertheless be placed reasonably near the light source, and certainly never in dark corners.

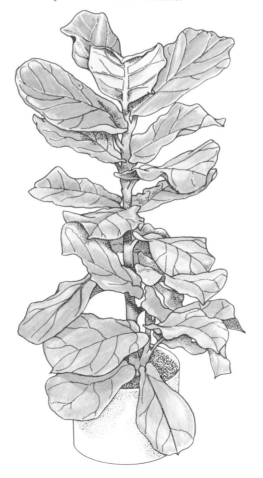

Ficus lyrata

Care of large ficus plants

Ficus plants in general should be inspected regularly when grown in pots standing on moist gravel or peat, as they are notorious for rooting through the holes in the bottom of the pot. This is one reason why it is often better to plant ficuses in boxes of compost where they can have a free root run, and grow much more rapidly and strongly as a result.

Being vigorous plants the majority of figs require regular feeding, and should be potted on once their roots have filled existing pots. A feeding programme similar to that recommended for the schefflera can also apply to the larger ficus plants. All of these will produce masses of roots that will make every effort to get out of the pot, either through the holes in the bottom or over the top, in the hope that there may be fresh soil for the plant to feed on. The weeping figs, once they have developed stems of reasonable circumference, will also have a tendency to produce thick roots from the stem of the plant. These are known as prop roots and act as very stout guy rope supports for plants when they are growing in their natural jungle environment.

Other suitable plants

A special favourite – Schefflera actinophylla

One of my particular favourites in the architectural range of houseplants, brings back fond memories of an old New Zealand friend, Mr Andrew Anderson. Many years ago he introduced the plant to me by writing the name *Brassaia actinophylla* on a greenhouse door and saying, with a finger stabbing at the name: 'This is a plant you must grow if you want specimen plants'. The plant, sold here as *Schefflera actinophylla*, deserves to be much more popular than it is, for it is a mixture of boldness and elegance; even a 15 ft specimen does not appear in any way heavy.

Negligence of either feeding or potting on when required will almost certainly have an adverse effect on schefflera plants, resulting in the loss of some lower leaves, and as there is no way of replacing these, the plant will forever look the worse for wear.

Feeding should be done regularly while the plant is in active growth. This could be continuously in a heated building and will mean feeding with a liquid feed about once each week. Alternatively, plants can be fed with plant food tablets that can be pressed into the soil. There they will gradually release beneficial nourishment to the roots. Usually purchased in a box of some kind, these tablets

Pandanus veitchii

come with full directions for their use – number of tablets required and frequency of application.

Not many pests attack the schefflera, but they are occasionally troubled by red spider mite, their presence being made known by a slight yellowing of the leaf. Treat with a proprietary insecticide.

Palms

Palms, like aspidistras, conjure up thoughts of the Victorian era and are not so popular today, though there are signs that they are returning to favour. Many of them make excellent indoor or office plants, and in a larger area well-grown plants of *Howeia belmoreana* or *Phoenix roebelenii* are well able to hold their own with more recent introductions. The lasting qualities of howeia are almost legendary; the phoenix is a little more difficult. Both require copious watering in the summer months, and regular potting on is essential, otherwise the mass of accumulated roots will begin to push the plant and compost upwards and almost out of the pot in time.

Pandanus

Screw pine. Easy
The vicious saw-edged leaf of the pandanus (the species *veitchii* is probably the best) make it essential that this plant should be positioned where passers-by will not come in contact

with the leaves. Failure to do so frequently results in costly replacement of laddered tights! This is generally an easy plant to grow, and ideal for brightening up a plant display that is tending to become too green. To preserve the variegated colouring a light position is essential, and water should be given when the soil is seen to be dry and not as a daily ritual.

Dracaena
Easy and Difficult
For that exotic Palm Beach effect, few plants can compete with the dracaenas (unless it is a palm, of course), and in particular *Dracaena marginata*. It is a fairly easy 'doer', that in common with most dracaenas sheds its lower leaves as it increases in height. Far from being detrimental, this process often gives the plant a more elegant appearance, with its dull red-margined leaves spiking out in all directions.

Two more dracaenas that are somewhat more temperamental, so not for the novice, are *D. deremensis* and *D. massangeana*. The former, which has grey-green striped leaves, must have a minimum temperature of 18°C (65°F). Watering must also be done with great care; it must never be too wet or the leaves will brown at the tips and edges. *D. massan-*

geana, which will also test the grower's skill, has strap-like leaves, margined green with mustard-coloured centres. It is probably a more attractive plant when it has reached a height of 4 to 5 ft, and certainly it is better if given sufficient space for the leaves to spread naturally.

Tetrastigma voinierianum
Easy
Lastly, the tetrastigmas, and in particular the species *Tetrastigma voinierianum*, which excites the interest of those who prefer their plants to have interestingly shaped foliage. Certainly it has an advantage over most other large plants in that it is quick growing. In ideal greenhouse conditions 'rampant' is probably a better word as tetrastigmas are difficult to keep in check once they have decided to become entangled with their neighbours. As with ficuses, they too present difficulties when their roots decide to go in search of something other than that which is available in their pots. Growth is kept in check by frequently winding it back and forth around itself; string is unnecessary, as self-clinging tendrils quickly attach themselves to everything and anything. The compost should be kept moist and frequent feeding is essential. However, guard against excessive wet which results in leaves – and, in extreme cases, actual growing shoots – being shed.

Dracaena deremensis

CHAPTER 7
Flowering houseplants

*R*ather than write a few brief words about a huge number of plants, I have in this chapter on flowering houseplants, endeavoured to discuss some of the established favourites in more detail, and to include a selection of the plants that have become popular in recent years.

In general, the needs of flowering plants indoors are very similar to those of other plants, as described in the chapter on routine culture. The way in which some plants are inclined to shed flowers, and sometimes buds, when introduced to room conditions often gives rise for some concern. Much of the flower drop that occurs can be attributed to buffeting in transit, and to the change in conditions in respect of light and temperature. More often than not it will be found that plants quickly settle down in their new environment, and that flower production indoors presents few problems. However, permanently saturated compost and dark corners will result in weak growth and flowers that will drop at a touch.

There is no doubt that the condition of a flowering plant when purchased can influence its future life in the home. Unless flowers are especially wanted to create a favourable first impression, the plants should almost all be purchased at the earlier stage of growth – to be more specific, when they have some colour showing and an adequate supply of buds, formed and forming. There are a few exceptions, however, two of these being the pot chrysanthemum and the poinsettia. The latter should be well coloured and the chrysanthemum ought to have a good percentage of buds open, though not fully.

Achimenes
Hot water plant. Easy
The hot water plant, as it is commonly named, will start into growth in February much more readily if the rhizome is first soaked in hot water. Flowers in many shades are produced throughout the spring and summer months. Keep moist, cool and in good light and they will repay you with a continuous show of colour until plants naturally die down in late summer. Keep warm and dry over winter, and pot into fresh John Innes No. 2 or a soilless potting compost annually.

Anthurium
Moderately easy
Here we have further proof of the importance of the aroid family to the houseplant grower. The large-flowered (or, more accurately, large-spathed) *Anthurium andraeanum* requires a minimum temperature of 21°C (70°F), and a very humid atmosphere, so it is only suitable as a temporary room plant.

A very interesting variety, *A.* Guatamalan, is less demanding, needing a temperature of about 18°C (65°F) and less humidity. It is also more shapely, and the orange-red spathes are produced much more freely. (Though expensive, mature anthurium 'flowers' have a water life of five to seven weeks from the time of cutting).

Smaller and more compact than the previous types, *A. scherzerianum*, is, understandably, better known by its common name of flamingo flower. This plant does well in a light but not too sunny window, and appreciates a thoroughly well-drained and open compost. Soft water, with the chill taken off it, is preferred; and if at all possible, the room temperature should not drop below 16°C (60°F). Soil, as such, is not important, the main compost ingredients being peat, leafmould, fresh sphagnum moss and a little dried cow dung – the object being to prepare an open spongy mixture. Crock the pot, and add a few crocks to the potting mixture as well, to further assist drainage. To improve their appearance, the spathes should be supported by a thin cane or wire; if wire is used, make a loop at the top in which to rest the stem, placing the wire just below the coloured spathe.

Above left *Achimenes, the hot water plant*
Above right *Anthurium scherzerianum. Inset shows flower from A. andraeanum*

Aphelandra
Difficult

There is little to choose between *Aphelandra* Brockfeld and *A. squarrosa* Louisae. The former has more attractive foliage and the leaves are stiffer and carried almost horizontal to the main stem. The latter is less attractive in respect of foliage, but produces several yellow bracts to each stem, whereas Brockfeld is more inclined to have a single bract.

Both varieties are, without doubt, among the most trying of indoor flowering plants to care for. Dry roots and starvation are the main causes of failure, and these need be neglected on only one occasion for irreparable damage to be done. Aphelandras fill their pots with roots in a remarkably short space of time, so, from the moment they are purchased, they need lots of water and lots of fertiliser (the manufacturer's recommended dilution can be slightly exceeded for aphelandras and no harm will be done).

Azalea
Indian azalea. Easy

The pot-grown Indian azalea is one of our most attractive plants, and is available in many colours for about six months of the year, from November onwards. At no time must it be allowed to dry out, and frequent syringing of the foliage will help to create the moist atmosphere that is so important to its well being. It is one of the few plants that one can be quite specific about in respect of watering. When purchased, almost all of the larger plants are in effect miniature standard specimens, having a short woody stem between pot and foliage. The properly watered plant should have a dark water mark about half way up this stem; if there is no mark the plant is too dry, and if the mark is near where the branches begin it is too wet. It is as simple as that.

Dead flowers should be removed regularly, and when the flowers have finished the plant is placed in a cooler room where it will require less water. During May, when frosts are less likely, the plant should be plunged to its pot

Azalea plants should be plunged in the ground outdoors when flowering has finished

rim in a sunny position in the garden, or in an airy cold frame that can have its cover removed during the day. Keep the compost moist and feed with liquid fertiliser during the summer months, when the foliage should also be sprayed over regularly. Before frosts are likely the plant must be moved into a cool room; and when buds begin to form, warmer conditions will encourage their development. When the plant is in flower the temperature can be reduced. The first year after purchase a plant might not flower so well, but once adjusted to the suggested routine it will provide a remarkable annual show of colour.

Begonia
Moderately easy

The humble green ivies are bought in huge numbers yet a serious attempt to popularise plants of the *Begonia corolicta, B. daedalea* and *B. mazae* types met with utter failure some years ago. Perhaps the public distrusted their fine foliage and exotic blooms. My experience suggests that these suspicions are quite unfounded, as I have successfully grown a selection of fibrous begonias over the years and find them less demanding than many of the houseplants normally considered.

At present the majority are in short supply, and so are difficult to acquire, but I feel that in time these plants will be given a second chance by the nurseryman, and they will then be more readily accepted by more knowledgeable and adventurous houseplant enthusiasts.

Some, such as *B. fuchsioides, B. lucerna* and *B. corolicta* become too large for the average room in time, but they almost all propagate with ridiculous ease, so there is no difficulty in starting a few fresh plants. All must have ample feeding when they are established, and potting on into larger containers should be made a spring chore.

Beloperone guttata
Shrimp plant. Easy

Much of the popularity of *Beloperone guttata* is due to the apt common name of shrimp plant, which it gets from the shrimp-like appearance of the dull orange-coloured bracts (the flowers are inconspicuous). Although normally quite small, reaching a height of about 18 in indoors, *Beloperone guttata* can be grown into a specimen plant in a comparatively short space of time. Some years ago, at the Paris Floralies, my eyes seemed to deceive me when I saw a shrimp plant of at least 5 ft in height, with a diameter of at least 3 ft and bracts almost 6 in in length. Later I had the good fortune to meet an employee of the

Beloperone with its shrimp-like flower bracts

nursery responsible for growing this monster. Taking his advice, an experiment was carried out, and we grew plants from a height of 12 in in 5-in pots in the May of one year to over 4 ft in 8-in pots by May of the following year. Regular feeding and potting on were the answer, plus the fact that all bracts were removed as they appeared, so preventing the plant using up energy in their production. (A useful tip for many flowering plants – build up a plant before allowing it to bloom). These plants were grown in a heated greenhouse, and would be an impossibility indoors, I imagine!

The feeding lesson can, however, still apply to the window-sill plant, but it is better to feed in spring and summer when new leaves are being produced. When bracts lose their attractiveness they should be removed, and at the same time plants can be pruned to a better shape. Firm trimmings, about 3 in in length, are not difficult to root if placed around the edge of small pots filled with John Innes No. 1 potting compost or a soilless cutting compost.

Chrysanthemum
Easy

By using artificial light to extend winter day length, or by covering the plants with black polythene in summer to shorten the day, the nurseryman is able to offer pot-grown chrysanthemums on any day of the year. Also, by incorporating growth-depressant chemicals in the potting mixture, the height of the plant can be restricted to between 15 and 20 in. Such plants should be purchased when showing a reasonable amount of colour and never when in tight bud. A good-quality plant in a 5-in pot will have about 20 flowers and can almost be guaranteed to last for a full six weeks indoors.

After flowering, they can be planted out in the garden, but, no longer being influenced by the chemical restriction on growth, the plant will attain the height of a normal garden chrysanthemum. Indeed, if planted out in time for the plants to develop a reasonable length of stem, it is possible for them to flower in their pots in the early part of the year, and for the same plants to flower later in the garden.

Cyclamen
Moderately easy

Almost all plants grown commercially are raised from seed and may take anything from 12 to 18 months before producing enough flowers to be considered saleable. During the major part of this time the plants are kept at a temperature in the region of 13°C (55°F) and ventilators are opened on every favourable occasion, so providing cool, airy conditions for most of the time. For seed germination the temperature is in the region of 21°C (70°F).

Having spent its entire life in light and airy surroundings, it is not surprising that a cyclamen plant quickly reacts against hot, dry room conditions by producing sickly yellow leaves and drooping flowers. A cool, light room provides ideal surroundings. Watering should be done thoroughly, allowing the compost to dry out (but never to become bone-dry) before watering again. The corm will not be damaged by water, but care must be taken not to get water in amongst the flower and leaf stalks, as they are inclined to rot.

A neighbour, who could keep a cyclamen in perfect health for anything up to five months, always swore by, and performed, a weekly ritual that she remembered reading of some years before. It involved having a bowl of about 12 in in diameter, in the centre of which she placed a block of wood about 1½ in in thickness. Water was then poured into the bowl so that it did not quite cover the surface of the block when this was held down in the centre of the bowl. The cyclamen pot was then placed on the wood, which remained permanently moist. Each Saturday morning the moment of the week arrived when boiling water was poured from a kettle onto the block of wood – enough to replace the amount of water lost to the atmosphere during the week. When required, the compost in the pot was watered in the usual way. Though the purist may frown – and I cannot decide whether to approve or not – the cyclamen obviously liked this treatment.

For every success there must surely be a score of failures when attempting to keep cyclamen corms from one year to the next. It does seem, however, that once a corm has been successfully treated in this way it can be kept for a number of years without too much bother. Under normal conditions, the plant so treated is seldom as good as those grown from seed in the greenhouse. Nevertheless, there is a sense of satisfaction when success is achieved, so the following advice is offered. When the flowers have finished and the leaves begin to yellow and fall, water should be gradually reduced until the soil is quite dry. For preference the corm is left in its pot, which is placed on its side under the staging in the greenhouse. If a greenhouse is not available, a cool room or sheltered corner outside is the next best thing. In May, the plant should be knocked out of its pot and some of the old soil carefully removed and replaced with John Innes No. 2 potting compost. The plant can be left outside until mid-September when it is gradually introduced to warmer conditions (too sudden a change of temperature can be damaging). When the plants are established, they should be fed with liquid fertiliser.

Fuchsia
Moderately easy

Not the best indoor flowering plants as they have an essential need for maximum light, in

Fuchsia

the absence of which they will shed flowers and buds alarmingly. A full-light location is needed – plants will often be happier on the window ledge outside rather than in. Easily raised from cuttings, plants in a marvellous range of colours can be obtained, and they will flower endlessly throughout the late spring, summer and into early autumn if kept moist, well-fed, and in good light. A superb, trouble-free plant for the conservatory or small greenhouse.

Hibiscus
Easy

These are excellent room plants that will greatly benefit from being exposed to the maximum amount of sunshine, though the temperature need only be moderate. The exotic flowers last for a day or two only, but as one dies there always seems to be another in bud promising pleasure on another day. Correct watering is important; the compost must not at any time be allowed to dry out during the summer months, as loss of flowering buds will be the inevitable result.

My plant of *Hibiscus rosa-sinensis* is about 4 ft in height and is kept in check by annual pruning in the autumn when it is obvious that no further flowers can be expected until the following spring. The variegated form, *H. rosa-sinensis cooperi*, has red flowers that appear infrequently. The graceful habit and light colouring suggests, however, that it may well be a promising plant for the future. A cool, light place is most suitable, as plants will lose much of their bright colouring if temperatures are high and light is restricted.

Left *Hibiscus*

Right *Hoya carnosa variegata*

Hoya
Wax plant. Moderately easy

Much prized for its exquisite, pendant clusters of flowers, *Hoya carnosa* is, nevertheless, not

Hydrangea

an easy plant to flower indoors. It is best planted out in the greenhouse, or conservatory, with the growth trained to overhead wires. The flowers will then be better appreciated and will also be more plentiful.

Hoya carnosa variegata is even more reluctant to produce flowers when its roots are confined to a pot, but the attractive foliage more than compensates for lack of flowers. Some of these have better coloured foliage than others, and it may well be worth while looking through your supplier's stocks in order to locate those with a pink flush of colouring. In common with all climbing plants, hoyas will benefit if supports can be provided for growth to twine around.

Hydrangea
Easy
The hydrangeas are ideal dual-purpose plants, obtainable in shades of pink, red, white and blue, though the blue colours are in fact pink varieties that have been induced to change colour by adding carefully controlled quantities of alum to the potting soil. Never allow them to dry out, feed them well and they will be little trouble if given a light position. When flowering has finished indoors they can be planted outside hence the 'dual purpose'.

When planting out it is advisable to select a protected location so that young buds are not damaged by spring frosts. Plants being kept in their pots for growing on indoors or on the terrace should be pruned back in September, kept on the dry side and offered protection from frost over winter.

John Innes No. 3 compost should be used for potting, with a bluing agent such as alum being added to pink plants if one wishes to experiment with producing blue colours. Getting the ideal blue colouring is a highly skilled operation and will entail a degree of experiment before finding the correct amount of bluing agent to add to your particular soil.

The pure white *H. macrophylla* Soeur Thérèse has few peers and one of the best deep pinks is *H. macrophylla* Alpengluehn. A pink variety that 'blues' effectively is *H. m.* Bodense.

Hypocyrta
Clog plant. Easy
This is a comparatively new introduction and makes an interesting addition to the range of flowering houseplants. It is commonly named the clog plant on account of the attractive orange-coloured flowers that resemble a miniature clog. Even when not in flower the mass of glossy, dark green leaves are an attraction in themselves and, provided it receives the standard treatment for indoor plants, it is not difficult to care for. Growth may be trimmed into shape at almost any time after flowering and if used as 3-in-long cuttings, the healthy trimmings will root readily. One or two of the lower leaves should be removed before inserting. It is an excellent choice for growing in a container or basket suspended from the ceiling near a light window.

Temperature-wise one should aim for a minimum during the winter months of around 16°C (60°F), with summer temperatures not mattering so much, provided rooms do not become excessively hot and dry. In summer it is also important to ensure that the soil remains moist without becoming totally saturated, while in winter drier conditions are better. Feed regularly while in active growth but be careful not to overfeed.

Impatiens
Busy lizzie. Easy
Ease of propagation has established the busy lizzie (*Impatiens sultanii*) as one of our most popular and homely flowering plants. They root quite quickly, either in a proper compost or placed in water, and it is interesting to grow them in a clear glass bottle so that roots can be

Increasing humidity

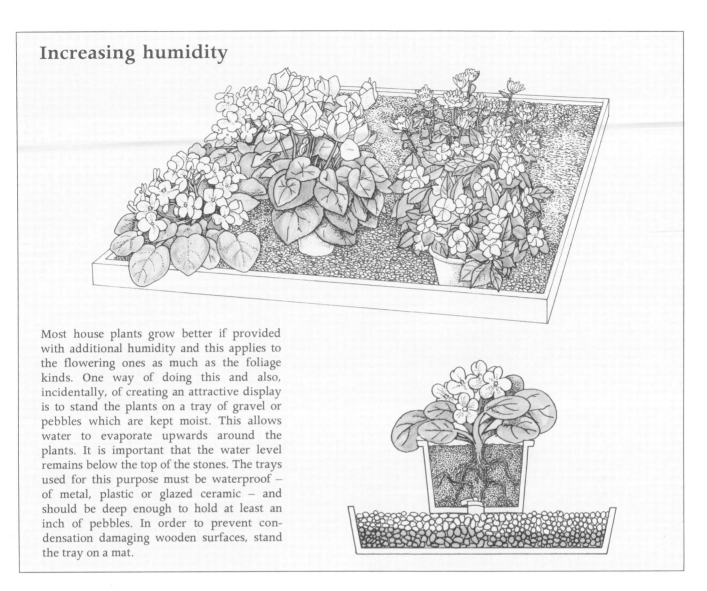

Most house plants grow better if provided with additional humidity and this applies to the flowering ones as much as the foliage kinds. One way of doing this and also, incidentally, of creating an attractive display is to stand the plants on a tray of gravel or pebbles which are kept moist. This allows water to evaporate upwards around the plants. It is important that the water level remains below the top of the stones. The trays used for this purpose must be waterproof – of metal, plastic or glazed ceramic – and should be deep enough to hold at least an inch of pebbles. In order to prevent condensation damaging wooden surfaces, stand the tray on a mat.

observed as they begin to grow. For growing plants a light sunny window is the place, and they should not be allowed to dry out, otherwise the flowers and buds will drop. They can be trimmed and reshaped at any time, and require regular feeding when in active growth if the leaves are to be kept healthy and green. If you want a plant as large as the one seen in the window down the road, pot your plant into a larger container using moist John Innes No. 2 potting compost or a soilless potting compost.

The newer species *Impatiens petersiana*, with dull red leaves and scarlet flowers will require more than the usual amount of fertiliser and more frequent potting on. A watchful eye should be kept on this impatiens for red spider; leaves becoming brown and dry are signs of their presence.

Besides raising new plants by means of cuttings, there is a wide range of F_1 varieties that can be raised from seed with little difficulty. Resultant plants will be much more compact than the older varieties and the colour range of flowers much more extensive.

For something new and an alternative to seed, early in the year I purchase the rooted cuttings of the range of impatiens referred to as New Guinea Hybrids. The majority of these have names relating to the circus, Big Top, Trapeze and so on, and will develop into plants of quite amazing size and colour if they are potted on into John Innes No. 3 compost and fed regularly once the plants are established.

While in active growth impatiens must never be allowed to dry out and a careful watch should be kept for greenfly, which seems to find the soft, succulent busy lizzie especially appetising. If aphids are discovered spray with soapy water or, if the attack is more severe, with malathion or liquid derris.

Ipomoea

Morning glory. Easy

Raised from spring-sown seed the morning glory is a fine annual plant for training around a windowframe during the summer. Intense blue, trumpet-shaped flowers last for one morning as the common name suggests, but the flowering period spreads over several days. Easily managed if kept cool, light and moist.

Ipomoea, morning glory

Poinsettia

Christmas flower. Moderately easy

Poinsettias have green leaves and insignificant flowers that are surrounded by brightly-coloured bracts, which are actually coloured leaves. The red-coloured plant is best known, though there are equally good white, pink and cream-pink varieties available. The modern poinsettia is surely one of the most remarkable plants of recent years. It has now lost its too-delicate-for-words image and become an established favourite that is thoroughly reliable. A sweeping statement, maybe (I know there are still some that fail inexplicably), but the way in which the public and florist alike have accepted the variety Paul Mikkelsen is abundant proof of its durability.

Although the greenhouse cultivation of this variety is in itself a fascinating subject, I will only very briefly comment on this aspect. New techniques and the use of growth-depressant chemicals are responsible for the compact plant, seldom more than 24 in tall, that is today offered for sale. Intense red bracts are no longer confined to the pre-Christmas months of the year, as the nurseryman is able to use black polythene to restrict the amount of light available to the plant, so inducing it to flower at an unnatural time. As with chrysanthemums, poinsettia flower buds initiate (that is first begin to form) when the day reaches a given length, and when grown naturally the poinsettia does so in about the third week of October. The light factor is probably the most important single reason why it is difficult to flower poinsettias indoors. In the home, they usually have the normal day length of light and are then subjected to an additional five to six hours of artificial light in the evening. Plants therefore continue to grow instead of developing flowers and bracts. The answer is to grow them in a room where they only get natural daylight. A sunny window will be ideal and will only be too hot for them on the very brightest of days. A temperature of around 16°C (60°F) will be perfectly adequate.

A golden rule with watering is to water when necessary and not at set times, nor just for the sake of it. Feeding is not important once the bracts have formed; before this, apply weak liquid fertiliser regularly.

Reports indicate that it is possible to have plants in colour for eight months or more from the time of purchase. This would, however, be the exception, and one would normally expect a flowering time of between six and eight weeks.

As the flowers in the centre of the bract begin to rot, or drop off, the bract itself will gradually begin to disintegrate. At about this time, the leaves will also begin to turn yellow and will fall at a touch. When the plant is no longer attractive the main stem should be cut back to a height of about 6 in from the soil surface. The flow of sap from the cut stem will do no harm and can either be left to dry naturally or can be checked by applying powdered charcoal or moist sand to the wound.

A week or two before cutting the stem, water should be gradually reduced until the compost is almost dry. If not considered unsightly, the plant can remain in the window; failing this it should be stored in a warm place, as cold conditions will lessen its chance of survival. While it is resting, the compost must be kept almost dry until new growth appears, when normal watering can be gradually resumed. At this time the plant can be potted on, or re-potted in the same pot after first removing some of the old soil; John Innes No. 2 potting compost is the best to use. If the plant is successfully flowered for a second time one should not expect indoor growth to produce quite such large bracts as those of greenhouse-grown plants.

Saintpaulia

African violet. Moderately easy

In the fascinating world of horticulture there is no plant that has caught the imagination and interest of the houseplant grower more than the humble African violet. It is without a doubt one of the most widely cultivated potted flowering plants. One good reason for their popularity is that they can flower throughout the year.

Since the first *Saintpaulia ionantha* was removed from its mountainside in Tanzania there has been a quite phenomenal amount of hybridising done. There must now be several thousand varieties of saintpaulia listed as distinct varieties, but it would be very foolish even to suggest that all of them are available, only the best are retained.

Besides variations in flower colour and shape, there is also a considerable difference between the varieties in the colour, shape and general appearance of many of the leaves: a comparatively recent and very pleasing introduction from Denmark has been *S. rococo* in both blue and pink colours. The flowers are an attractive semi-double and the leaves are particularly interesting for their shorter stalks

and the contrasting pale green colouring where the leaf is attached to the petiole. These would seem to constitute an interesting new strain which will encourage further developments and improvements in the same way as other positive strains have done such as the varieties developed from the Holtkamy Rhapsody strain from Germany and the Balli strain from America. Most of the plants within these groups have, like racehorses, retained the essential characteristics of the parents. So, rather than present a lengthy list of difficult-to-obtain plants, I would suggest that one should contact a good supplier to see what is available. Alternatively, join a group that has African violets as a special interest, and you may well be able to participate in a plant exchange arrangement.

African violets are among the most perplexing of all our indoor plants, and almost everyone seems to have attempted growing them at one time or other. Most people shake their heads in disbelief when they see a really well-flowered plant, saying they have tried saintpaulias unsuccessfully so many times. The natural follow-up question is, 'What is the secret?'

Mrs Murray, an old friend and true expert on the subject, attributes her success to a mysterious ingredient which she refers to as TLC – tender, loving care. Though TLC is important, there is a great deal more to it than that, as our expert well knows. To achieve success there are, to my mind, three essential factors that cannot be ignored: light, adequate temperature and proper watering.

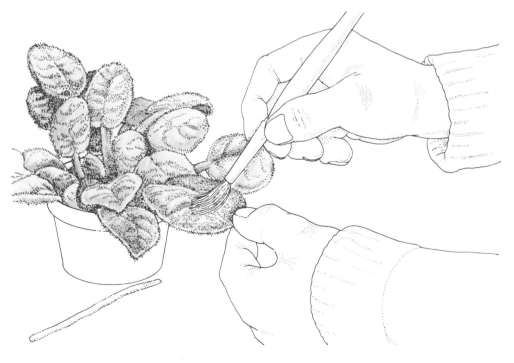

African violet leaves should be gently cleaned with a soft brush

According to most of the recognised experts, saintpaulias should have approximately 14 hours of light each day. So it is a question of the lightest possible window during the day, and supplementary artificial light in the evening. I have found that most of the greatly improved strains of saintpaulia now on sale will do perfectly well on a sunny window-ledge, needing protection from only the strongest mid-day sun. Have a care, though; sunshine on wet leaves will be damaging, so avoid wetting leaves when watering.

Often I have listened to the tale of woe as someone has described how wonderfully well their African violet did in the steamy kitchen window during the summer, only to gradually succumb with the approach of winter. It is the common fault of inadequate temperature that is responsible for leaves becoming darker in colour and beginning to shrivel as cold conditions and fluctuating temperatures have their effect. Although plants will survive at lower temperatures, I have found that a minimum of 18°C (65°F) is essential if plants are to be in good health and produce fresh leaves at the same time.

Some time ago, on recommending the use of tepid water for saintpaulias, I was just a trifle nonplussed when a listener, in all seriousness, asked where it could be purchased! As hot water can be more harmful than cold, care should be taken to use water that has just got the chill off; I find that a container of water placed in a warm room overnight is ideal for use the following morning. Water must be kept off the leaves and away from the central crown of the plant, and is best given by placing the pot in a shallow saucer of water and allowing the plant to drink up all it requires before tipping away the surplus. Never allow plant pots to stand in water for any length of time.

Damaged leaves and dead flowers must be removed as soon as they are seen in order to prevent rot setting up in the centre of the plant. When cleaning plants in this way, it is important that the complete leaf or flower stalk should be removed, leaving no pieces that are likely to rot if left attached to the plant.

Cuttings present little difficulty: firm, clean leaves are inserted in a peat and sand mixture. Endeavour to maintain a temperature in the region of 18°C (65°F). They will also form roots in water. When the young plants clustered around the parent leaf are large enough to handle, and have a reasonable amount of root attached, they should be gently teased apart. A number of individual little plantlets will result; handled carefully, these can be potted up individually, or spaced out in a seed box filled with a mixture of two-thirds John Innes No. 2 potting compost to one-third clean peat or a soilless potting compost. (This mixture will be suitable for saintpaulias at all stages of growth). Treated in this way, plants with single crowns will result and flowers will stand boldly away from the overlapping rosette of neat leaves. If left undivided flowers and leaves intermingle and present a less attractive plant. In order to build up strong plants it is advisable to remove the first, and sometimes the second, flush of flowers; by so doing the plant's energy will be directed to leaf development, and it will, in turn, flower more freely.

Spathiphyllum wallisii
White sails. Moderately easy

Protection from direct sunlight is essential if one is to succeed with this aroid, and the compost must never be allowed to dry out if the glossy green leaves are to retain their appearance. Regular feeding and annual potting on in early spring are two more essentials that will have to be attended to if plants are to remain in good fettle. Propagation, by division of the root clumps, is not difficult, and may be done at almost any time other than when plants are in flower. The stiffly erect, creamy-white flowers are ever popular with

Spathiphyllum wallisii

the florist and flower arranger; even when they have dulled to green they still have an attraction for some.

Strelitzia

Bird of paradise flower. Easy

Strelitzia reginae is a plant bearing a splendid proper name and an equally fascinating common name – bird of paradise – derived from the bird-like appearance of the exotic blue and orange flower. The combination of name and flower, brings the plant immediately to notice but it really is not the best of plants to have indoors. The leaves are unattractive, and in order to produce its long-awaited flower, plants must be in very large pots.

Seed is generally freely available and is not difficult to germinate, but from seed it will probably take at least six years (or more) for plants to produce flowers. They require a fairly heavy potting mixture, such as John Innes No. 3, cool, light conditions indoors, and a full sun location out of doors in the summer. Water freely, giving a little less in winter. Pot on when roots push out of the pot.

Streptocarpus

Cape primrose. Easy

This plant is a particular favourite of mine. The variety Constant Nymph freely produces violet-blue flowers throughout the spring and summer and never fails to attract attention. Besides the blue, there is also a white form of *S.* Constant Nymph which offers a pleasing contrast. Possibly the most important step in respect of hybridisation of these plants has been taken by the John Innes Institute who have produced many more compact varieties in a splendid range of colours. They all have girls names: 'Tina' with magenta markings; 'Fiona' which is pink with a white throat and 'Diana' which also has a white throat and is principally cerise in colour. Perhaps the greatest difficulty will be in locating a source of supply, as the brittle leaves that overlap in the pot make it almost impossible to pack without damage and nurserymen are loth to grow it. Probably the best answer is to try your local nursery, which does not have to contend with packing problems. Failing this, find an owner who is willing to sacrifice a medium-sized, healthy leaf from his plant. The lower portion of the complete leaf, inserted in propagating compost, will be reasonably easy to root. Alternatively, new plants will not be difficult to raise by division, splitting older clumps after they have flowered and potting them in John Innes No. 2 compost or a soilless potting compost, or by growing them from seed sown in heat in January.

Streptocarpus

Orchids

Many orchid plants are much tougher than is often supposed, and considering that many of them are epiphytes, it goes without saying that they must have a tough constitution to survive in the extremes of wet and dry conditions that must prevail in their natural habitat.

There are orchids that like cool conditions, those that like to be on the warm side and countless others that fall between. It is therefore impossible to recommend ideal temperatures. This very diverse and extensive family of plants makes generalisation very difficult, but for the easier plants that one may care to try indoors it can be said that a temperature in the region of 16°C (60°F) should be the aim. Also, a light, airy and humid location should be provided, and any potting should be done with a properly prepared orchid mixture that drains very freely and offers maximum aeration.

The best indoor orchids that I have seen were growing in a deep window that had been built out from the house, so that it resembled a small greenhouse attached to the wall – a sort of bay window at conventional windowledge height. In such a window the plants can be provided with their own micro-climate, the glass can be shaded to offer protection from the sun and a great deal can be done to incorporate the maximum number of plants by suspending them from the roof and around the walls. Likewise, there are numerous plant cases of reasonable size available in which

continued on page 108

Flowering pot plants provide a long-lasting source of pleasure especially in winter when cut flowers are scarce

Far left A large azalea plant in full bloom is a blaze of colour

Left Chrysanthemums are always popular gifts and can be planted out in the garden after flowering indoors

Below The humble impatiens (busy lizzie) will grow into an impressive plant with good care and the regular pinching out of the shoot tips

plants can be provided with specialised conditions that are quite different to those prevailing in the room in which they are located. In more temperate regions plants can be placed out of doors in a warm and sheltered area during the summer months.

The indoor orchid requires a fairly high humidity level in the region of 70 per cent, which will mean frequent misting of the foliage with a fine spray of tepid water. With individual pots on window sills it is difficult to maintain humidity, so it becomes necessary to provide a tray of some kind filled with moistened gravel on which plants can stand.

In better equipped commercial establishments, new plants are propagated from seed and are raised in highly specialised conditions that would be far beyond the means of anyone other than the specialist grower. For example, from the time of germination, seedlings of cattleyas will take five to seven years before they eventually produce flowers – one of the reasons for the plants being costly. A simpler method used with many varieties that will result in much earlier flowering is to remove mature pseudobulbs and plant them up individually, or by dividing actual clumps of plants and potting them individually. Cattleyas, cymbidiums and paphiopedilums (the comparatively easy slipper orchid) are examples of plants that can be increased by division.

Angraecum sesquipedale
A plant well worth considering if the owner is prepared to sell you one, certainly a nice name to roll off the tongue. I include it here out of sheer devilment. I have been reading that it is a plant for the stove greenhouse (temperature around 21°C (70°F)), yet I recall growing this plant in a sort of slatted wooden box in very spartan conditions and it did splendidly. The foliage is very ordinary, but the glistening white flower with an extremely long white spur was a rare but regularly appearing sight in spite of the rough conditions. When in flower, it came indoors and was treated no differently than the many other indoor plants which surrounded it.

This plant, and its treatment and conditions of growing, is mentioned by way of encouragement to anyone who may be offered an orchid and is unsure of taking on something with the reputation for being exotic. Exotic maybe, but you could well be surprised by the manner in which many of these plants will settle down and do perfectly well indoors – perhaps giving the feeling that you have at last got a brush of the old greenfingers magic!

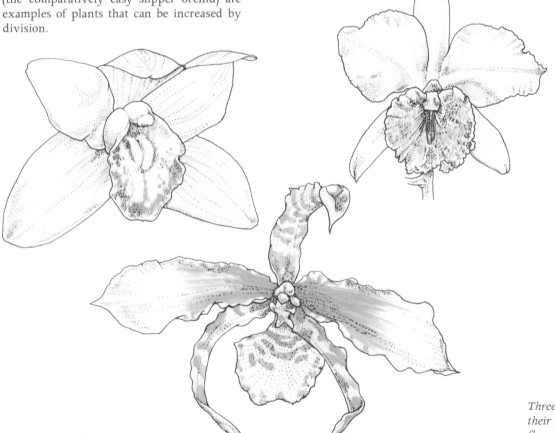

Three orchids, showing their stunning varied flowers

Cattleya

Anyone sufficiently interested could well set up a collection composed entirely of these very fine plants and the many hybrid forms, which are generally not difficult to obtain from the specialist grower. Plants rest in winter when less water is required, but the mixture in which they are growing must at no time become excessively dry. Provide a light growing position in winter and a spot that offers protection from strong sunlight in summer.

Cymbidium

These are the backbone of the orchid business, producing spectacular flower spikes in an infinite range of colours, particularly through the winter months. In time the plants become very large and require ample space, but they are not in the least difficult to care for as far as orchids go, and will tolerate a wide temperature range as long as there is a buoyant and airy atmosphere.

Compost must be free draining, and it is important to water thoroughly – for smaller pots that can be handled easily this will mean plunging the plant pot in a bucket of water and allowing all air bubbles to escape before the pot is removed. If flowers are to be cut they must first be allowed to open fully on the plant; individual flowers are much used in floristry.

Dendrobium

Very wide ranging with more than 1,000 species, many of which leave much to be desired when not in flower; the flowers do make up for any deficit there may be in the foliage. Higher temperatures are generally required, but there is some variation depending on the type, so it is well to get growing instructions with the plant when purchased.

Miltonia

For limited space and maximum pleasure this could well be the choice, not only as an orchid but as an indoor plant in general, certainly so if one possesses a heated conservatory. Those with flowers resembling pansies are especially attractive and could well be the perfect plants for that extended window 'greenhouse' mentioned earlier. Being epiphytic they can be used in many interesting ways other than as simple potted plants.

Odontoglossum

Allied to the miltonia and requiring a growing temperature in winter of about 16°C (60°F) minimum. Will do best in a lightly shaded moist atmosphere and can be propagated by division.

Overleaf Poinsettias have become the traditional 'Christmas flower' and so make excellent gifts. In recent years new varieties have been developed which are easier to look after than their predecessors and a whole range of colours is now available from white through all shades of pink to red. This photograph shows two extremes of the range – a greenish white and lovely rich red. When giving plants as gifts do not wrap them up too long in advance. Keep them in optimum conditions for as long as possible.

Paphiopedilum
Slipper orchid

A tongue twisting name for the slipper orchid which does well if kept moist in a lightly shaded, reasonably warm location. A small collection of different varieties provides a succession of flowers.

The attractive, pansy-like flower of miltonia

CHAPTER 8
Climbing and trailing plants

With houseplants, the aim is to have a variety of healthy plants displayed to their fullest possible advantage, and in this respect there cannot be anything better than an attractive trailing plant cascading from a hanging pot or basket.

Hanging baskets

An extensive selection of decorative pots has been developed to display on shelves, from wall brackets or be suspended from the ceiling. A natural extension of the latter has been the need to provide something to hold the pot in its mid-air position; macramé is the most popular solution. Macramé is the time absorbing craft of intricately weaving string and similar materials into all sorts of beautiful patterns (beautiful patterns may be a rather sweeping statement, as some of the creations done in heavier or synthetic materials can be quite hideous). However, the majority of the macramé items will enhance the appearance of the plant, the container and the room in which they are placed.

Multihangers, holding three or more pots are suitable for rooms with high ceilings, and must have firm anchorage; three pots with plants, soil and weight of water are surprisingly heavy and must have a stout hook from which to hang. The same applies to hanging baskets which will hold a number of plants.

Most decorative pots for hanging plants are without drainage, so care must be exercised when watering to ensure that the compost does not become too soggy. There are pulleys available with which one can raise and lower plants from their elevated positions. This feature is especially useful for heavier plants and will greatly simplify the business of watering – for one thing it will be much less hit and miss.

With hanging plants, both out of doors and in, it is better to have the container suspended at about head level, which will make it possible to regularly check the condition of the soil, without needing to find a stepladder first. When feeding hanging plants it is much easier to use fertiliser in tablet form – tablets are simply pushed into the soil at intervals as recommended by the manufacturer.

Watering hanging plants

Returning to watering, there are several ingenious devices available to assist with watering plants at higher levels. One in particular is useful for the person with a number of plants – a lightweight hosepipe is attached to the domestic water tap and at the other end there is an extension pipe for reaching the basket. Water is then controlled by the operator with a special on-off switch that works admirably. As with almost all houseplants, one should water hanging plants thoroughly and allow the soil to become reasonably dry before watering again.

Suitable plants for hanging baskets

Many ordinary houseplants will develop into fine climbers or trailing plants if their supporting stakes are removed so that they can trail downwards. Two of the best plants in this respect are the grape ivy, *Rhoicissus rhomboidea*, and the sweetheart plant, *Philodendron scandens* – both green foliaged plants that are better out of constant direct sunlight. In macramé hanging pots, a pleasing effect can be achieved with both these plants by allowing some of the strands to climb the string support, while the main part of the plant is allowed to trail naturally over the basket edge.

One of the very best trailing foliage plants for a position out of the sun is *Scindapsus aureus*; it is particularly suitable as a hanging plant when grown by one of the water culture methods. Growing plants by one of these

continued on page 116

Left A tower pot is a
suitable container for a
collection of saintpaulias
(African violets) with their
varying flowers and leaves.
The cyclamen adds a splash
of pink in the background
Top left The colourful bract
and interesting leaves of
anthurium
Top right A cymbidium
orchid
Bottom right It is easy to
see how *Strelitzia reginae*
acquired the common name
'bird of paradise flower'

methods in an elevated position is something that has not been taken full advantage of. Control of watering is very simple, and the water indicator in the container can be so located that one should be able to read it from floor level.

If offered a light position in the window, many of the busy lizzies (impatiens) do splendidly in hanging containers. Not requiring quite so much light, but needing even temperature in the region of 18°C (65°F), *Columnea banksii* is a fine plant with oval shaped evergreen leaves, and a wealth of exotic orange flowers in early spring. These plants will usually flower more freely if the soil is kept on the dry side during January and February; at other times regular feeding and watering will be necessary.

The humble tradescantia in its several forms is the perfect trailing plant for the home; when they become a bit ragged around the top of the pot, as they invariably do, one can rectify the situation by inserting cuttings in the top of the pot to sprout afresh. Ivies for lighter and cooler rooms will also do well, and for warmer and slightly darker locations the creeping fig (*Ficus pumila*) is excellent, but it must at no time be allowed to become too dry.

Flowering trailers

Pendulous begonias, trailing varieties of fuchsia and *Campanula isophylla*, with its lovely star flowers, will only retain their flowers if offered good light. The first mentioned pair really being only suitable for the glassed-in porch or conservatory.

Climbers

To complement the hanging plants there are also a number of natural climbers that can be used for covering wall areas, or providing divisions of greenery between one part of a room and another. Most majestic and far and away the most popular of the climbing or upright plants is the monstera which tolerates a variety of conditions and treatment. Possibly tougher in its constitution and if anything more adaptable is *Rhoicissus rhomboidea* which, as mentioned earlier, is quite prepared either to climb or trail down. For various methods of training see page 120.

Most rampant of the climbers is the vine *Tetrastigma voinierianum* which, if happy with its treatment, will almost seem to have continually moving growth as it covers the wall or supporting framework.

Cacti & succulents

Trailing cacti or succulents are also a possibility, with hearts entangled, *Ceropegia woodii*, providing a yard-long cascade of heart-shaped leaves that are primarily grey-green in colour. Though not having such long trails, the rat's tail cactus, *Aporocactus flagelliformis*, is interesting. *Sedum morganianum*, though not for the beginner, is an interesting trailing succulent with ropes of blue-grey leaves that are roughly tubular in shape.

Tetrastigma voinierianum

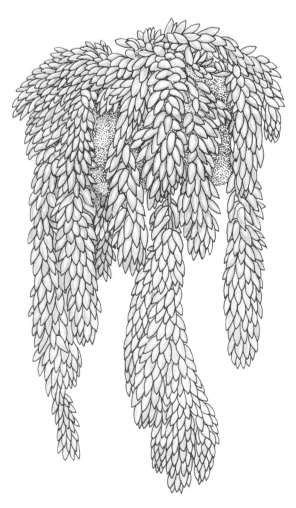

Suggested plants

Columnea
Moderately difficult
These and allied plants, such as aeschynan-thuses (syn. trichosporums) are not too difficult despite their exotic flowers. Being naturally trailing in habit, they should be placed where growth will trail down and show the flowering bracts to better advantage when they appear. When older plants become untidy new ones may be started from cuttings rooted in moist peat in warm conditions; whole strands will root if laid on the surface of the peat.

Ficus pumila
Creeping fig. Easy
It is not always realised that the creeping fig, *F. pumila*, a charming green plant of easy culture, can be encouraged to climb if a mossed stake, or piece of cork bark, is provided for the aerial roots to cling to. It is essential that the support should be kept moist and equally important that the compost should not become saturated, so fill a scent spray with water and use this for damping the support.

Above left *Sedum morganianum*

Above right *Ficus radicans*

Ficus radicans
Difficult
To succeed with the variegated *radicans*, a propagating case or a damp mossed stake would appear to be essential, as plants quickly deteriorate in the dry atmosphere of the average room.

Trailing peperomias
Three trailing peperomias, ideal for edging plant troughs and containers, are *P. scandens*, *P. glabella variegata* and the more recently introduced *P. tithymaloides*, which has mottled green and gold variegations. The latter produces occasional green shoots that are not unattractive and, indeed, help to set off the variegation. No more than three or four green pieces need be left, as any more would quickly outgrow the more colourful pieces.

Platycerium alcicorne
Stag's horn fern. Moderately easy
One of my favourite houseplants, the stag's horn fern, as it is called, is much less difficult indoors than its appearance at first sight suggests.

As the platyceriums are epiphytes, better results will be achieved if plants are attached to a piece of bark, or absorbent timber; or they can be planted in an old log or tree stump. The method employed is the same as that described for cryptanthus (see page 53). Once established on their anchorage, platyceriums can remain there literally until they grow

continued on page 121

Climbing and trailing plants
offer a great deal of scope
for decorative ideas
Left *Philodendron scandens*
is a very versatile plant and
has been used here in a
fun, jungle-type
arrangement, giving an idea
of what it would look like in
its natural environment
Right As a contrast a trailing
plant, columnea, is used to
good effect in a light
conservatory

Training plants

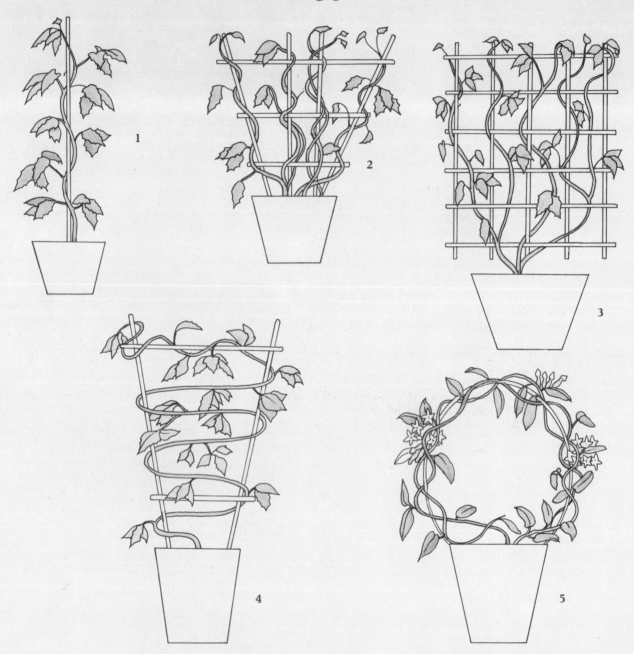

Imaginative training of climbing plants greatly increases their scope for use as display features in room decoration. The following are some of the most popular methods: 1. The simplest way is to twine the stems round a single cane. 2. A plant can be trained up a small trellis which can be bought ready-made or constructed from canes firmly tied together. 3. A larger trellis can be used to create a leafy room divider or wall decoration. 4. The stem of the plant can be wound round two canes in S-shaped loops. 5. Some plants can be trained successfully round a circular loop of strong plastic-coated wire.

When training plants in this manner handle them carefully; remember that if a stem is broken or bent at too acute an angle the flow of sap will stop and the plant die off above the break. Tie stems to the support with twine or paper– or plastic-covered plant ties, choosing whichever blends best with the plant's natural colour.

For best results choose a fast-growing plant such as *Cissus antarctica*, *Rhoicissus rhomboidea* or *Tetrastigma voinierianum*. Stephanotis is a suitable plant to grow round a circular hoop.

Platycerium alcicorne

it is most essential that a moist support be used into which the plant can work its roots.

Stephanotis floribunda
Madagascar jasmine. Easy
The heavily scented flowers of this plant are an almost indispensable part of the better-quality bridal bouquet. The scent of only a few 'pips' indoors will find its way into every room – unless, of course, you happen to live in a mansion. I am experimenting with a plant indoors at the moment, to see how it reacts to room conditions, but I have not had it long enough to form a proper opinion. Reports of great success from various owners of stephanotis plants have, however, surprised me; and there does not appear to be any special treatment, other than a light window position and a temperature of about 16°C (60°F). When training plant growth to supports use a trellis, or hooped wire, so that growth can be wound backwards and forwards, thus checking the flow of sap and encouraging flower development.

themselves out of house room. As some indication of their potential, I once measured a plant that was 6 ft in length and the same across. The hanging basket in which it had been originally planted had long since disappeared in the heart of the plant.

When attached to bark it is usual for stag's horn fern to be hung on the wall so that their antler appearance can be set off to full advantage. There is an obvious precaution, however; the wall must be made of brick, or some other material that will not be harmed by moisture.

Watering is simply done by plunging both plant and anchorage in a bucket of water and allowing the surplus water to drain away before putting it back in position. A little liquid fertiliser mixed into the water is beneficial, care being taken that the fertiliser is used according to the manufacturer's instructions.

Scindapsus aureus

Scindapsus aureus
Money plant or devil's ivy. Moderately difficult
Scindapsus aureus is an attractive plant that will respond to the treatment generally recommended for philodendrons. With leaves of similar shape and shorter internodes than its parent, the variety Marble Queen lives up to its name for it has white marbled foliage. It is not an easy plant, the leaves being prone to browning at the edges when the plants are young and the roots weak. Once the plants have established themselves they are not so troublesome. When grown as an upright plant

The
Hall

Plants for the hall must be choosen with great care to suit the conditions in your own home. Remember that all plants hate a draughty position. The arrangement **below** would only suit a warm, draught-free hall. It includes *Ficus benjamina, Aechmea fasciata, Dracaena deremensis, Begonia rex* and *Nephrolepis exaltata*. A cool, light hall **(right)** makes a good home for a large fern, with a small leaved ivy and *Rhoicissus ellendanica* on the low window sill.

CHAPTER 9
Cacti and succulents

According to at least one survey these are the most popular of all indoor plants, which seems odd when one meets so many people who cannot bear the sight of the prickly and unfriendly things!

Perhaps this popularity can be attributed to the ease of their propagation and, if one discounts the rare kinds, the fact that they are just about the easiest of all potted plants to care for. My own collection seems to thrive on minimal care. But the one sure way of killing them off is to provide conditions that are a combination of cold and wet. The majority of them, however, will not object too much to cooler temperatures provided they are not wet at their roots.

With such a wide-ranging family of plants it is difficult to generalise in respect of care and attention, but by the same token it would be impossible to cater for all their needs in these few pages. But, to be bold, may I suggest that indoors they should all have a light position in which to grow (most in full sunlight), and water that is given freely and regularly, say once weekly during the growing season. The growing season is usually from spring to autumn, during which period the compost should be kept moist. From about mid-October to early March the majority of them will be better without water. Temperature is not important provided it does not become excessively cold; average room conditions are fine.

This may seem spartan treatment, but it will keep plants in better condition, and a much greater number of plants in your collection will produce flowers during the following early spring and summer. The flowers of cacti and succulents can be a considerable bonus, as most have flowers of the most brilliant colouring, although some of them may last for a fleeting few hours only.

Because of the somewhat general advice in respect of plants and watering, it may be found that some plants which appear to be suffering as a result of the drought conditions will require a little water in winter, but it must never be excessive. Succulent types may need more water.

Given proper conditions and ripe seed many of these plants will germinate like mustard and cress and, if time is on your side, it is far and away the best and cheapest way of starting a collection. Compost for growing cacti is now freely available, and with the addition of a little extra sand this will be fine for seed sowing. A shallow seed box is the best container – the soil should be gently pressed into position and the seed sown thinly on the surface with perhaps a fine scattering of sand over the seed. Water it all with a very fine rose on the can, place a sheet of glass over the box, and then newspaper over the glass, and wait for the tiny seeds to sprout. Given reasonable warmth (in the region of 18°C (65°F) it will not be long before the box begins to fill with minute pinheads of growth that will in time develop into the weird and wonderful shapes we know so well. From a few packets of seed an amazing assortment will often result.

There is no urgency for removing the seedlings from the box – they can be left until they produce firm young plants that can then be potted into individual small pots using an appropriate porous cactus compost.

Propagated in this way, there will obviously be many duplicated varieties, and one then has to be selective in retaining only the best, perhaps donating the others to friends.

Fortunately, these plants are not much troubled by pests (other than overwatering on the part of the too attentive owner), though mealy bug, which manifests itself as a tiny ball of what appears to be cotton wool in the more

continued on page 128

Right A dish garden planted up with various kinds of succulents makes a long-lasting decoration

Opposite page
Top Cactus flowers come in a range of bright colours appropriate to their natural sunny surroundings
Bottom left The flower of *Schlumbergera gaertneri*, the Easter cactus
Bottom right An epiphyllum flower – Dobson's Yellow

inaccessible parts of the plant, can be a problem. The actual bugs have the appearance of tiny white woodlice – the young bugs being protected in the cotton wool-like substance. Dabbing methylated spirits onto the pests by means of a small paintbrush or piece of cotton wool tied to a matchstick will destroy them.

On a south-facing windowsill I have a 4-ft-long plastic window tray in which there is a layer of about three quarters of an inch of sand, and placed on the sand there are twenty square plastic pots holding one cactus each. These fill the tray perfectly making it a fine display. There are mammalarias, echinocactus, rebutia and similar plants of exquisite symmetrical shape, that give me immense pleasure. The south facing aspect is very hot and sunny in summer and often quite cool in winter, but these plants have proved to be the ideal occupants for the location.

On account of their prickly, inhospitable appendages some of the cacti are problem plants when it comes to potting them into larger containers, not that this is a frequent necessity. New pots should be only slightly larger than the old pots, and potting should be done in the spring. However, there may be the additional need to take the precaution of using a folded newspaper in the form of a collar to hold the plant while it is being placed in position. A properly prepared quick-draining compost is most essential.

Aporocactus flagelliformis

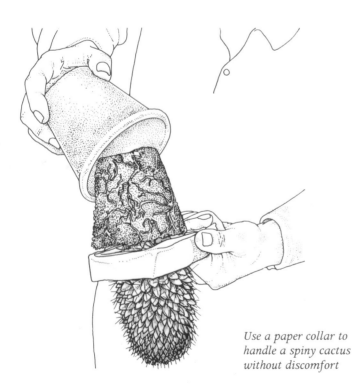

Use a paper collar to handle a spiny cactus without discomfort

Favourite varieties

The following list only scratches the surface, but could prove to be an interesting basis to a collection. Few are difficult, and most of them will add interest by producing flowers.

Aloe variegata
Partridge breast aloe
Commonly named partridge breast aloe on account of interesting variegation in shades of green. Flowers, borne on tall stems, are tubular and reddish orange in colour. Can be increased from seed or offsets, and requires no special care other than warmth and light.

Aporocactus flagelliformis
Rat's tail cactus
The rat's tail cactus may be grown in a hanging pot, as it has cylindrical trailing stems from which appear attractive hose-in-hose pink flowers of deep pink colouring. Requires reasonable winter warmth.

Cephalocereus senilis
Old man cactus
Slow growing and covered in long silvery hairs that give it the common name of old man

cactus. Would you believe that the hairs can be washed and combed when dirty? My own twenty-year-old plant has never had this treatment, but it is a fine specimen nevertheless, and no trouble to care for. Occasional watering, a light windowsill and an average temperature are all that it requires.

Cereus peruvianus

Easily-cared-for plant that will give some height to a collection. Develops into stereotype 'wide-open-spaces' cactus in time, with attractively ribbed stem. Besides this one there are any number of attractive cereus to choose from.

Crassula lycopodioides

Tiny leaves form branches of square and interesting stems that sprout further stems to eventually give a miniature tree-like effect. Flowers are insignificant, but it is a trouble free plant that is easily propagated from pieces of stem.

Echeveria

Lots of different varieties of these, almost all with fascinating leaf colouring and regular summer flowers. A windowsill filled with flowering echeverias presents an unbelieveable range of colours. Keep water off the leaves and they are little bother.

Echinocereus grusonii
Barrel cactus

The round barrel cactus with prominent yellow spines is one of the most splendid of all plants. Quite the pride of my small collection, it has grown at twice the pace of the other plants, yet has no special attention. A must in any cactus collection.

Epiphyllum

There are many hybrids of these succulent plants with large spatula-shaped leaves and flowers of unimaginable colour and brilliance. Needs slightly richer, moisture-holding compost, but tolerates very variable conditions with no marked ill effects.

Euphorbia splendens
Crown of thorns

This is the very spiteful crown of thorns (a jab from the thorns produces a nasty rash) and has small but brilliantly coloured red flowers. It will grow anywhere in reasonable light and temperature. Cuttings, allowed to dry for a day before inserting, will root readily in warm temperature of around 18°C (65°F). A careful watch should be kept for troublesome mealy bug on older plants.

Overleaf A variety of plants creates a happy working environment
1   *Neanthe bella*
2   *Adiantum cuneatum*
3   *Scindapsus aureus*
4   *Howeia forsteriana*
5   *Rhoicissus rhomboidea*
6   *Philodendron scandens*
7   *Ceropegia woodii*
8   *Billbergia windii*
9   Saintpaulia
10 *Sansevieria trifasciata laurentii*

Kalanchoe daigremontiana

At one time known as bryophyllum, the principal fascination of this plant is the way in which completely formed plantlets develop along the edge of the leaf. These root easily in almost any growing medium, and new plants will grow like a weed.

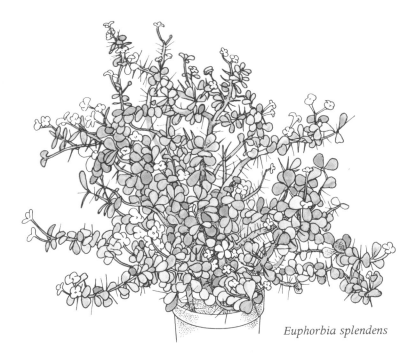

Euphorbia splendens

Cactus garden

Cacti and succulents are often shown to best advantage when planted up in a bowl arrangement. In this way the shapes help to compliment each other and the finished effect is not only attractive but can survive with minimal care on any sunny windowsill. However, such arrangements should consist of either all cacti, as shown here, or all succulents; to mix the two types creates cultural problems.

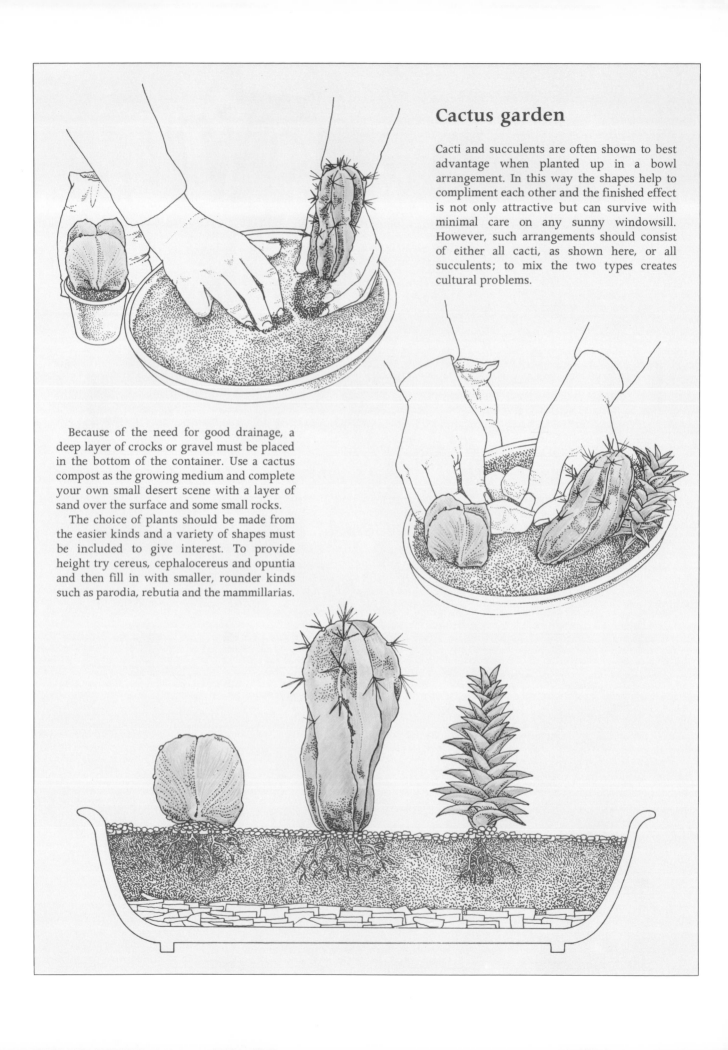

Because of the need for good drainage, a deep layer of crocks or gravel must be placed in the bottom of the container. Use a cactus compost as the growing medium and complete your own small desert scene with a layer of sand over the surface and some small rocks.

The choice of plants should be made from the easier kinds and a variety of shapes must be included to give interest. To provide height try cereus, cephalocereus and opuntia and then fill in with smaller, rounder kinds such as parodia, rebutia and the mammillarias.

Lithops
Living stones

On close inspection these will be found to be quite varied in shape and colour, but they all resemble small stones or pebbles, hence the common name of living stones. Can be raised from seed which is very expensive, so every care should be exercised when sowing and a constant temperature of around 21°C (70°F) should be provided. These are always seen at their best as a collection in a shallow pan.

Mammillaria

No collection of cacti could possibly be gathered without including these lovely barrel-shaped plants in their neat, symmetrical forms. *Mammillaria rhodantha* has lovely spines and produces tiny red flowers in the summer. My *M. hahniana* has the appearance of a ball of grey wool as a result of natural straggling hairs that completely obscure the plant. *Mammillaria elongata* has an attractive tubular body, is an overall dull yellow in colour and forms a neat cluster.

Notocactus leninghausii

Develops into a tallish cylinder of sulphur yellow growth that is lopsided at the top, which adds considerably to the attraction of the plant. Slow to mature, but age greatly enhances the appearance of this fine plant. Does not normally flower in its early years but well worth having, nevertheless.

Opuntia
Prickly pear

The prickly pears are among the best known of all, and have pads of growth that are viciously spined, or have countless bristles that stick into everything and anything that comes into contact with them.

Dark green pads of *O. leucotricha* carry the most incredible armoury of spines, but if one remembers to handle it with care, it develops into a magnificent plant. The varieties of *O. microdasys* have bristles rather than barbs but also require care when handling. Almost all are easily managed and root readily from pads removed and treated as cuttings.

Parodia

These are rewarding plants that are easily raised from seed, hence the many varieties available. All will flower freely over a long period, and have the added benefit of coming into flower at a very early age. Ideal for restricted space, as the compact rounded shapes take up little room. A collection of these small plants makes an ideal display for a sunny windowsill.

Rebutia

For the average grower of cacti on the windowsill the many hybridised kinds of these could well prove to be the most appealing of all. Because of their neat round shape and clustering habit they require little space, and can be almost guaranteed to produce flowers. Can be raised from seed, or by peeling off offsets and rooting them individually.

Schlumbergera gaertnerii
Easter or Whitsun cactus

Produced in vast quantities as a flowering pot plant, these are better known as Whitsun or Easter cactus, and need good light to do well. Once in flower the plant should remain in a light window position, and they will benefit from being placed out of doors during the summer months in a sheltered, sunny location. Cuttings of individual, or two-pad leaf sections will root readily. Keep moist and feed them with weak liquid fertiliser once established.

Zygocactus truncatus
Christmas cactus

Very similar in appearance to the foregoing, this one has the common name of Christmas cactus simply because it flowers at that particular time of year. Plants should never be allowed to become bone dry, but the soil should never become saturated.

Three cacti – opuntia, Cephalocereus senilis and rebutia

Bulbs can always be relied upon to provide a cheerful display of flowers
Top left Hippeastrum, sometimes known as amaryllis
Top right *Clivia nobilis*
Left A colourful spring display of irises and crocuses
Right The ever popular hyacinth, grown for its heady scent as well as its attractive flowers

CHAPTER 10
Bulbs, corms and rhizomes

One of the cheeriest sights of spring is a golden bed of daffodils swaying gently in the breeze. Their vibrant colour lifts the doldrums of winter and heralds the new growth of the year. Lately, many people have been discovering that a breath of spring can be enjoyed before the onset of the actual season by planting up containers of bulbs to flower indoors during late winter.

Most bulbs are suitable for indoor growing, hyacinths, popular for their heady scent, being the most familiar. When buying the bulbs it is very important that they should be in prime condition. Look for signs of eelworm and don't bother with dried-up specimens. Many garden centres supply bulbs which have been specially prepared for early forcing, again hyacinths are the most common, being prepared to flower at Christmas. If, however, you see the bulbs on sale before the middle of August, you can be sure that they will not have had the time to be properly prepared and will not flower as expected.

Potting

Bulbs for indoor growing should be potted sometime in late summer (August–September). Use a large shallow container rather than the conventional pot; do try to use one that has drainage holes. If this is not possible, put a layer of gravel mixed with charcoal in the bottom of the container; charcoal will help to keep the soil sweet.

When planting, specially prepared bulb fibre is the usual recommendation, but I find that my own bulbs respond very well to potting in John Innes No. 2 with a little peat added.

Fill the bottom of the container with compost and then put in the bulbs, placing them close together – nothing looks worse than a few lonely 'daffs' sticking up out of a vast

container. By planting the container with a number of bulbs placed at two different levels you can achieve a colourful massed display.

Wrap the containers in large black refuse bags or similar and store them in a cool dark place for at least 10 weeks, or until you see the first signs of growth.

When the shoots are about 2.5 cm (1 in) tall, bring the bulbs into the warmth. Do not put them in direct sun (although they do like a light position) and keep them moist.

Types

Clivia
Not strictly speaking a bulb, this plant has a thick, fleshy base to its stem. It needs a minimum temperature of around 16°C (60°F). Very durable with glossy strap-like leaves and bearing clusters of orange flowers on stout stems. Put in a reasonably light position and water regularly, feeding when established. John Innes No. 3 required when potting on.

Crocus
Use shallow bowls with drainage holes, and cover the holes with crocks before half filling with compost. Press bulbs almost touching into compost then cover with soil. After flowering, let the leaves die back, dry off the soil and then plant the bulbs in the garden.

Gloriosa rothschildiana
Tender subjects that should be planted several to a large pot filled with John Innes No. 3 to which extra peat has been added. These are best started in a warm greenhouse and will require several canes at least a yard long to support this normally quick growing plant. The brightly coloured scarlet flowers appear in summer. Place in good light, but not strong sun and keep moist. Dies down in winter, when the tubers should be kept warm and dry.

Planting bulbs

Many types of bulbs can be grown in bowls indoors to create a colourful spring display e.g. narcissi, tulips, hyacinths, crocuses, snowdrops and grape hyacinths.

Bulbs can be planted close together (but not touching) in a single layer or, for a fuller display, can be layer-planted. The diagram shows the two layers correctly placed so that the lower bulbs can grow up through the spaces left between the bulbs in the upper layer.

After planting, the bulbs should be plunged outside in a garden frame until growth starts (about 10 weeks). If a frame is not available wrap the containers in black polythene and store in a cool place such as a garage or garden shed.

Haemanthus

Odd is a suitable word to describe these bulbous plants with their broad strap leaves that are very short. In time they will produce a peculiar white, red or orange flower that resembles a somewhat ragged shaving brush! Best planted in early spring with the tip of the bulb just showing above the soil. If kept warm and almost dry in winter it is no trouble to care for.

Hippeastrum

Expensive, large bulbous plants with strap leaves and extremely exotic trumpet-shaped flowers that stand proudly on stems which may attain a height of a yard or more. After flowering in early spring keep the plant watered and fed and place out of doors in a sunny position during the summer. Take care that watering and feeding are not neglected during this period. As the end of summer approaches, allow the plant to dry out and then store it in a warm spot in autumn. Then pre-heat the bulb in warm water before starting into growth again at the end of the year. For success all that is necessary is to purchase good quality bulbs and provide warmth, light and moisture.

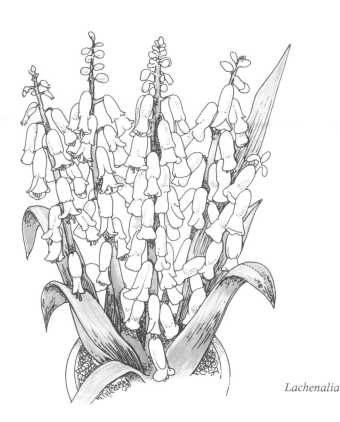

Lachenalia

Lachenalia

Another tender bulb originating from South Africa and commonly named Cape cowslip. Growth is from September to June when flowers of orange-yellow colouring appear. Six to eight bulbs in a hanging basket produce a good display, and they should be brought in to the warmth in September to start into growth. After flowering keep bone dry and place out of doors in full sun.

Lilies

There are many of these to choose from, some needing different types of soil in respect of acidity, so information must be sought from the supplier when the bulbs are purchased. Information on culture varies, but I find bulbs purchased and potted in mid-winter (January–February) will flower perfectly during the summer. Buy the shorter varieties for preference. Offer cool conditions after potting. Keep compost moist and put in a lightly shaded spot and a fine display of colour will result.

Narcissus

There are many varieties to choose from some scented, double-flowered or dwarf and a really grand display can be made as follows: fill an 8 in pot, that has been crocked to about half its depth, with John Innes No. 3, put in a layer of bulbs and cover them with soil. Then place another layer of bulbs on the layer of soil before filling the pot to just below its rim with

compost. Try not to overlap the bulbs. The double layer will ensure a superb display when flowers appear.

Nerine

Hardy South African bulbs that are kept dry and dormant during the summer months, preferably on a greenhouse shelf in full sun. Sun baking will encourage the flowers which are carried on 45 cm (18 in) stems and are mainly in pink shades. Indoors they should have good light and be allowed to dry out between each watering.

Tulip

Pot in September, using John Innes No. 3. Once indoors, water freely and place pot in a light position. Shorter stemmed varieties are more suitable for indoor decoration.

Zantedeschia

Zantedeschia

The arum lily, *Z. aethiopica*, is not everyone's cup of tea as an indoor plant, but it grows well enough and produces spectacular white flowers if kept moist and well fed, and given reasonable light. Less water and feeding is required in winter, and during summer months the plants can be placed out of doors. When potting on use John Innes No. 3 and pot firmly.

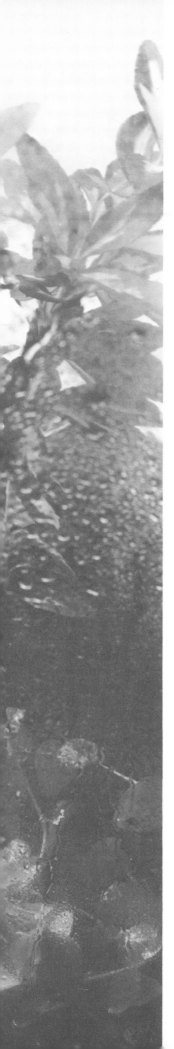

CHAPTER 11
Bottle gardens

ottle gardens are adaptations of the Wardian case principle of keeping tender, moisture-loving plants in an environment that would otherwise be difficult to simulate in the average living room. Dr Ward, after whom Wardian cases are named, was a keen plantsman who discovered that tender ferns lived for many years, virtually without attention, in the atmosphere of his ingenious cases, which were first used in about 1830.

When cases are hermetically sealed, watering is unnecessary, as moisture transpiring from the plants' leaves condenses on the inside of the glass container, and eventually finds its way back into the soil. Completely sealed containers are, however, less attractive than those with a small opening because the film of moisture which forms on the inside of the glass obscures the plants from view. Bottle gardens with open tops will require a little water very occasionally, when the plants are seen to be flagging, or when the soil surface is obviously dry. Trickle the water gently on to the soil surface by means of a flexible rubber hose pipe.

Disused carboys make excellent bottle gardens, as they are spacious inside and permit the use of slightly taller plants, though sweet bottles and clear glass jars of various kinds may also be used for smaller, or even individual, plants. Almost the first step on acquiring a carboy will be the need to give it a thorough cleaning with detergent, both inside and out, in order to remove stains and any harmful residue. Be warned, however, that the use of hot water is positively not advised, because of the risk of cracking the glass. Finally rinse it out well with clean water.

is in fact a disused fish tank – these are roomier, more accessible, and much more attractive when plants have been established.

A further benefit is that the fish tank will almost surely have its own built-in strip light. Presence of soft lighting will greatly enhance the appearance of the plants, and the gentle warmth that is given off will considerably improve plant growth. Not that one wants plants to grow too quickly, but it is more agreeable to watch them prosper rather than shrivel and die.

When planting the fish tank one should apply the same principle as for the bottle garden – you require about a 6-in depth of compost that has had some charcoal worked into it to prevent it becoming sour. The compost should be laid over a bed of gravel which will collect surplus water. A pleasing contoured effect can be achieved on the surface of the compost by putting in stones or pieces of bark before introducing the plants. If the tank is large enough you could scatter pebbles on the surface of the compost to give the appearance of a path.

The object should be to design and plant up a miniature garden, using tall, medium and creeping plants with stones and so on setting them off as one would expect in a well arranged garden, rather than to just fill the tank with lots of different plants!

Another advantage is that a fish tank does not place so many restrictions on choice of plants as does the conventional bottle garden – somewhat larger plants can be used, as their encroachment on other plants can be simply remedied by means of pruning.

Plants to choose

Next, and most important, is the choice of plants. Here it must be emphasised that only slow-growing plants should be used. See the list at the end of the chapter for an idea of suitable plants. A florist friend informs me that his charge for dismantling overgrown carboys is more than his charge for arranging plants initially – so beware. The same friend illustrated his point when he showed me a carboy that had been planted up less than one year previously with the apparently harmless dead nettle, *Gynura sarmentosa*. In a matter of months the plant had filled all the available space in the carboy and had a few shoots inspecting the prospects outside the bottle!

Plants to avoid
The use of flowering plants presents problems, for when flowers fade and die they become vulnerable to fungus diseases, which will quickly spread to other plants in the container if left unchecked. Having warned against the use of flowering plants, I can see in my mind's eye an established bottle garden in perfect condition, in the centre of which nestled an African violet in full flower and obviously not in the least concerned about having been an 'intruder' for the previous two years. In general, however, though you may be tempted to experiment, it is better to concentrate on foliage plants when making your selection.

Purchased plants ought to be in pots no larger than 3 in in diameter if they are to pass conveniently through the neck of the bottle. Plants in larger pots, besides being too tall or spreading in themselves, suffer considerably from having their roots damaged in the planting process. Also, care must be taken to choose plants with flexible leaves that will bend easily as they are lowered into the bottle.

The planting operation

Before planting begins the following materials should be at hand: sufficient pebbles $\frac{3}{8}$ in in size (ballast from your local builders' merchant, is ideal) to provide a 2-in layer in the bottom of the bottle (these should be thoroughly wetted before putting in position); a small amount of charcoal (from any gardening shop) for mixing with the compost to prevent it becoming sour too quickly. Sour soil inevitably results in the formation of an unsightly coating of algae on the surface of the compost. Large carboys will need about a 5-in layer of compost, which should be of an open texture. John Innes No. 2 potting compost would be a suitable medium with the addition of two handfuls of sharp grit to improve drainage.

Use a funnel, shaped from a piece of cardboard, to pour the materials through the narrow neck of the bottle and into the desired position.

Simple tools as planting and cultural aids
Some simple tools will be needed for planting, pruning and cleaning. Mine are nothing more than a few 2 ft canes, to the ends of which I tie a teaspoon (as substitute for a trowel), a table fork (for a rake), and an old cotton reel wedged

1. *No special equipment is required to start a bottle garden. The tools are merely ordinary household items tied firmly to strong canes*

onto the end of a cane, which is used for firming the soil around the roots after planting. For pruning, my favourite tool is a razor blade secured into a cleft in the end of a cane. For a scavenging tool I follow in the steps of the park keeper and tie a nail to the end of a cane; this is used for spearing yellow leaves and severed pieces that the pruner has dealt with.

A trial run
To obviate the need for difficult manoeuvring of plants in the confined space of the containers it is better to do a mock-up outside the bottle first, in order to achieve the desired effect. Do this by preparing a bed of compost of approximately the same dimensions as the surface of the soil in the container, and on this

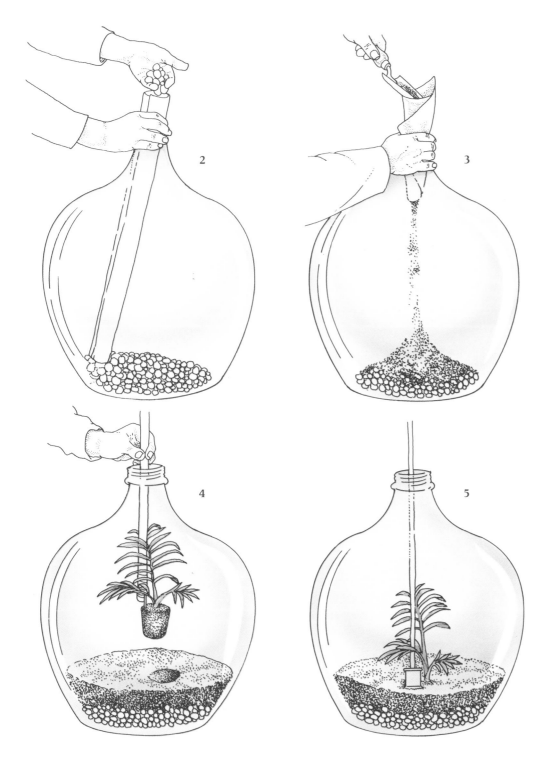

2. An even layer of small pebbles is introduced to the carboy by means of a cardboard tube
3. The potting compost is the next layer to go in through a paper funnel
4. The plants can be manoeuvred into position by placing a spiked stick firmly through the rootball
5. The planting operation is completed by using a cotton reel to firm the plants in

*A finished bottle garden
planted up with a selection
of small delicate plants*

arrange the plants to your satisfaction; it is then an easy matter to place them accordingly in the bottle. The standard carboy will accommodate five or six small plants; if more than this number are planted they will quickly become congested.

Positioning the plants
Great care will be needed when the actual planting operation takes place. Although it may appear harsh, I find that using my park keeper's prodder to spear through the root ball is the simplest way of inserting plants and manoeuvring them into position. One of the other tools can then be used to hold the plant firm while the prodder is withdrawn. I often feel that the dextrous use of elongated chopsticks would be the perfect answer to planting. Or, as an acquaintance once suggested, bottle gardens should be fitted with zip fasteners! Dr Ward would seem to have had the ideal answer when he fitted a door in the side of his more ornamental Wardian cases.

In common with the majority of foliage plants, your carboy will require a light position and protection from strong sunlight. Ornamentation in the way of stones, bark, twigs, wee men and such like is purely a matter of personal taste. These can be used to good effect if they are placed with care and used sparingly.

Suitable plants

Acorus gramineus variegatus Erect golden grass.

Adiantum cuneatum The delicately-leaved maidenhair fern.

Asplenium nidus Only for larger bottles, as eventually the plant becomes rather large.

Begonia boweri This plant will pay for the bother of finding a supplier.

Begonia Cleopatra Makes neat hummocks of dull green and bronze-coloured foliage, with the prospect of pale pink flowers coming as a bonus.

Begonia rex Only the smaller-leaved sorts. There is a danger of mildew attacking the leaves of these plants in close, damp conditions.

Cocos weddelliana Fine feathery fern that can be utilised as a background plant for the arrangement. When too large, it can be removed and potted into a conventional container.

Codiaeums (crotons) Many of these develop into very substantial plants, often outgrowing the small greenhouse, let alone the bottle garden – so select with care.

Codiaeum pictum and C. Apple Leaf Both Codiaeum pictum and the variety Apple Leaf will remain reasonably small, though their colouring, yellow and green, is rather dull when compared with the rainbow colours of most codiaeums.

Cryptanthuses In many varieties – choose those with smaller leaves and more compact rosettes.

Dracaena godseffiana Florida Beauty See description on page 71.

Dracaena Rededge With a combination of dull green and equally dull red foliage, this is another plant that will form a pleasing background.

Dracaena sanderiana Becomes tall in time, but useful for providing a little height in the centre of the arrangement.

Episcia There are a number of these that will be admirably suited, as they are mostly compact and will enjoy the warm and close conditions.

Euonymus japonicus aureopictus A hardy ourdoor plant with attractive golden foliage that can be pruned to shape at any time.

Ficus pumila A quick grower, but regular pruning will keep it in check.

Ficus radicans With attractive pale green and white variegation, this plant will appreciate the close and warm conditions of a bottle garden.

Fittonia argyroneura The dwarf miniature form of this plant is probably a better choice, but either will be well suited to the humid and warm conditions. This dwarf variety is commonly known as little snakeskin plant on account of its leaf markings.

Fittonia verschaffeltii See description on page 73.

Hederas (ivies) Select the small-leaved variegated ones and cut them back when they spread too far.

Hoya carnosa variegata Easily checked by pruning if it becomes too invasive. Can either be used as a ground-cover plant or be tied to a short cane to give a little extra height in an arrangement.

Maranta leuconeura erythrophylla A fine plant capable of being a feature if planted by itself in the bottle garden, with only the odd bit of ivy or *Ficus pumila* to act as a foil.

Maranta l. kerchoveana Only for larger containers.

Neanthe bella A trouble-free miniature palm.

Peperomias *Peperomia magnoliaefolia, P. hederaefolia* and *P. caperata*. The last two form large clumps that will be difficult to prune, so use them only in more spacious bottle gardens.

Pteris cretica One of the many smaller ferns that are perfect for this purpose.

Saintpaulia In their many fine colours, these will give a lot of pleasure in the fish tank where it will be possible to remove dead flowers without difficulty.

Sansevieria hahnii variegata Expensive and scarce.

Sansevieria trifasciata laurentii Not one of the best, but it offers a pleasing change of leaf shape.

Selaginella Makes clumps of mossy green foliage which are perfect for the bottle garden.

Tillandsia Compact bromeliads in many varieties. *T. cyanea* is one of the best if there is a choice.

Tradescantias Many kinds, some rather invasive, but even those can be pruned if in a fish tank.

An old fish tank is much easier to plant up and care for than the traditional carboy

Ficus pumila and pteris are two excellent small-scale plants suitable for bottle garden arrangements

CHAPTER 12
Plants for the office

The growth and popularity of house-plants has been something quite remarkable in itself, and it would seem even more remarkable that following on to their popularity in the home, there has been created a desire for plants among people at their places of work. In the hotel foyer or restaurant this is quite understandable, but it is remarkable that the interior of many offices have almost become miniature botanic gardens.

The office windowsill plant is still very much in evidence, but such plants have now given way to much bolder schemes whereby entire floors of offices are planned with as much emphasis placed on the location of plants as there is on the desks that at first sight would appear to be more important.

Although we may refer to them as office plants they are, in fact, no different from the general range of houseplants now available. In many cases they are, however, subject to much harsher treatment than their counter-parts in the living room window. Where the home gardener will purchase a plant with the express intention of giving it every possible care, Mabel in the office receives it as a birth-day gift from her colleagues and looks at it with bewilderment, wondering what on earth she is going to do with it. Generally speaking, given a week or two of the inexperienced, and not always interested, care of Mabel, and there is no doubt what should be done with it!

Most plantings are confined to large con-tainers with a selection of plants that are either growing conventionally in soil or, as has been the trend in recent years, they are growing in a mixture of water and nutrients with plants being anchored by pebbles of some kind. There are a number of different systems whereby plants can be grown very successfully in this way.

The plants will, in most instances, have been installed by a plantsman specialising in this field and this person will usually be responsible for the maintenance of the plants in the office, ensuring that they are watered, fed and so on. It is usual for the company owning the offices to enter into a contract with the plant supplier, in which case you usually require the latter to replace any plants that may be ailing. Such an arrangement is usually much more satisfactory than simply allowing any person in the office who is available to care for the plants.

Even the supplier will make stipulations when plants are being considered as a possibility for any particular office. Besides a minimum year round temperature in the region of 16°C (60°F), the most important need will be adequate light to enable plants to grow. The average office, well lit with banks of fluorescent lighting and evenly controlled atmosphere and temperature will be about right.

Plants in dark corners simply will not do well unless special lighting is installed above the plant display; there are pendant lights made especially for this purpose. These lights are suspended about 4 ft above the plant and possess qualities that, as far as the plants' requirements are concerned, are not dissimilar to natural daylight. If spotlights are to be used to highlight the beauty of the plants, these should be placed considerably further away, otherwise the plant foliage may be scorched.

The problems

There are several problems to be overcome if office plants are to survive: excessive heat, dry atmosphere, inattention at week-ends and lack of any sort of facility for performing so much as the simplest potting operation, to name but a few. Plants will probably have to suffer high temperatures, though following the advice given in the chapter on routine culture will help to relieve the harmful effects of the dry atmosphere. Lack of attention at week-ends may be overcome to some extent by purchasing plants in pots of reasonable size; such plants will be better able to stand several consecutive days without attention. The soil in small 'tots' or 'thumb' pots soon lacks nutriment, and dries at an alarming rate when plants are stood for any length of time on a sunny windowledge.

Lack of attention at week-ends
Brief respite from watering and general care is a blessing for the plant that is treated like an only child and is provided with all the attention that this book describes, plus a little more for good measure. But, for the office plant that often has its share of neglect during the week, a good baking on the window-ledge in dry soil at week-ends can prove fatal. So, have a care, and move plants into a shaded corner on Friday evenings where they will be much happier over Saturday and Sunday.

Rarely can the need for adequate light be overstressed if plants are to succeed, but equal emphasis must be placed on their need for protection from strong sunshine. In the modern office block consisting of concrete and acres of glass, plants will have ample light in almost any position. Morning and evening sun is comparatively harmless, but mid-day sun, magnified by the glass, will quickly reduce indoor plants to a few dry, shrivelled leaves. Some plants appear to tolerate these Sahara-like conditions reasonably well, but even they would benefit from some protection. Among the few in this category are chlorophytum, tradescantia, sansevieria, impatiens (sometimes growing astonishingly well), ivies and the occasional kangaroo vine (*Cissus antarctica*), though the last-mentioned is inclined to become very hard and yellow in appearance eventually. Perhaps the main reason for ivies, chlorophytum, and tradescantia being so prevalent is their ease of propagation, which ensures an ample supply.

The radiator problem
Office radiators present a further problem, as these are frequently placed along the wall immediately under windows. This is ideal for office staff on a cold winter's morning, but death to any plants in the direct stream of hot air on the windowledge above. Should there be no alternative to the window position above the radiator, care must be taken to increase the width of the shelf with a piece of hardboard or similar material – hot air will then be directed above the plants and not through their leaves. Where radiators are fitted in the home, this precaution also applies.

Suitable plants for the office

Aspidistra lurida (cast iron plant)	Light, shady position. Minimum temperature 13°C (55°F)
Cacti and other succulents	Good light. Minimum temperature 10°C (50°F)
Chlorophytum (spider plant)	Good light. Minimum temperature 7°C (45°F)
Cissus antarctica (kangaroo vine)	Shady position. Temperature required: 10° to 18°C (50° to 65°F)
Coleus	Good light. Minimum temperature 16°C (60°F)
Euonymus japonicus aureovariegatus (golden bush)	Likes cool conditions but plenty of light. Hardy shrub
Fatshedera lizei	Reasonable light. Minimum temperature 10°C (50°F)
Ficus elastica (rubber plant)	Good light but not full sunlight. Minimum temperature 13°C (55°F)
Heptapleurum	Light shade. Minimum temperature 7°C (45°F)
Impatiens (busy lizzie)	Good light. Minimum temperature 13°C (55°F)
Kentia (palm)	Good light with shade from strong sunlight. Minimum temperature 18°C (65°F)
Monstera (Swiss cheese plant)	Light shade. Minimum temperature 16°C (60°F)
Philodendron scandens (sweetheart vine)	Light shade. Minimum temperature 16°C (60°F)
Sansevieria trifasciata laurentii (mother-in-law's tongue)	Good light. Minimum temperature 10°C (50°F)
Schefflera (umbrella plant)	Light shade. Minimum temperature 13°C (55°F)
Tradescantia (wandering Jew)	Good light but avoid strong sunlight. Minimum temperature 7°C (45°F)

Hot air from a radiator may be deflected over the plants on the windowsill by placing them on a piece of hardboard. This tip can, of course, be used in the home as well as the office

An interesting trial

Although we are continually being reminded of the need for potting plants on into larger containers when it becomes necessary, astonishing results can also be achieved by regular feeding. On record there is proof of an interesting trial that may help to prove the point. By way of experiment, a rubber plant (*Ficus elastica*) was taken direct from a peat cutting bed and 'potted' into Sorbo rubber material fashioned in the shape of a pot. A deep slit was made in the rubber, into which the cutting was inserted, and the 'rubber pot ball' was then snugly fitted into a 5-in pot. In the space of three years the rubber plant in rubber 'soil' grew to a height of 30 in and had 20 firm leaves. The leaves were slightly smaller than those of plants grown in ordinary compost, though it is interesting to note that no leaves were shed during this period. Similar experiments, equally successful, were carried out with bromeliads and *Begonia masoniana*. 'Compost' of this kind, because of the slower rate of growth of the plant and the extra attention required, is not a commercial proposition, but it did prove that the potting medium is not quite the important factor that it would appear to be. I mention the experiment purely as a matter of interest, and would not expect plants to prosper under normal room or office conditions unless they were potted in a suitable compost. Compared to other plants, those in the Sorbo rubber required more frequent watering, though there was the advantage that the water drained away rapidly, thus preventing waterlogging. No extra feeding was required.

Holiday periods

In the course of time the observant plant owner gets to know almost the exact requirements of particular plants in respect of watering and feeding. During holiday periods, such information can be a considerable asset, as one can give precise instructions to the person entrusted with the care of plants during one's absence. The inexperienced person, having the misguided impression that too much is better than too little, is almost invariably tempted to over-water and over-feed plants left in his or her care. In respect of plant care, there is no doubt whatsoever that too many cooks spoil the broth, so, when absent from the office for any length of time, select one person to administer to the needs of your plants, and give precise instructions concerning the amount and frequency of both watering and feeding.

Feeding

As already mentioned, another drawback is lack of facilities for carrying out simple potting operations. The office manager may considerably fail to notice a few clean plants in clean containers standing in saucers and ashtrays, but the line is firmly drawn when sacks of John Innes potting compost appear in the 'typing pool'. Therefore, if potting on is out of the question, the need for regular and adequate feeding is doubly important. As indoor plant fertilisers are all packed in neat boxes or bottles these days, there should be no objection to their presence among the paper clips.

CHAPTER 13
Plant hygiene

Standing your plants outside in the rain, is often mentioned as being a simple way of cleaning plant leaves. Perhaps the lady who wrote to me from Burnley in February and complained that her rubber plant was looking decidedly sad following its recent spell in the rain-drenched garden had done just this. Possibly a warm gentle summer rain is harmless but here it would be wise to compare plants with human beings, and one shudders to think of standing unprotected in a Lancashire garden in mid-February!

Plants with leaves of a rough or hairy texture will be damaged if cleaned with a sponge or cloth. Many such plants, *Peperomia caperata* for example, can be cleaned of dust by placing your hand over the top of the pot and inverting the plant in a bucketful of tepid water. Gently move the plant to and fro through the water, and this will remove all loose dust and greatly improve the appearance of the plant. Hairy-leaved plants, such as saintpaulias, can have dust removed by using a soft camel hair brush.

For all other plants, proprietary leaf cleaning preparations are available, and reasonably good results may also be achieved by using a mixture of equal parts of milk and water, or neat brown ale. One of the white-oil insecticides will also improve the appearance of plants if used at a strength of one dessertspoonful to one gallon of water. Liquid paraffin (not paraffin-oil) weakly diluted in water is also suitable for tougher-leaved subjects. Oil preparations give an unnatural appearance to leaves if used at an excessive strength, and will have a tendency to turn the edges of leaves brown if used too frequently. Actual cleaning of leaves in the average home need only be done every six to eight weeks, although plants with larger leaves benefit from regular dusting. Some of the aerosol sprays are excellent for cleaning the leaves of shiny-leaved foliage plants, such as monsteras, rubber plants and glossy-leaved philodendrons. But there are a few precautions that one should take, and the most important of these is never to use cleaning chemicals on leaves that are exposed to direct sunlight. Equally important, plants that have been cleaned with any form of chemical should not be subjected to low temperature until the effects of the chemical have worn off.

Drastic treatment

My local railway station generally displays a reasonable collection of foliage plants that are lovingly tended by a semi-retired member of the staff. Summoned by an urgent message from the gardener one spring morning, we arrived at the station to inspect his fly- and dust-ridden ivies, some of which had trails almost 6 ft in length. The man whose charge they were, looked on with some concern when buckets were produced, malathion solution prepared, and his plants unceremoniously plunged in the mixture and given a good scrub. All dead leaves, greenfly, dust and a few sound leaves were removed in the process, but the treatment certainly did them a power of good.

The 'spring clean'

Such treatment would be a trifle harsh for the less dusty plants growing indoors; nevertheless, it is wise to give them a good spring clean to set them on their feet for the new season. Insert new stakes where necessary, remove dead leaves and pot on any plants that may be in need of a larger container. Although potting on may not be necessary, almost all plants will benefit from having the top inch or so of soil removed and replaced with fresh compost.

Use a pointed stick (a pencil is ideal) to disturb and remove the old soil, being careful not to probe too deeply.

Recommended insecticides

Malathion and liquid derris are two insecticides that can be safely used on the majority of indoor plants to control pests, provided the manufacturers' instructions are carefully followed. Take the precaution of wearing rubber gloves, and treat plants outside to avoid unpleasant smells indoors. Smaller, and trailing plants that will fit into a bucket are best treated by immersing them in the solution you intend to use. Larger plants should be drenched with the insecticide by spraying it on, using a small hand spray and paying particular attention to the underside of the leaves where most pests make their home.

Besides leaf cleaners, there are all sorts of other chemicals that, for convenience, are contained in aerosols. Many of these can be lethal as far as the average indoor plant is concerned, and plants should, therefore, be kept well out of the way when they are being used. Aerosols in general use such as hair-sprays, furniture polish and fly-killers can be damaging to plants indoors. Plant insecticides are now available in aerosol form and they are very easy to use making it possible to treat both sides of leaves effectively. For the person with a small collection of indoor plants these sprays are by the far the cleanest, safest and most effective. But, as with all chemicals and fertilisers used in connection with potted plants, be they in the home or in the greenhouse, one should use discretion and never be tempted to apply them too frequently, or in contradiction to the manufacturers' recommendations.

Besides more conventional insecticides there are systemic kinds that, as the name implies, are taken in through the system of the plant, so that insects that survive by sucking the sap are destroyed. These are usually made-up in a liquid solution which is watered into the soil around the plant. Again, for the safety of you and your plants, be sure to follow the manufacturer's instructions.

The pests

The following list describes some of the pests you are most likely to encounter on house-plants and describes the symptoms of their presence and the best way of treating an attack.

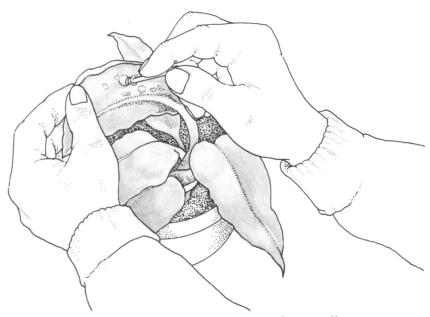

The most effective way to get rid of mealy bugs is to dab them individually with methylated spirit

Mealy bug
Mealy bugs are one of the more easily detected pests, being white in colour and resembling small woodlice in appearance. Making contact with the young mealy bugs, which are protected by a cotton-wool-like covering, presents a problem when spraying. It can be overcome by dabbing them with a piece of cotton wool (tied to the end of a match stick) that has been soaked in methylated spirits.

Red spider
Red spider mite, much smaller than the mealy bug, is difficult to see with the naked eye, and its presence is often only detected when leaves become brown around the edges and take on a generally dry appearance. Plants badly infested will eventually have small webs on the undersides of the leaves. However, they may be detected earlier when tiny pin-prick holes appear on the underside of the leaves, or by using a magnifying glass to see them busily going about their business of slowly sucking the life out of your plant. The perfect breeding ground for red spiders is a plant kept in hot, dry conditions; so, where possible, frequent spraying of the foliage with water will help to deter them.

Other mites
Perhaps the most damaging pests of all are the almost invisible mites, though fortunately they are less common these days. They seem to have a particular attraction for the ivies and African violets. Their trade mark is hard and distorted pit-marked foliage, badly infested ivies being eventually reduced to leafless

stalks. Unfortunately, there is no simple cure that can be recommended for general use. Control can only be carried out swiftly and effectively in nursery conditions by using a highly toxic insecticide that has to be treated with the greatest respect. One can also exercise some control by cutting affected plants hard back to the point where they are almost devoid of leaves, in the hope that new growth, when produced, will be clear of mites. Should other plants in a collection be vulnerable, affected plants must be disposed of, preferably by burning.

Greenfly

Greenfly is sometimes troublesome, but simply erradicated, either by using one of the earlier mentioned products, or, more cheaply, by immersing the plants in soapy water. Larger plants can be sprayed with the same inexpensive solution.

Scale insects

The scale insects are hard-backed pests, coloured light brown when young and almost jet black when adult. These are predominant on the underside of the leaves, but are also to be seen on the stems. A sponge that has been soaked in malathion can be used to wipe them forcibly from where they are attached, remembering always to wear rubber gloves when handling insecticides. Scale insects that still persist may be removed with a well-directed thumb nail.

An important reminder

When using insecticides the maker's directions should be followed to the letter. If uncertain of your plant's reaction to a particular insecticide, it is advisable to experiment first by treating only one plant, or, if you have only one specimen of a particular plant, you should treat part of it in order to note the reaction.

Diseases and disorders

Symptoms	Possible cause	Treatment
Yellowing leaves	1 Old leaf	None required if it is one of the lower leaves that is affected.
	2 Too little light	Change position but avoid strong sunlight.
	3 Underfeeding	Feed during growing season with proprietary house plant food applied according to manufacturer's instructions. Repot.
	4 Sucking insect such as red spider mites	Improve humidity by spraying foliage regularly, spray with insecticide.
Variegated leaves loose colour	1 Too little light	Move nearer to source of light.
Leaf tips and margins go brown	1 Overwatering	Allow compost to dry out again before watering.
	2 Temperature too low	Move to a warmer room.
	3 Overfeeding	Check on amount and frequency of feeding and adjust if necessary. Do not feed when plant is not actively growing.
	4 Draughts	Move to draught-free position – not in line with windows and door.
	5 Lack of humidity	Take measures to increase humidity.
Brown or yellow spots on leaves	1 Sunscorch	Move plant away from strong direct sunlight. Do not leave water drops on leaves when watering.
	2 Draughts	Move to a draught-free position.
	3 Overwatering	Allow compost to dry out, take more care with watering.
	4 Overfeeding	Check on amount and frequency of feeding and adjust.
Leaf drop	1 Underwatering	Check plants regularly and water when compost is dry to the touch.
	2 Sudden changes in temperature	Avoid moving plants from room to room or place to place, especially in winter.
	3 Draughts	Avoid a position between door and windows.
Leaves and/or stems rotting	1 Overwatering	Reduce amount of water and do not allow water to remain on leaves or around base of stems.
Plants wilt	1 Too much heat	Move away from windowsill or heat source, watch watering.
	2 Underwatering	Give more water or water more frequently.
	3 Overwatering	May cause waterlogging of soil and kill roots. Allow compost to dry out before watering again.
Leggy growth	1 Too little light	Move nearer to a source of light.
No flowers on a plant which should flower	1 Too little light	Move nearer to a source of light.
	2 Temperature of room too high in evening	Move to a cooler position in evening but not into a draught.
	3 Plant too immature to flower	Wait.

CHAPTER 14
Simple propagation

Indoor plants can be increased by a variety of methods, seed sowing, leaf and stem cuttings, and division of plant clumps being the most practical. The nurseryman rarely resorts to the use of pips, date stones or pineapple tops in order to increase his stock, but a number of interesting plants can be produced in this way. Although increasing difficult plants that require constant high temperatures and high humidity may be out of the question, many of what one might call 'every-day plants' are comparatively easy to propagate.

Hygienic conditions
Hygienic conditions play an important part in successful propagation so pots, boxes, compost, and anything else that cuttings and seeds are likely to come into contact with, must be kept scrupulously clean. The propagating medium is equally important, so a potful of soil from the garden cannot be expected to give satisfactory results. One cannot go far wrong when using John Innes No. 1 potting compost, a soilless seed and cutting compost or clean moss peat with a little sharp sand added to it. Once rooted cuttings should be potted into a proper growing medium.

Pot sizes and cutting material
When starting smaller cuttings in pots, it will be found that the smaller pots, up to 3 in in diameter, give better results. Small cuttings inserted in large potfuls of compost rarely do well, as the medium tends to become sour long before the plant is able to establish itself. Tradescantias, and other plants that produce ample propagating material, do infinitely better if several pieces (up to seven) are put in one pot; these take on a mature appearance almost as soon as they have rooted. Rosette-forming plants do better when grown from individual pieces.

Simple propagating cases
An adequate temperature is a further pre-requisite of success. A constant temperature in the region of 18°C (65°F) is ideal for most subjects, and if the soil temperature can be maintained at the same level, then the need for 'green fingers' becomes relatively unimportant. Simple wooden propagating cases are easy to construct at home, and an ever-increasing range of models is on offer at almost any gardening shop. The majority of the latter are made of plastic and need little more than a supply of electricity for them to become operative. In these propagators, space is always at a premium, so it is wise to use shallow seed boxes for cuttings and for seeds in order to make maximum use of the available area. Light is of course essential for growth of cuttings and germinated seeds.

The polythene bag 'propagator'
Where one's purse, or need, does not extend to something as grand as a propagating case, reasonably good results may be obtained by covering cuttings with a polythene bag, or by placing both pot and cuttings in the bag and sealing the top. The object here is to reduce transpiration, thereby permitting leaves and stems to remain turgid while the rooting process takes place. Should there be no propagator, or polythene bag, cuttings will dry out and become limp, so lessening their chance of producing roots of their own.

Hormone rooting powder
Though by no means essential, the use of one of the proprietary hormone rooting powders will induce cuttings to root more readily, particularly if they have hard, woody stems. The severed ends of the cuttings should be moistened and then dipped in the rooting powder, before inserting them in the rooting medium.

To propagate tradescantia plants, take several healthy cuttings and insert them round the edge of a pot. These will soon root and form a new, attractive plant

Cuttings

The young gardener is forever being advised by the more experienced old hand that, when propagating, he must remember that the best new plants are almost invariably the result of using strong, unblemished material in the first place. This is indeed the case, and it goes without saying that the best propagator always accumulates the most rubbish. The important difference is that the efficient man can detect good from bad when preparing his cuttings, so he accumulates rubbish at his feet and not in his propagating beds. Though the greenhouse propagating bed containing thousands of cuttings may seem a far cry from the home-made propagator in the spare room or kitchen, the principle still applies. So, when attempting to increase one's stock by vegetative means, it should be borne in mind that eventual success owes much to the quality of the parent plant from which leaves or cuttings are taken.

Cuttings with very soft top growth (for example, early spring growth of ivies) should be discarded as they seldom grow well. When started from firm cuttings with two leaves on the stem, and cut about half an inch below the lower leaf joint, the ivies, vines (*Rhoicissus rhomboidea* and *Cissus antarctica*) and smaller-leaved philodendrons are among the easiest houseplants to propagate. The majority of these plants will also be better, in the long run, if they have their growing tips removed once they have become established as this will encourage the growth of side shoots.

A polythene bag can be used as a home-made propagator. A loop of wire inside the bag will keep the moist polythene from touching the leaves of the cutting and causing them to rot

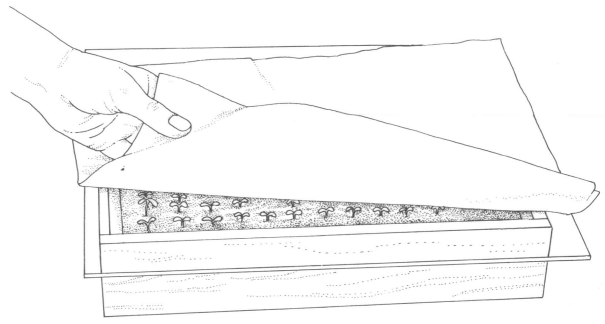

A warm dark environment is required for germinating seeds. This can easily be created by using a pane of glass and an old newspaper

Seed sowing

Seed sowing is relatively simple and, if instructions are provided on the seed packet, they should be followed. Make sure that the pots to be used and the soil mixture are clean. Also moisten the soil mixture before sowing the seed. On the whole, seeds of houseplants should be sown thinly and lightly covered before damping the soil surface with tepid water applied with a watering-can fitted with a fine rose. Germination time will be reduced if a sheet of glass is placed on top of the pot; there should be about half an inch between the soil surface and the glass, and to avoid excessive condensation the glass should be turned daily. It is also helpful if the glass is covered with a sheet of newspaper until such time as germination occurs. The paper can be dispensed with when growth appears, and, at the same time, it will also be beneficial if a wedge is placed between the glass and the pot to permit the entry of a little fresh air. Seedlings should not be exposed to strong sunlight, and a temperature in the region of 18°C (65°F) is preferred.

It is common knowledge that the majority of flowering pot plants are raised from seed in their millions each year; for example calceolarias, cinerarias and primulas. For practical purposes, however, it would be unwise to purchase packets of seed in order to grow a few plants on the window-sill. Where a few

plants only are required it is very much better to purchase young plants ready for potting up, or buy established plants in small pots and to pot them on into slightly larger containers as soon as purchased. Having too many plants to handle properly, which could result if one sowed one's own seed, almost inevitably results in them all becoming congested and few doing as well as they might.

The layman is frequently surprised to learn that many of our bolder plants are, in fact, grown from seed, and not from cuttings as might be expected. Among them are monstera, *Grevillea robusta, Fatsia japonica, Schefflera actinophylla* and *Dizygotheca elegantissima*, which is really more graceful than bold in its early stages of development.

Comparatively easy to propagate from leaf cuttings, the African violet (saintpaulia) may also be increased by means of seed. Here again it is important that seedlings be spaced out as soon as this becomes necessary, and only sufficient to meet one's need should be kept – with just a few extras for special friends! Saintpaulias and other plants with very fine seeds should be thinly sown on the surface of moist compost and left uncovered, except for the glass top cover. To encourage growth, saintpaulia compost should be moistened with warm water before sowing; and, when germination takes place, growth will be more active if the seedlings have the benefit of artificial light for a few hours in the evening.

Division is one of the simplest methods of propagation.
1. *The plantlets are teased apart and separated with a sharp knife*

2. *Ensure that each portion has plenty of roots and then pot individually in the usual way*

Division

Division of pot plants is a simple operation that is similar to separating a clump of garden plants of the Michaelmas daisy type. Generally speaking, as with propagation of most indoor plants, it is a task that ought to be performed in the spring when the plants are becoming active again. Before separating root clumps the compost should be thoroughly saturated so that the roots can be more easily pulled apart. If it is necessary, use a sharp knife to cut through roots that have become matted together. Complete the operation by potting the separated clumps into individual pots in the usual manner, using John Innes No. 2 potting compost or a soilless potting compost and 3½-in pots.

The following are some of the plants that may be increased by means of division: *Acorus gramineus, Aspidistra lurida, Isolepis gracilis.*

Air layering

For this, one should have to hand the following items: a sharp knife, a 2 ft cane, two handfuls of wet sphagnum moss, a piece of polythene about 8 in by 6 in (a stout polythene bag slit down the side and along the bottom is suitable), string, a piece of matchstick and some one to assist with the operation. Begin by removing a leaf at the height you wish your plant to be. Follow this by getting your helper to hold the stem in position while you cut halfway through the main stem about 1 in below the joint from which the leaf was removed. Then bend the stem carefully, and very slightly so that the knife can be turned to make an upward cut through the actual node. (The flow of latex will do no harm, though care should be taken not to get it on one's clothing,

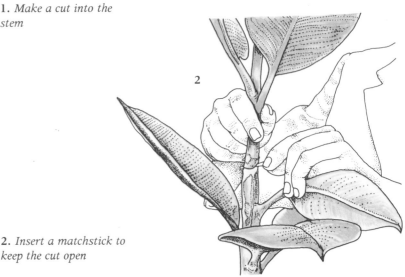

Air layering is particularly suitable for ficus plants (rubber plants) that have lost their lower leaves
1. *Make a cut into the stem*

2. *Insert a matchstick to keep the cut open*

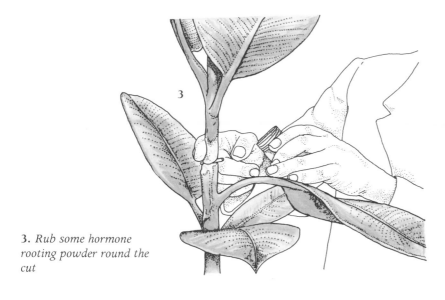

3. *Rub some hormone rooting powder round the cut*

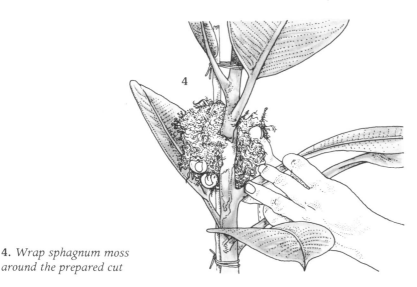

4. *Wrap sphagnum moss around the prepared cut*

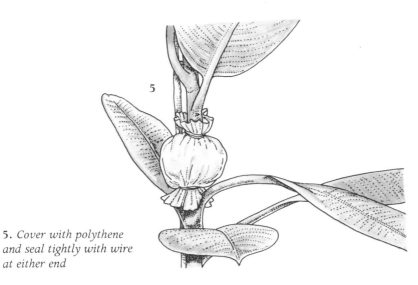

5. *Cover with polythene and seal tightly with wire at either end*

as such stains are difficult to remove). Insert the piece of matchstick in the cut to hold it open, then dust with one of the hormone rooting powders. The cane should now be tied in position above and below the cut mark in the form of a splint and inserted in the pot. This will obviate the possibility of the stem keeling over and breaking off.

The wet moss is then placed on either side of the cut mark and tied in position. Wrap the moss around with the polythene and tie it tightly above and below the moss. After some six to eight weeks, when a plentiful supply of white roots can be seen inside the polythene, use secateurs to sever the rooted section just below the moss ball. Allow the severed end to dry, and carefully remove the polythene before potting the plant into a peaty compost, with the moss ball intact. The compost is watered in to settle it down and is then kept on the dry side until the plant is obviously seen to be growing away in the mixture, when normal watering can begin.

The remaining lower portion of the plant will then produce shoots from the topmost leaf joints, but in the process, it is usual for the plant to shed some of its lower leaves.

Layering

Several houseplants can be increased by this method, which is probably the most reliable of all as the parent plant continues to nourish young plantlets while they are producing roots of their own. One of the best-known examples of this method of propagation is the production of new strawberry plants from strawberry runners.

Common indoor plants that can be produced in this way are chlorophytum, *Saxifraga sarmentosa* and *Tolmiea menziesii*. The operation is simply performed by pegging down the young plantlets into small pots of compost, using a hairpin, or similar piece of bent wire. John Innes No. 1 potting compost with a little extra sharp sand added, is a suitable growing medium or a soilless compost including silver sand. When young plants are obviously growing away on their own roots, the stalks attaching them to the parent plant can be severed.

Other plants that can be increased in much the same way are the hederas, *Ficus pumila*, *F. radicans*, columneas, *Gynura sarmentosa* and the smaller-leaved philodendrons. For these, rather than peg growths down into individual pots, I find it better to place the parent plant in the centre of a shallow box that contains a 3-in layer of John Innes No. 1

potting compost or a soilless equivalent. Longer growths from the plant can then be pegged down in the compost. When rooted, they can be snipped away from the parent and potted up into individual pots using a similar compost. The leaves in the area of the roots should be removed, to prevent them rotting and causing disease. At least three rooted strands should be put into a 3½-in pot, to form an attractive display.

Leaf cuttings

For successful results with this method of propagation, especial care should be taken to provide ideal growing conditions. These include a humid atmosphere and a temperature of 16–18°C (60–65°F). A small propagating case is the easiest way of providing these conditions, but it is not essential. Choice of suitable propagating material is doubly important here, so the use of firm, unblemished leaves is particularly important.

The best-known houseplant propagated by leaf cuttings is the saintpaulia, which roots with little difficulty either in a proper compost, or when the leaf stalk is placed in water. For the latter method a narrow-necked bottle should be used, so that the petiole (leaf stalk) is in the water and the leaf is supported by the neck of the bottle. *Peperomia caperata* and *P. hederaefolia* can also be increased by this method.

If the leaves are to be rooted in compost, rather than water, the severed ends of the leaf stalks can be treated with a hormone rooting powder before inserting them. An open sandy compost should be used into which the leaf stalks can be gently pushed without bruising them. They should not be inserted too deeply, just far enough for them to remain erect. In reasonable conditions, new growth will be apparent about six weeks after insertion of the cuttings.

As mentioned elsewhere, it is a simple matter to propagate streptocarpus from firm, and mature leaves which have been cut into about 4 in lengths. These sections are put into

Chlorophytum plantlets pegged down into small pots will soon form roots and grow away into new plants

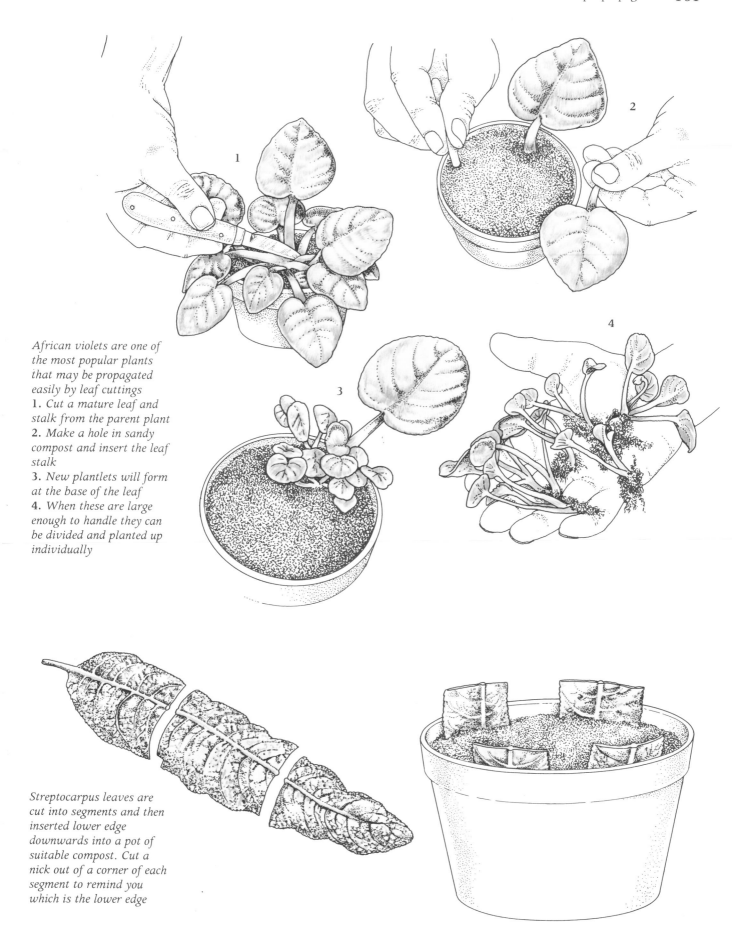

African violets are one of
the most popular plants
that may be propagated
easily by leaf cuttings
1. Cut a mature leaf and
stalk from the parent plant
2. Make a hole in sandy
compost and insert the leaf
stalk
3. New plantlets will form
at the base of the leaf
4. When these are large
enough to handle they can
be divided and planted up
individually

Streptocarpus leaves are
cut into segments and then
inserted lower edge
downwards into a pot of
suitable compost. Cut a
nick out of a corner of each
segment to remind you
which is the lower edge

the compost; care must be taken that the sections are put in the right way up that is, with the portion of the leaf which was nearest the stem downwards. It helps if a small piece is removed from the bottom corner of each leaf piece.

Stand each piece upright in a mixture of peat and sand, provide the necessary warm, moist conditions and rooting soon takes place.

The Christmas and Easter cactus (Zygocactus and Schlumbergera) are among the easiest of plants to increase from leaves. Segments are removed in the summer when the plants are not in flower, and placed around the outer edge of a small pot filled with peaty potting mixture. Water in lightly, then keep moist and warm.

Another type of propagation in which leaves are used is one in which the leaves are cut up into pieces. This method is particularly suitable for begonias of the rex type. Again, choice of material is important, and crisp leaves of medium size should be selected.

These are cut up into small pieces a little larger than a postage stamp, then placed on moist peat with the coloured side uppermost. It is important that the compost should only be moist; if it is too wet the cuttings will rot, while if it is too dry they will shrivel up. As a rough guide, the soil is sufficiently moist if one can just squeeze moisture from the peat, or compost, when a fistful is tightly compressed. Cover the pot with a small piece of glass (turn it daily) and keep the temperature at around 18°C (65°F). Direct sunlight on the cuttings will be damaging, but a light position must be provided, and additional artificial light in the evening is an advantage. About six weeks will elapse before the first tiny leaves appear.

Offsets

Many plants form perfectly shaped miniature replicas of themselves around the stem base of the parent plant, and when reasonably mature these can be very easily cut away with a sharp knife and potted up individually in small pots. The bromeliads respond especially well to this method of propagation. Although not all of them produce offsets at their base, those that do (*Aechmea rhodocyanea* and *Neoregelia carolinae tricolor* in particular) offer what must be one of the most reliable means of propagation of almost all indoor plants. At all stages of growth, from propagation onwards, the bromeliads should have a peaty and free draining potting mixture in which to grow.

Other methods

At the beginning of this chapter, mention was made of the fact that nurserymen rarely resort to other than traditional methods in order to increase their stock. However, there is no reason why the amateur should not display in his collection a wide variety of interesting plants that have been raised from date stones, pineapple tops and the like.

Pips and stones
Given a temperature of 18°C (65°F), oranges, grapefruit, lemons, lychees, avocado pears and a host of other interesting plants can be raised indoors from pips or stones. Growing these is one thing, getting them to produce a crop of fruit is quite a different matter. Although plants will occasionally and quite inexplicably bear fruit when little more than 18 months old, it is more likely that eight to ten years will elapse before any fruit develops, by which time the plant will be more suited to the

Christmas cactus plants are easily propagated from leaf cuttings. Segments are removed when the plant is not in flower and placed round the edge of a pot filled with peaty compost

spacious greenhouse or conservatory, having
outgrown its welcome indoors. Though a
source of keen interest, it is unfortunate that
many of the plants that can be grown from
pips and stones of tropical fruits do not in fact
develop into plants that are attractive or even
suitable for indoor decoration; this seldom
deters an interested person.

Should you have a mind to experiment, it is
important to follow the advice given in this
chapter for the sowing of seed, and to pot the
resultant plants on into standard houseplant
potting mixture as the seedlings increase in
size. Also, it is important to allow the seed of
citrus plants, avocado pears and dates to dry
off before they are sown.

Avocado pear stones

One of the more attractive plants to grow from
a stone is the avocado. The very large stone is
best started into growth in water, although it
will also germinate in soil, but this takes
longer. The stone should be suspended to
about half its depth in water. This can be done
by inserting three cocktail sticks around the
circumference of the stone and placing it in a
glass of water so that the sticks rest on the rim
of the glass. Roots will sprout in the water,
and when the stone splits to produce leaves
the stone can be planted in peaty soil with the
leafy top section exposed. The plant can then
be grown on in a moderate temperature in a
cool room. Bushy growth can be achieved by
pinching out the growing tips regularly.

Pineapple tops

Propagating pineapples in the home is not easy,
but, if successful, it does give one that bit of an
edge over one's friends who are also indoor
plant enthusiasts. When attempting this,
several methods may be employed, but I have
seen the following succeed, which is some
recommendation. A pineapple with a healthy
green top should be selected and the top
should be removed with a sharp knife, leaving
just a sliver of the fruit still attached. A 5-in
pot is filled with bromeliad potting mixture
(see page 56), and a thin layer of sharp sand
scattered over the surface. The pineapple top
is then placed on the sand, and pushed gently
into the compost, which should be kept moist.
A temperature of at least 18°C (65°F) should
be maintained. Roots will form more readily
in the sand, and having done so will then find
their way into the compost underneath. Once
rooted, culture is the same as that advised for
other bromeliads (see pages 52–56).

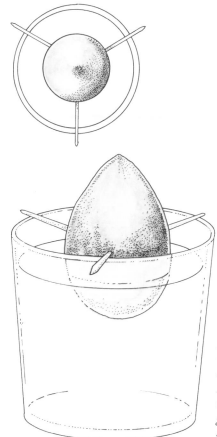

*Avocado stones are best
started into growth in
water. Insert three
cocktail sticks into the
stone as shown above and
rest them on the rim of a
glass of water so that the
stone is half submerged*

Some common problems

Over the past thirty years houseplants have advanced from very humble beginnings to the point where they have become one of the most popular hobbies, competing strongly with such well-established pastimes as fishing and outdoor gardening. Unfortunately the more plants there are the more problems arise and the more one is beset by questions.

I find that whatever the company, if it leaks out that I am involved with houseplants, there is an inevitable flood of questions from all and sundry enquiring about their rubber plant, African violet or dumb cane. Taking part in a regular monthly 'Phone-In' programme I have learnt that the subject of houseplants runs second only to pets in the numbers of questions asked. Being a sort of Aunt Agatha for one of the world's largest producers of houseplants, I am also obliged to cope with a vast number of written questions, as well as dealing with the endless queries and problems following talks on houseplants. Flower shows, such as Chelsea are another time for answering questions when floods of visitors ask about every conceivable sort of plant.

This chapter is devoted to some of the questions that I am most frequently asked together with a few which are less common but interesting nevertheless.

Green poinsettia

Q I have kept my poinsettia plant in beautiful condition from last year, but the red bracts that were on the plant when it came will not form. Is it possible to get them to develop again?
A Modern poinsettias are, in fact, very much easier to care for and to keep from year to year than they used to be. In order to get bracts in subsequent years, plants must not be exposed to artificial light from the end of September through until Christmas. They are what is termed short-day plants. This means they flower naturally during the shorter winter days of the year, therefore it is essential to ensure that during this period they are not exposed to any artificial light in the evening. It is, however, important to ensure that plants have the lightest possible location during the hours of natural daylight.

The shrimp plant

Q Having flowered for most of the summer, the bracts of my shrimp plant are now beginning to fall off, and some of the leaves are changing colour to a reddish-brown. What is the cause, and can cuttings be taken from my plant?
A It is usual for the shrimp plant, *Beloperone guttata*, to stop producing its colourful bracts in the autumn, and for existing bracts to lose much of their colour. When these are no longer attractive they should be removed. Plants may also be pruned to shape in the autumn; firm trimmings, a few inches in length, will root readily in any good potting mixture. When growing conditions are cold and wet, the leaves have a tendency to change colour and may in some instances drop off, but, unless this loss of leaves is excessive, it should not give rise to concern. After the plants have flowered, the compost must be kept on the dry side until the following spring when normal watering can be resumed. A winter temperature in the region of 55°F (13°C) should be maintained, and the parent plant can be potted on into a larger pot in early spring.

Sansevieria in flower

Q My sansevieria plant, which I have cherished for the past four years, is now in flower; is this unusual?
A It is unusual for smaller plants to do so, but older plants flower in mid-summer with reasonable regularity, though there is no way of ensuring this.

Ungainly aphelandra

Q I have an *Aphelandra squarrosa* plant that has lost its lower leaves, but has two strong healthy shoots at the top. Is there anything I can do to improve the appearance of my plant?
A Although little can be done to improve the appearance of your plant, there is no reason why the two healthy shoots should not be removed and used to propagate two new plants. Do this by allowing the shoots to produce two pairs of firm leaves before severing them with a sharp knife from the

parent plant and inserting them in 3-in pots filled with John Innes No. 1 potting compost. To prevent the cutting from drying out, place both pot and cutting in a sealed polythene bag and protect the latter from strong sunlight; the temperature should be in the region of 65°F (18°C). Cuttings should be started in individual pots, and as soon as they have rooted through to the sides of these they must be potted on into 5-in pots using John Innes No. 2 potting compost. After removal of the growth from which the cuttings are made, the parent plant will be of little further use and should be disposed of.

Wilted cyclamen

Q Is there anything one can do to revive cyclamen plants that have wilted as a result of becoming too dry?
A Simply giving the plant water will not result in the flowers becoming erect again, although the leaves will stiffen and take on their natural shape. Florists, who are frequently faced with this problem, adopt the practice of watering the plant well before wrapping it fairly tightly in newspaper. This results in the flowers standing erect while they draw up water, and remaining so when the paper is removed.

Bud drop

Q I have an hibiscus that is quite healthy but sheds its flower buds before they open, and a Christmas Cactus that behaves in the same way. Why does this happen?
A Insufficient light is the short answer. Both these plants need a light location to flower well, and will benefit from being placed out of doors in a sunny, sheltered position during the summer months. The Christmas cactus is also very sensitive when it is about to flower. If this plant is moved from its normal growing position by a light window it will tend to shed buds before they have opened; so if they are about to flower the best thing is to leave them alone to get on with it.

Dividing saintpaulias

Q For some years I have been growing an African violet (saintpaulia) which has now developed into a large, bushy plant. What I would like to know is if it can be split up in order to make more plants, and if so, when would be the correct time?
A Yes, this can be done, but you would probably get better results by propagating

plants from individual leaves, as described in the chapter, Simple propagation. The plant can be divided up into smaller pieces at almost any time when it is not in flower, though the best time is probably April to May when the divided pieces will root more readily into fresh compost. The plant must be well watered before removing it from its pot. Follow depotting by gently teasing the matted roots apart and pot the separated pieces into small pots filled with a peaty compost. After potting, water the soil with tepid water and then keep the young plants on the dry side until new growth is evident. Normal watering can then begin.

Flowerless saintpaulias

Q I have some beautiful African violet plants that get bigger and bigger, but never produce any flowers. How can I get them to bloom?
A This has become a very popular question in recent years, as better heating has improved growing conditions for saintpaulias indoors. We hear so many reasons for the reluctance of plants to flower, but my view is that there are two very simple answers. One is poor light; it is of the utmost importance that saintpaulias should have very good light if they are to flower. This will usually mean placing the plant by a sunny window during the day and under a table lamp in the evening. This treatment will almost certainly give markedly better results. The second suggestion is that one should try feeding with a fertiliser that contains a higher proportion of potash such as a tomato fertiliser. The usual high-nitrogen houseplant fertilisers are fine for producing bigger foliage plants but will not encourage production of flowers.

Naughty pussy

Q My cat has done its business in the Swiss cheese plant. This was actually asked, to my horror, on a live radio programme one morning!
A The lady questioner in fact wanted to know why the cat should have done such a thing and what she could do about it. My answer was that she should not invite the neighbours in for a few days! On a more serious note I told her to remove the 'business' with as much of the surrounding compost as possible. The resultant hole should then be filled with fresh compost, and a lid made for the pot to prevent any repetition. (I never cease to be amazed by the odd problems that confront many growers of indoor plants.)

Ailing fatsias

Q My *Fatsia japonica* plant, given to me some months ago, is now looking very sad and is reduced to two large and one small leaf at the top of the stem. Can anything be done to restore it to its former appearance?

A Alas, when growing in the home, very little can be done to revive house plants when they have been reduced to the condition you describe. There is no reason, however, why you should not plant your *F. japonica* out in the garden in a sheltered position. For best results, summer planting is advised. In time the fatsia will develop into a very fine garden shrub, which seems to thrive even in smoke-polluted districts.

The rubber plant's sheath

Q Should I remove the pink-coloured covering from around the new leaf of my Rubber plant in order to help it open?

A Certainly not! The sheath is Mother Nature's way of protecting the young leaf and should be allowed to fall off naturally when it has completed its protective function. Many ficus leaves are irreparably damaged by removing the sheath prematurely; also by inquisitive fingers handling the sheath before it has opened.

One big leaf

Q My Rubber plant, purchased recently, has one leaf turning yellow – what is the cause? It is the bottom leaf of the plant, and is much larger than the others.

A This means simply that the leaf you mention is the one that was attached to the parent piece of stem when the plant was propagated as a cutting, and having completed its function it is quite natural for it to turn yellow and eventually die. Many nurserymen remove this leaf before dispatching plants, using a sharp knife to carefully cut it off below soil level.

Problems with flowers

Q My flowering pot plants always look lovely when I take them home, but the flowers soon die and some of the buds fall off before they even open. What is going wrong?

A Usually poor light is to blame once again. It is essential that all flowering plants in the home should have good light in which to grow if flowers and buds are to function correctly. In good light flowers will have a brighter colour and remain attractive for much longer than if they are in poor light. Hibiscus, in particular, find life difficult in poor light, and will usually shed their flower buds before they open.

When placed by a window most plants will need some protection from very bright sunlight, but it is most important not to place them in poorly lit corners if you wish to get the best from them.

Brown spots

Q Lots of my plants have developed irregular brown marks and spots for no apparent reason but the condition doesn't seem to spread. What's the problem?

A There are numerous possibilities, but the most common reason for damage of this kind is the use of aerosol sprays near to where the plant has been standing. Examples of guilty products are furniture polish, hair lacquers and fly sprays. On plant foliage you should only use sprays and insecticides that are specifically intended for them. All other sprays should be kept well away or the plants themselves moved to a safe place when you are polishing.

Damage may also result through using leaf-cleaner sprays intended for plants either too generously or too frequently, while plants are standing in the sun or when the temperature is very low.

Limp leaves

Q My African violet plants have become mottled around the edge of the leaves, which have also become rather limp to the touch. Why is this so?

A Almost without question this is due to low temperatures, and is usually more common during the winter months. To do well saintpaulias should have a minimum temperature of not less than 18°C (65°F). They will survive at lower temperatures, but to grow well they must be warm. Quite often damage of this kind can occur in a cold shop before the purchase is made, or as a result of carrying plants home on cold days with insufficient wrapping. When buying plants it is worth inspecting the leaves to see that they are firm and free from blemishes.

Treatment of Ficus benjamina

Q During the summer I potted my 3½-ft-tall plant of *Ficus benjamina* into a 9-in pot, using John Innes No. 3 Potting Compost. Two months after potting I started giving the plant regular applications of liquid fertiliser, a little each time the plant was watered. Many of the leaves are now turning yellow and the plant appears to be sick; I am wondering what could have gone wrong?

A Almost everything! First, a 9-in pot is much too large for a ficus plant that is only 3½-ft in height, and the John Innes Compost used would have been better for the addition of a little extra peat or leaf-mould in the mixture. Also, plants potted indoors in mid-summer should not need any form of fertiliser until the following spring at the earliest; unnecessary feeding damages young roots, the consequence of which is yellow leaves. It would be better now if the plant was kept on the dry side in a warm room until it shows signs of recovery.

Variegated ivies and tradescantias turning green

Q Why, after a few months, do my variegated ivies and tradescantias turn green in colour?
A The reason for this is almost invariably lack of light. Plants purchased in the summer months retain their colouring while growing in a light window, but quickly revert to green in the winter if maximum light is not provided. It is odd, however, that cuttings taken from the green growth of ivy plants will frequently sprout with variegated colouring. Tradescantias, besides being kept in a light position should have any green growth removed as it appears, as it is much more vigorous and will quickly predominate.

Leggy Ivy

Q My hedera has become very thin and leggy. Is there anything that can be done to improve its appearance.
A The best treatment really is to plant the ivy out in the garden, preferably against a wall where it can climb naturally. The larger-leaved ivies, such as *H. canariensis*, make superb climbing plants, while the smaller-leaved ones are excellent ground cover subjects. Indoors ivies require cool and light conditions to give of their best.

Red spider mite on ivy

Q Why has my *Hedera canariensis* plant taken on a dry appearance with browning of the leaf margins?
A The short answer is red spider mite. These minute pests thrive in very dry and warm conditions, and have a particular liking for for the *canariensis* ivy. These pests can be detected by the naked eye if one knows what

one is looking for, but it usually requires a magnifying glass to see their tiny bodies moving around. Where there are very bad infestations these mites will produce tiny webs between the leaf and leaf stalk. Erradicating red spider mite is not easy, but perseverance will usually bring its reward. A suitable insecticide should be mixed according to the manufacturer's directions then applied to both the upper and lower surfaces of the leaves, ensuring that the plant is completely saturated. Whenever one is treating plants with insecticide rubber gloves should be worn and the job should be done out of doors or in a shed. Choose a still warm day if the job is to be done outside and keep treated plants out of the sun.

Red spider mites dislike moist cool conditions, so it is a good idea to mist the foliage over regularly with a fine spray of water as a deterrent. Inspect all your plants periodically for signs of infestation as prevention is much better than cure.

Decreasing monstera

Q The leaves of my monstera plant seem to be getting smaller and they don't have the usual cut marks in them. Why is this happening?
A Poor culture is the main problem usually allied to less than adequate light conditions. Poor culture can mean a number of things. The drainage may be poor or the temperature may be too low – if it falls below 16°C (60°F) too often the plant will begin to suffer. The plant may be in need of potting into fresh compost or feeding. Any of these factors in combination with cold, dark and wet conditions make the worst environment for any plant and it is not surprising that its appearance begins to deteriorate.

Roots of a Swiss cheese plant

Q What can I do with the long things hanging down from my Swiss cheese plant?
A These are aerial roots and a natural part of the plant. In the wild they spread out over the forest floor and into water holes seeking moisture and nutrients for the plant. Removal of some of these will not be harmful, but it is unwise to take them all off. The best method of keeping them under control is to tie the roots loosely in around the stem and when they are long enough, poke them into the potting compost. An interesting exercise can be conducted whereby the roots are directed into a container of water standing adjacent to the pot. They will then draw up moisture from this source and the soil the

plant grows in need not be watered so frequently.

Brown marks on foliage

Q Some of my plants are getting funny brown marks on them but I cannot find any sign of pests. What could be the cause?

A I am asked this question so often at flower shows or in letters through the post accompanied by samples of the damaged leaves. Almost invariably, dry brown blotches, more particularly streaks, on otherwise healthy leaves are the result of placing plants too close to window panes on very sunny days; this can be especially harmful if the glass has a frosted pattern. The window pane acts as a magnifying glass, increasing the intensity of the sun's rays which literally burn the surface of the leaf. Even old rubber plants that one might think would resist any such damage are vulnerable.

Plants for a dark room

Q What sort of plant can you recommend for a dark room that is not very well heated?

A There really is very little that one can suggest with confidence, as reasonable light is essential for almost all indoor plants, and, if they are to have any chance of producing new leaves the temperature should be maintained at around 16°C (60°F). Some will tolerate less, but this is a minimum for most plants. Darker locations are really only suitable for the tougher green foliage plants such as the aspidistra, rhoicissus and *Philodendron scandens*.

House plants and central heating

Q I recently moved into a new house with large windows and central heating that maintains a minimum temperature of 65°F (18°C). Could you please suggest a small collection of plants that would be suitable for a beginner in these conditions?

A Ideally, you should choose plants that are both easy to grow and able to withstand the conditions prevailing in the temperature you mention. Some of the easier plants, ivies and *Cissus antarctica* for example, do not grow particularly well at higher temperatures. A selection from the following plants will give you a good mixture that will be reasonably easy to care for; *Maranta leuconeura kerchoveana, M. l. erythrophylla,* monstera, *Philodendron scandens, Rhoicissus rhomboidea,* peperomias, pileas, *Hypocyrta glabra, Anthurium scherzerianum* and *Sansevieria trifasciata*

laurentii. It is wise to experiment with a small collection of this kind, getting to know the individual requirements of particular plants, before attempting more difficult sorts.

Effects of gas and paraffin heaters

Q Are gas and paraffin fumes harmful to plants?

A Yes, fumes of either polluting the atmosphere would almost inevitably result in plants shedding leaves and in flowers failing to survive. In this respect both tomato plants and cut flowers of carnation are especially sensitive, and could well be used as vectors for harmful fumes. However, modern appliances burning natural gas are generally not harmful. Paraffin heaters in sealed rooms that are seldom aired will be detrimental to some plants and fatal to others. Calor gas fires are not by any means suitable for all plants, and should be the suspected culprit if topmost, or young leaves show signs of distress.

The benefits of cold tea

Q Is cold tea good for plants?

A If my experience of listening to growers of houseplants extolling the virtues of cold tea is anything to go by, then I would most heartily approve of this liquid that is often treated with a certain amount of amusement. The benefit lies in the fact that the water has been boiled so all the impurities have been removed and cold tea is almost the perfect example of tepid water; whether or not the tea itself has any nutritional value is a different matter.

Fertilisers for houseplants

Q With so many different fertilisers being offered for sale I find difficulty in choosing the right one for my indoor plants. Could you please advise? Also, could you give me some advice on how often and when I should feed my plants?

A The formula for indoor plant fertilisers varies very little and there is no reason why they should not all give equally good results if used according to the maker's directions. Some of the more vigorous plants, such as aphelandra, will benefit, however, if fertilisers are applied at shorter intervals, or slightly in excess of the recommended strength. As to their use, the principal precaution here is to ensure that the soil in the pot is moist before applying the fertiliser, otherwise root damage may result. They should be used mainly in spring and summer when the plants are producing new leaves, although weak feeding in winter may also be necessary if the plants are actively growing. Feeding plants that are sick and have ceased to grow during the normal growing season will only be detrimental. Such plants should be carefully nursed back to health and fed only when growth is again active.

Potting composts

Q Can you please tell me if ordinary garden soil will be suitable for potting my house plants into? If not, what do you recommend?
A In the first place, there is no such commodity as 'ordinary' garden soil, as soil varies from district to district and even from one garden to the next. Garden soil, unless of particularly high quality, is generally considered to be too heavy and lacking in porosity for the majority of potted plants. For many years now the emphasis, as far as the majority of commercial house plant growers are concerned, has been on an open mixture that contains a high percentage of peat. The success of peat-based soilless composts helps to prove this point. These mixes and the John Innes range of composts can be purchased in handy packs that are clean and labour saving. John Innes compost should have extra peat added to it for the majority of house plants. When purchasing compost it is wise to buy sufficient for one's immediate needs only, as composts tend to dry out and deteriorate when stored for any length of time.

Planting of foliage and flowering plants

Q Could you please tell me how to care for a container of mixed foliage and flowering plants given to me as a Christmas present?
A Most bowls of assorted plants are prepared for festive occasions and contain at least one colourful flowering plant that will probably die a month or two after purchase. When no longer attractive the flowering plant should be removed, and the hole which is left can be filled with fresh compost. As many of these containers have no drainage holes, water should be given sparingly to prevent the compost becoming waterlogged. Although not all plants are compatible, it is surprising how well many will grow when planted together in this fashion.

Plant care at holiday time

Q I own a number of indoor plants and am wondering what I should do with them while on holiday.
A For the summer vacation, it is usually best to get a friend to see to watering for you in your own home during your absence. Plants can be taken to the friend's house, but they seem to resent change once they have adjusted themselves to particular surroundings. It is of the utmost importance that the chosen person should be given precise directions concerning the amount and frequency of watering and fertilising, as the novice is inclined to go to extremes, one way or the other. Failing this, the plants should be removed from sunny windows and given a good watering before grouping them together in a large watertight plant holder, or basin. A 4-in. layer of wet sand in the bottom of the basin will help to keep the compost moist in your absence; packing the pots around with moist peat, moss or wet newspaper will also be an advantage. During the winter months plants will be faced with the additional hazard of low temperatures, which makes it essential that they be moved to premises with similar conditions to those of your own home whilst you are away.

Exhibiting houseplants

Q Our local flower show is including a section for house plants this year for the first time – have you any advice to offer a would-be exhibitor?
A Many flower shows now have a class for house plants, and judges are presented with many problems when assessing the merits of the large number of plants that come under this general heading. Some of them are comparatively easy to care for, while others are downright difficult. Naturally enough, healthy plants will catch the judge's eye, but when faced with plants of equal merit he will look for other points in their favour. So plants should be clean and neat, which will entail the removal of dead and damaged leaves, and the tying-in of untidy growth on plants such as ivies and philodendrons. Even pots should have their share of titivating, as clean pots set off plants to much better advantage. The naming of plants will also be a consideration, so ensure that the names, and the way these are spelt, are correct.

INDEX

Metrication table

Imperial	Metric
$\frac{1}{2}$ in	1 cm
1 in	2.5 cm
$1\frac{1}{2}$ in	4 cm
2 in	5 cm
3 in	8 cm
4 in	10 cm
5 in	13 cm
6 in	15 cm
7 in	18 cm
8 in	20 cm
9 in	23 cm
10 in	25 cm
11 in	28 cm
1 foot	30 cm
2 ft	60 cm
3 ft	1 m